HEPHZIBAH
GOD'S DELIGHT WITHIN HER

BY ANGELA DAVIS

Hephzibah: God's Delight Within Her

Trilogy Christian Publishers A Wholly Owned Subsidary of Trinity Broadcasting Network

2442 Michelle Drive Tustin, CA 92780

Rights Department, 2442 Michelle Drive, Tustin, CA 92780.

Trilogy Christian Publishing/TBN and colophon are trademarks of Trinity Broadcasting Network.

Cover design by: Grant Swank

For information about special discounts for bulk purchases, please contact Trilogy Christian Publishing.

Trilogy Disclaimer: The views and content expressed in this book are those of the author and may not necessarily reflect the views and doctrine of Trilogy Christian Publishing or the Trinity Broadcasting Network.

Manufactured in the United States of America

10 9 8 7 6 5 4 3 2 1

Library of Congress Cataloging-in-Publication Data is available.

ISBN: 979-8-89041-218-8

E-ISBN: 979-8-89041-219-5

Table of Contents

Chapter 1

Good morning, my love; thank you for waking me up this morning. Abba, I love you with all my heart, mind, and soul. When I think back on my life over the years, to see where I've been and what I've gone through, and to know that you never leave me, I'm so grateful to you for your love. Now, I can see the big picture of everything, the pain and hurt I've been through; it was the path that I had to take. I didn't understand it then, but now I know.

God, you have made me into your own image, which I'm so thankful for; a lot of people don't like themselves for what they see, but you look at the inside of man and search out our inner most hearts. That's what makes you God all by yourself. When I think back on my youth and where I'm at today, you have been so good to me.

Being the youngest child was no picnic in the park; everyone was always looking out for you but, at the same time, beating the crap out of you. Now I know how to keep my mouth shut, and sometimes, I just let it run wild and put myself into more hot water. I always tell people my mind; sometimes, I should just use wisdom and not say anything. Like I say, you learn from your own mistakes, which I've learned the hard way. Life was always great until that moment of problem came around to test you and take your joy away; is this a part of life's journey? Did we choose some of our own problems, or was it a plan of God? A question I ask myself most of the time. I've tried not to think about it, but when you are a parent, you worry about a lot of things in life in general.

I can remember one event when my older sister had run away from home; she wasn't being abused or anything. She chose to have fun, but her fun caused pain that my parents felt was unspeakable. It didn't bring them together; it drove them apart. Everyone had the blaming game going on. Whose fault it was, and who was not there enough? As the youngest child, they tried to not involve me in any situation at all; after all, I was just a kid. I saw the pain in my mother's eyes each night I went to bed; she didn't sleep at night. She was always on her knees talking to that man named Jesus. I didn't know him that well, but it seemed whenever she talked to him, he helped her. I wasn't worried one bit because I knew that once Mother went on her knees, Jesus never failed her yet. My dad, on the other hand, didn't talk too much to God. He cursed most of the time, I didn't know the term truck driver talked, but that was my dad's second language. These two people went through a lot looking for my sister; I sometimes wonder what Dad was thinking because he didn't talk much; our parents had five children together, and my mother had our oldest brother Gary. He is more of a protector for all of us except Marlene, the one who ran away. They were always fighting and arguing with each other.

Our parents couldn't stop them at all; only they could explain it. This went on for a long time, living with both of them. I could understand Gary, but Marlene was the favorite in our family. She was Dad's first child, and they shared the same birthday, so what more can a girl really ask for? She was our grandma's favorite, and so was Althea; they loved her so much. Mother was always on the street searching while Dad was home with the rest of us; he wanted to make sure that we were okay.

Mother kept praying and trusting God as always; she knew what she had to do. At the same time, going back and forth to hospitals and funeral homes wasn't any picnic either. This went on for too long now, so Mother took matters into her own hands and called a couple of my dad's friends, who he knew worked at the newspaper and the radio station. My dad used to play cricket for our country, Jamaica, and he knew a lot of important people, but he was never conceited. My dad was very humble, but he had a mouth like a sailor.

He is everything like my brother Edson, my dad's only son. He's spoiled and everything; I follow him in the birth line, while Althea and Karen were the other two girls who followed Marlene, who ran away. The day my brother was born was the happiest day for Dad and Mother, I was told. His name would live on, Davis, that is. Only time could help us now. Mother never gave up one bit; she kept praying and talking to God. I knew all of this because I slept with them. I knew when she got up to pray and when she came back to bed. One thing I can say, she talked to Jesus a lot. Sometimes, she thought that I was sleeping, but I heard every prayer she made to the man Christ Jesus.

I could never forget that Saturday evening when my mother got a call from our cousin. She saw that my sister was missing, but Marlene was with her all this time. Mother just dropped the phone and put her hands in the air and was just thanking the Lord; she cried and thanked him. I just looked at her with tears rolling down my face. She couldn't contain herself; I couldn't explain it. She was just crying and thanking Jesus. Dad looked as if a load was just taken off of his back.

Everyone in the house was happy that she was all right; this was an experience that I don't think any parents should go through. This made our parents think twice if they were there enough for us. The day Marlene came home, Mother didn't even wait for her to get inside the house; she ran to the car and grabbed her. The hug that she gave her was breathless. She hugged her so tight; she never wanted to let her go. As the tears roll down her face, I watch them embrace each other. Dad just looked at both of them. Only God knows what was going through our parents' minds. One thing I know, whenever I have a problem, I should go to this man Jesus because he answers my mother's prayers.

As the days went by, we were back to the same daily life routine. Dad went back to work, which was sad because he worked at Alpart bauxite company. So, he would be gone for the whole week, and Mother would have to take care of all six children. She washed and cooked while everyone else had their own work to do. Edson and I, on the other hand, didn't have much to do; I thought it was because we were the youngest. My brother Edson was always making something, if he wasn't a genius or something. He would make trucks out of milk containers; anything came to his head, and he would fix it.

One day, he went too far and put a hair pin into the electric plug. I don't need to explain what had happened to him; he was shaking a lot; our dad always told us to stay together because if anything happened to one, the other sibling would be there to help; Edson and I were twins while Althea and Karen were both paired up too. Marlene and Gary didn't get along at all. They were like water and oil; over all, I think we were happy in spite of our differences. As the days went by, our dad was coming home. I had a job from my brothers and sisters. They would tell me to watch out for Dad. I didn't know what it was all about; I did what they told me. I took the family dog with me and waited patiently for Dad. When I saw him coming, I would sound the alarm. Then I would cry out really loud, "Sammie is coming!" I did this about three or four times... really loud. Even our neighbors knew that he was home. I don't know what that did for them, but Dad was upset. They were happy, and so was I because I knew I was going to get goodies from him. How I love this man! He was a wonderful man, even though I knew I would have to sleep with my brothers and sisters that night. I didn't mind at all because Althea and Marlene would sing songs for us. Althea had the most beautiful voice ever; she sounded like an angel as I listened to my sisters sing those beautiful gospels. I didn't know when I fell asleep.

The next day was fun for me because Edson and I were always on the move to do something. He was always trying to fix or make something he saw my dad do. I was more his supervisor to see if things made sense. Edson didn't care what I had to say or not. He still did what his heart told him; everyone was busy doing their chores while we went on our exploring. We knew when it was time to get back for lunch or before our brother Gary came looking for us. Life was fun growing up, but nothing lasts forever. As life went on, I felt like we were doing the same thing almost every day. When it wasn't school, it was some kind of drama with my siblings. Whether at war with each other or with people in the neighborhood, life for us was the same as always.

On Sunday mornings, our dad would wake us up to help him with his bowling for his cricket games. When he had a match to play, we were his bowling men. Dad would let each of us throw the ball; then, he would bat it in the yard. You really had to be skillful to do this. Karen was always first, then Edson; I was always last and stayed the longest. I couldn't understand it; when we were finished with him, we would get ready for church. I loved church because we would get dressed up, and after church, Marlene would take us to the store to get candy. When we got home from church, Mother would be done with dinner, or Dad would be playing music, if he wasn't at one of his games.

One thing I loved about this man was, whenever Dad got home from his games, he would call us to come and sit with him while he ate dinner. Mother didn't like it at all, but I guess he wanted to make sure we had dinner with him. I was always on his lap while Althea shared the rest with Karen and Edson, even though the dog was there waiting for him. Our dad was a lot of fun. On Monday mornings, he would wake me up for breakfast at 5:00 a.m. This was good because I didn't have to share it with anyone. The reason for this was because I slept with them while the others slept in the next room.

This was my life being the smallest; as time passed, it seemed like a pattern. You knew what was coming next; school was out for the weekend, then came Dad on Friday night with our goodies. Saturday, he went to play his games, and we were on our adventure as always. Sunday morning, we helped Dad bowl and then get ready for church. One thing I noticed was my mother was getting sick a lot on the weekend when she knew that Dad was coming home. She was always in the room in bed while everyone seemed distant. I didn't let what they were doing bother me at all because, at the end of the day, I was a child, and I must be seen and not heard.

I can never forget that Saturday evening when Dad didn't go to practice. Our aunt came over to visit our mother, and Aunt Ciscly spoke and laughed. Dad was home that weekend; he was there waiting to strike. That evening, I followed my mother to the bus stop with Aunt Ciscly; while we were at the bus stop waiting for a bus, I didn't even see Dad. He came up to Mother in front of everyone, yelling. He didn't ask her anything, but he was letting her know that if Marlene was pregnant, she could not stay at the house, which was followed by a lot of bad words. As the tears rolled down Mother's face, she was embarrassed about what he had done in front of all those people at the bus stop.

My aunt went on the bus, and my mother and I walked away. I didn't know where Dad went, but he was mad. Mother took me back to the house and told me to go inside, and she kept on walking. I didn't know where she was going; when I went inside the house, it was dark and quiet. Everyone was in their room, Marlene was crying a lot, and the rest of them were speechless.

I went into the room, and Dad was on the bed, shaking his legs. I just stood there, upset. I looked at him, and he didn't say another word at all. Mother didn't sleep with us that night until Dad left for work.

This was one moment when you wished everything was the same as before; it seemed as if our lives were changed for good. As tension grew in the house, Mother was trying to find ways to fix the whole situation. I noticed she wasn't talking to the man Christ Jesus like before. She was doing a lot on her own, which brought a lot of pain as the week went by. Our dad was coming home, and the tension was in the house as always. Our parents were always arguing, and everyone was on edge. Mother couldn't take it anymore, so she decided to take my sister Marlene to our aunt's house in the country. This aunt was my mother's youngest sister. Mom had three sisters: two lived in Jamaica, and the eldest lived in England.

My mother's mom had four girls; they were from three different men, and it seemed as if she got married. Her husband left her with my aunt Audrey. He never wrote or visited, so she moved on with my mother's father. When my mother was two years old, he came back, and my grandmother had to say goodbye to my granddad. Her husband didn't stay long with Grandma because he got her pregnant and then left her once more. So she was left with three children and no husband. Not before long, she got involved with someone else just to help her with life itself.

It didn't work out either; our grandmother went through a lot, I was told. She died a week after giving birth to her fourth child. My mother was with her dad at the time this happened, while Aunty Audrey was with family members, and the other girls were somewhere else. Grandmother died alone, without her family around her. My grandmother's family told her who to marry and who she should stay away from. If she didn't listen to them, they would leave her to the mercy of God to take care of her. She got sick alone with her baby, and Aunt Cislyn was only two years old. So she died alone; to this day, my mother doesn't know where her mother's grave is because the government had to bury her.

Her children were taken like kittens; everyone wanted one. Thank God my mother had a father who wanted her, so he took Mother and left her sibling behind. Granddad had his story as well. He was handsome, so you know what that meant—lots of women. So Mother didn't have a stable life because she was from house to house with these different women. Mother didn't talk much about her past; she never wanted us to be separated at all. Due to what she went through, now it seemed her nightmare came back to her.

Chapter 2

One Friday evening, Mother packed up Marlene's things and took her to our aunt's house in the country. Now Althea was in charge of us until Dad got home that night; things weren't the same. I still went to the corner and waited for Dad. When I would call out, it seemed as if no one cared. Mother wasn't there, and everyone was unhappy. I told Dad that they had left. When he came inside the house, Althea would tell him what had happened. He didn't say another word; he just took the same route. Now this was our daily life. Every Friday, Mom was gone, and we were on our own until Dad got home; Sunday evening, she would come home to make sure we were okay for the rest of the week.

My life wasn't the same at all, but Edson and I didn't let this get the best of us; now, we would stay longer on our adventures. This time, we were going all over the place. We didn't care if our brother Gary caught us on the road. We would find bottles and sell them; then, we would buy cookies and play pinball at the local bar. No one was watching us; we were doing our own thing. Dad would come home, and now his sister would come over to take care of her brother; after all, Mother wasn't there at all.

Aunty P was his oldest sister. Dad was the youngest of six children. My dad's father died when he was in his teens; my dad's oldest brother was in England. I don't know what was wrong with these people; it seemed as if they would give away their oldest children. At the same time, his other sister and brother were in the United States. So my dad and his big sister were left behind. My dad's mother's story wasn't bad like my mother's.

My paternal grandmother's family was more like a family net; they stayed together no matter what, more controlling people as well. My mother wasn't loved by my aunts, but my dad's mother loved her very much, and she did the same. When my sisters Marlene and Althea were growing up, Grandma grew them so they were loved by our dad's family. On the other hand, Karen and I were strangers to them. Edson was the only boy, so he got most of the attention; no one hid it. I didn't care at all; once I knew that my dad loved me, that was all that mattered.

Every week was the same. I still went to the corner of the street to meet Dad. He was happy to see me there with the dog waiting for him; he knew I was there for the goodies and him as well. I never let him down on Friday afternoon; no one knew how he felt to do what he did. He missed them both, but he had to do this for the rest of us. I remember we would talk at night; he would ask me if he was a bad father.

I would tell him no, but he cursed too much. I didn't like it at all; then, he would tell me not to be afraid of anyone. I was too tired to listen to him as he talked, but I got some good advice from Dad. He wasn't a bad man at all; he just put up this wall around him. He only wanted to protect his family. My dad never drank or smoked; I never saw him hit my mother at all. What I saw was a father who worked to keep his family alive. He was more of a provider, a protector, and a guider as well. One thing with him, I would rock myself to sleep, and it didn't bother him at all, while Mother made a big thing out of it.

Marlene was the eldest of our dad's children, and she was getting all the attention. I missed my old life; it might seem as if everyone was sad, even our dog Beddy was unhappy too. This went on for months that seemed like years; the house felt like a dark cloud was over it. One Saturday night, my dad got a call from his sister in the US; he was so happy to hear from her.

They talked and laughed; I didn't see that in a long time. He looked happy and was just shining as if he had gotten some good news. When he hung up from her, he asked me how I would feel if my sister and the baby came back home. I just looked at him, smiling, because this meant Mother would be home too.

Dad told me that I would not be the baby anymore, but I could take care of the child when it was born. He said that I would be the youngest aunt around. I thought I could boss another one around, other than my brother Edson. I just smiled and told him yes. I liked the sound of that. When Mother came home that Sunday evening, she was so happy. I had to sleep with those kids. I didn't like it at all, but my parents were happy once more, and so was our family.

I knew that Mother couldn't wait to tell Marlene the good news; I couldn't wait to boss this kid around. The week went by so fast; I couldn't believe it was Friday already. My dad was coming home, and I would have to take my pose with Beddy, our dog.

The dog was a part of our family; now, we had to share him with the new baby that was coming. As I waited to see my mother and my sister with her baby, there was no sign of them. Then Mother would come home by herself; I couldn't understand why. Then she told me that I had to wait until the baby was born, then I would see it. These couple of months were the longest ever; I gave up hope for this kid. I remember my mother didn't come home that Sunday, then we got the call that the baby was born, and it was a boy. The look on Dad's face was priceless; he was so happy; you would think he was the child's father. As we waited for them to come home, there was another story.

The baby was sick, so they had to wait until he was well. I guess Marlene had too much candy, which wasn't good for the baby. I totally gave up on them; whenever mother came home, she would tell us how handsome he was and how his complexion was cool. I could hardly wait to see my handsome nephew. Every day, I would have to wait on this kid. I gave up; this was too much for me.

One day, Edson and I were playing ball in the backyard when Karen told us the baby was home. I dropped the ball and went to the front of the yard; that's when I saw Marlene smiling and Mother holding the baby. I ran and hugged my sister so tight, and I turned to see the baby.

Mother stopped me in my tracks; she told me to go wash my hands; I even washed my face. Now I was about to look at this baby that I had waited to see when Mother gave me the baby to hold. I was so shackled; he was nothing she had told us. I didn't keep my thoughts to myself. "This baby is not handsome; where is the handsome child you told me about?" At this time, everyone's face was surprised, and my mother came over, took the baby away from me, and sent me outside. I felt so bad for what I said; everyone was talking about what I said. My mother let me feel as if I wasn't her child. Marlene didn't say anything; she just looked at me. I was so embarrassed to even look at them.

I kept hearing the voice in my head telling me that was wrong. I went outside and just sat down. I know that I was in a lot of trouble. I kept away from the baby because I didn't want to say something bad or hurt anyone's feelings. I could hardly wait until Friday to see my dad. He would understand. The weekend was here, and Dad was so excited to see them; I just watched them, Dad didn't even notice me, but I was still waiting for him to realize I was in the room with them. When he was finished with his grandson, then he came over to me. I got my hug and my goodies. Life was well when Dad was around; I didn't feel left out at all whenever Dad was home. The weekend went fast, and Dad was gone once more.

Chapter 3

One day, I came home from school, and my sister Marlene was washing the baby's clothes. This child was crying a lot. I went and told her that the baby was up and crying. Marlene said she had heard him, and he just had to wait until she was done. I couldn't handle the noise, so I went over to Oliver. When he saw me, he would stop crying. The minute I moved from the bed, he started to cry once more. I went to Marlene again and told her the baby was still crying. She told me the same thing as before; I couldn't deal with the noise, so I went and got my hands washed and went back in the room to him.

I don't know if I should stay with him; after all, Mother told me to stay away from him. As I looked at Oliver and he looked at me, I started to make funny faces at him. He didn't even smile at all; he kept looking at me. I guess he was still upset about what I had said about him; he started to cry, then I just told him that his mother was washing his clothes and she would be done soon. He just looked at me as if he understood. Then he started to cry once more; I just did the next thing I knew best. I sang to him. This brought me some time before his mother was done. This child seemed to be a handful, but I was okay with it.

The next day, I could hardly wait for school to be over so I could sing to Oliver. It seemed as if he liked my voice, even though Althea's voice was the best. School was over, and I went to Edson's class. I told him to hurry up. I didn't have much time to waste. He just shook his head and walked as fast as I was walking. In some way, I think that he was happy that Oliver came in the picture because I wasn't around him and his friends much. I had a new job now, which I loved.

This went on for some time. I knew my new job was a lot of work. I still find time to go to the corner of the street to wait for Dad; Beddy, the dog, never missed his pose; he was always on time. I don't know how he knew what time it was. Then Dad came to the street where we always waited for him. Beddy was barking, and I was yelling, "Sammy is coming!" I did this for a while until he got near, then he told me to be quiet. I just smiled and talked to him; he now asked about the baby and Mother. I told him they were fine, then he asked for Edson and the others. I told him the same thing; they were all fine.

I asked him how his week was. He would smile because he knew what was coming next. "So Sammy, what did you bring for me?" He would look into his bag and give me a bag of peanuts to share with Edson. When I called Edson, I began to share the peanuts. I would rob him so much: "One for you, two for me, then two for you, and three for me." I don't know if he knew that I was robbing him blind. Edson didn't care one bit, but that voice kept appearing and telling me that it was wrong. *How I love my life, apart from Mother sometimes telling me things to make me feel less of myself.*

As the months went by, my dad came home in the middle of the week. When I came home from school and saw him, I was happy. Dad, on the other hand, didn't look too well at all; he was sick. Mother asked him if he wanted to go to the hospital. He told her no, he just wanted some rest from work; his body was run down, he told her. I told him everything would be all right. I asked my mother if she wanted me to sleep with the rest of the kids, and she said that it would be fine.

A week had passed, and Dad was feeling better. He would start to notice things in the house that needed to be fixed, he would call Edson, and they would fix what needed to. Sometimes, Dad would yell a lot at Edson if he wasn't doing it right. Mother didn't like it one bit; I guess they didn't like the fact that Dad was home. He would see everything; then he decided to paint the house. He started it; then he got sick again. Mother told him that she thought he should go to the doctor just to see if anything was wrong or not. He didn't go at all; he was stubborn. I heard my mom crying out loud; it was my dad. He was vomiting blood; my mother panicked and was crying. We all were crying at this point; then she realized what she had done. She told Althea to call the neighbor to see if they could take them to the hospital. They got dressed, and off they went. Althea went with them while we were left with Marlene. I just cried because that was my best friend. Marlene told us to go back to bed because we had to go to school. I didn't know what in the world she was talking about school—my dad was sick! She insisted that we go to bed. That night I didn't sleep at all; my mind was on my dad so much.

I didn't know when I fell asleep; the next thing I knew, Marlene was waking us up for school. I asked her if they had come back, and she told me not yet. I went into the bathroom and got ready, and then Edson went in next. Karen would have to go by herself because Althea wasn't home yet with our parents. I didn't know why Marlene even sent me to school because I wasn't even paying any attention to what was being taught. My mind was on my dad; I couldn't wait to get home.

Soon school was over, and when I got home, they were not home yet; at this point, the only thing to do was wait. The house was so quiet; you could hear a pin drop, and even Oliver was calm. Edson was with Beddy, the dog; the two of them were in another world.

It was about 2:00 or 3:00 p.m. when we heard Mother talking to our neighbor. Althea came inside the house; she didn't say anything at all. She went into the bathroom and took a shower; when Mom came in after, the tears were rolling down her face, and we all asked her if Dad was all right. She said that he didn't look well at all.

Althea came out of the bathroom, then Mother went in. She took her shower, and then she was packing Dad's things to take to the hospital again. She didn't waste any time at the house, she told Marlene what to do, and she was out. The doctors had to run a lot of tests on Dad first; then, she would know what was wrong with him. Still no answer. I asked Marlene why she was sending me to school as she knew I wasn't learning anything. Then Gary, my eldest brother, told me to shut up and go to bed for school. I didn't like the way he treated me at all; he was always hitting me or telling me a lot of bad words, but Marlene would save me most of the time. The rest of them were afraid of him, but Dad told me not to be afraid of anyone.

Our dad was in the hospital for almost three weeks; he wasn't getting any better. The doctors didn't know what was wrong with him, now our dad's sister was there a lot. When Mother had the morning shift, she would do the night shift. This went on for some time. Mother was getting discouraged over the fact of our dad's sickness, and she didn't have any money to pay the bills and send us to school. She did the thing she knew best; she talked to the man Christ Jesus. She prayed and cried and cried and prayed. Then she told him thanks. I didn't hear God talk to her, but she did because I heard her thanking him. I didn't hear him one bit, but she did. The next day, Mom called Dad's friends and told them what was going on. I don't know what Jesus told her, but she was putting important papers together. The following day, she left the house and went only God knew where.

I didn't know how to talk to Jesus the way mother did. I knew that I said my little prayers at night, and Jesus didn't say much. On Sunday, when we went to church before Oliver was born, I would love to go to church for just the candy because I didn't understand anything at all. I knew whenever I did anything wrong, I would hear a small voice telling me that it was wrong. I was always sleeping in church; when service was over, they would wake me up. So I didn't hear too much of God talking.

Sunday school was too much; you would have to know Bible verses, which I was dumb, so I didn't know much. Church was okay, I thought, but I needed to go and pray for Dad. The weekend went fast. The following Monday, Mother got a call from one of my dad's friends. It seemed as if our dad was going to the USA. I guess this was what Mother and Jesus were talking about; they got him a visa for the USA so that he could see the doctor in America.

I was so glad that our dad was going to get the proper care he needed. Everything was going so fast; Mother was on the phone with our uncle. He was Dad's middle brother; he was coming to get Dad and take him to the US. All of this didn't take that long; before we knew it, our dad was on his way. I was crying, and so was everyone else. When he left, everyone was happy; we knew that he would get the help he needed. Mother was relieved of the stress; she did what she had to do.

We had food to eat, and she saw to it that the bills were paid; we didn't see Dad for almost seven months. I missed him a lot but not that much. Due to the fact that he was never home that much, I would just imagine that he was at work. This did a lot to me; I kept wondering if he still loved us. He didn't call at all, if he did. He only wanted to talk to our mother; that was all right with me; I still had Oliver to boss around.

One day, my mother asked me a question; she wanted to know how I felt about Dad coming home. I told her that I had missed him, but I didn't like the way he cursed too many bad words. I didn't like it one bit; she just smiled and said, "I know." Mother didn't talk much; she was just fixing the place up; she saw to it that the house was painted and what was broken got fixed. She even got a new mattress for Dad to sleep on and gave my sisters the one we slept on.

When everyone was busy working, I was just wondering what Dad would look like and what he would bring me from the US. The time came, and Mother left to go to the airport to get Dad. At this time, I would have to stay in the yard because I didn't know what time he was coming or which street he was coming on. When I heard the car pull up at the gate, I was smiling all over.

My best friend was home! Mother was all right, but Dad was the one I could get away with most of the time. When I saw him, I didn't even recognize him. Dad was so fat and was looking good; I was just watching him as he went over to the dog Beddy and hugged him first. I was wondering, *What in the world is wrong with my dad?* I was standing there, and he walked by me. Finally, he noticed me and said, "Where is my hug?" I didn't have words to answer him; I just hugged him so tight, as if I didn't want to let him go. When Dad greeted all of us, he took Oliver and was playing with him; I was so happy to see our family so happy again. Of course, that night, I would have to sleep with my siblings. I was fine with that.

The next day couldn't come any sooner; Dad got up early, and, of course, I was up too; I couldn't put my hands on it; my dad wasn't the same person I once knew. Dad's action was different, but I'd watch him really well to see if he would come back to me. I guess he didn't miss us anymore because it was seven months since he lifted us to get treatment in the USA. I watched everyone get mad at each other for no reason; it seemed as if something was taking over our home. Mother didn't pray like before; she did more complaining than ever, which wasn't helping our family at all. Dad was a totally different person.

One day, mother came to us and said that she had a surprise; I didn't like surprises at all because they came with a price. She said that when Dad got sick, and she was left with all of us to take care of, it was really hard. She saw where she couldn't handle it at all, and before she let anything happen to us, she would die.

I just watched her because I was just waiting for her surprise. Then she hit us with her going to the USA for six months and getting a job to help our dad with some of the bills, not to mention us as well. I didn't care about things from the USA. I just wanted my life back; I did everything I'd known to do just to make my mother feel guilty. She didn't listen at all. I asked her who would comb my hair or look over my homework.

I even told her I couldn't sleep by myself, anything for her to change her mind. She is a tough cookie to break, so I went to Dad to see what he thought about her leaving us. He was in the same boat as me; I didn't know what my brothers and sisters felt. I didn't ask them; I didn't care at all. Dad would be gone all week and come home on the weekend; no Mother to cook our dinner and wash our clothes. This wasn't right; I needed her more than ever. I was stuck with my siblings.

The day came, and Mother was all packed and ready to leave us; my heart was full. I just cried and cried; she didn't care at all. She went into the car with Dad and his friend. That evening, the house was quiet; everyone was in their own world. Dad, too, was quiet. He looked at me and said, "It's me and you, Bubup." I just looked at him and started to cry. I was nine years old; I'd never been without this woman. I saw her cry and talk to Jesus. She even talked to our neighbor, Dad, and everyone else. I didn't know if I could live without her.

It was Sunday morning, and our dad woke us up early to bowl him for his game as always; soon, our dad's sister came over.

She knew that Mother was gone; now dad wanted her to watch us while he went to work. This woman was on a trip. She found all the faults she could; she didn't like the fact that I was in the room with my parents. We had only two bedrooms, and it was eight of us. I guessed she wanted me on the floor. My aunt was my dad's oldest sister; she didn't like my mother at all. I was the only one who looked like my mother, so I was her number one target. She told me herself that she hated me; she even told me that I was ugly and a dunce.

Dad was at his cricket game, so she was there, and she cooked for us that Sunday. I knew my luck with her, so I stayed away from her presence. Karen and Gary were on her hit list as well. Aunty P wasn't afraid to show her favorite that evening when Dad came home from his game. He did what he did best. He called Edson, the dog, and me to the dinner table. It was his custom to do. So I went and sat next to Dad; soon, she came out of the room and saw us next to him while he was eating.

She started to yell at us, "Get up and move away from him!" She called us greedy kids and let us know that it was our fault that her brother was sick. I looked at my dad to see what he would say to her. He didn't say a word. I just went outside and cried. It really hurt because he didn't tell her to stop; after all, I was not the one that went around the dinner table; he called me.

While I was outside, Althea came and told me that our dad was calling me. I wasn't afraid of her, but I didn't like to be embarrassed at all. When I went inside the house, Dad shared my little dinner just for the fact that he wanted to eat with us. She didn't understand it at all; she looked at me as if I was a disease. I knew she hated me, and she didn't hide it one bit. I sat next to Dad, and she was just going on and on; she told him that we were spoiled and needed discipline.

While I was eating the food he had left for me, I could feel her eyes piercing me. Not before long, the phone rang; it was our mother. My heart felt much better, and everyone was happy to hear from her. Dad was looking at me to see if I would let her know that his sister was mean to me. I said nothing; I told her that I loved her and missed her. Mother then spoke to everyone else. My dad's sister got mad, which she didn't need to because she was a crazy woman herself. She went outside, talking to herself. I just smiled.

I knew that Monday was coming, and we would be left with that evil woman who didn't like us in the house, and my brother Gary didn't like us on the street. Edson and I didn't know where to go; we sometimes went over to our neighbor's house after school. I knew if Mother had been here, this could not have happened. I guess this was what we had to go through for a better life. We had to get used to this situation; this woman wasn't going anywhere. So we stayed out of her sight; I noticed that if I stayed away from Dad, everything would be all right with her. One day, she told Marlene that she had to go to her house for a couple of days, so we were left with our sibling.

We were so happy; at this time, everyone was doing their own thing. Edson and I were on the street most of the time; whenever we could go on the street, we were picking mangoes from our neighbor's tree at night; we didn't ask them if we could take them. I was the lookout girl because I was good at that, while Edson did the climbing. When we got our mangoes, we ate and were full. Our next mission the following day was the beach. Edson and I, with Beddy, the dog—it was the most dangerous adventure for me.

Everywhere we went, dogs were running after us because of Beddy. I jumped the fence I didn't know I could do; I could really go into track and field. It felt so peaceful when we reached the beach; I sat on the rock while Edson and Beddy went in the water. I sat down, and I felt a piece come over me; everything was just quiet. Then I heard the sound of the waves; I felt the cool breeze from the beach. Edson wanted to know if I was going into the water or not. I just shook my head and went in; I couldn't swim at all, so I stayed close to the shore. Beddy was having the time of his life; that was one of the happy moments I saw him have. We didn't stay too long because it was a long way home. I knew we had to do a lot of running until we got home.

Chapter 4

Out of all the days Marlene decided to look for us, I couldn't understand it at all. I guess she was all over the place because the neighbors asked us where we were. Edson told me not to answer them, but what could I have said? Our clothes were almost dry. No one would have known; the only thing that gave us away was my hair; it was still wet and had sand in it. I womaned up and took my beating well while Edson was outside with Beddy hiding. The dog was lucky no one disciplined him. I told Edson that Marlene's hits were not bad like Gary's, so he should get over it; moreover, she wouldn't tell anyone that we were missing because it would look bad on her.

He came in and took his beating like a man. I don't think that the beach was a good adventure for us because it came with a price. We stayed with our cooking and selling bottles and mango picking; if our neighbors ever knew, then that would be another beating. Life was fun; we got used to what to expect from our family. Oliver was too young to follow us, so he stayed home with his mother while Althea and Karen were into puppy love with their boyfriends. I should be playing with dolls, but Edson couldn't. We had a lot of fun until that woman came to our house.

I knew Dad was on his way home, so Beddy and I did our usual thing. This time, I didn't call out, "Sammy is coming," because they knew it was his time to get home. So I sat on the street corner with Beddy. When he saw Dad, his ears went up, so I smiled because I knew that Dad was near us. I stood up, and we both ran and met him. I asked him how his day was, and he told me fine; then he asked how our week was. I dared not tell him what we did. I said fine too; he just smiled and gave me the bag of peanuts to share with Edson. I didn't go inside because of that woman. Then Dad called me to come inside the house.

Marlene told me not to tell Dad that she beat us; I was no dummy; I knew if he found out, that would be the end of our freedom. Our mean aunt would have to live with us until Mother came home. I didn't think that I could handle it well enough. The weekend came, and I took my mental abuse from my aunt; she would make fun of our mother a lot while the others laughed as if it was funny. I didn't because what she was doing wasn't right at all; I knew that Gary wanted to give her a piece of his mind, but he had to be cool.

She would let me feel unworthy and ugly, not to mention dunce and stupid. In some way, I believed her because no one ever told me not to. They all looked at me as if it was true; even at school, it was the same thing with the teachers. I was a dunce that wasn't going anywhere in life. I started to believe everything they told me, so

I did the best thing I knew how. I would start fights at school, even if I couldn't handle them.

I would threaten them by telling them that Edson and his friends would give them a good beating. If only he knew what rumors I was telling. I was a bad cookie who didn't care at all; I found myself singing a song that Mother loved to sing—"I'm Nobody's Child" by Hank Snow. I would sing that song most of my life. This was everyday life; you had to do what you had to do.

The weekend was gone, our aunt stayed with us, and then she left; this time, she didn't leave any food for us to eat. I didn't know if she forgot or what. Marlene had to borrow money to buy food for us; I didn't know what was going on, but we had only oil, flour, and sugar. Althea made sugar dumplings, which we call *gungola*. This was our meal most of the days; Gary would cook tinned mackerel with rice or dumpling. I was sick and tired of it; they would beat me to eat it. Oh, I hated tinned mackerel; I guessed I had to eat it or else.

Every Friday evening when Dad was on his way home, his sister would go to the grocery store and buy the best things for our dad, so he thought that we were getting the same things he was getting. We didn't tell him at all because we didn't want him to get upset. So we kept our mouths shut; this went on for some time. I got so used to what to expect; it was the norm. We knew how to handle it very well; Dad came home and was gone most of the day; we were on our daily mission as usual.

One night, Gary went out; our dad's sister decided to lock him out of the house. When he came home, she refused to open the door. He was so upset that he started to curse her out; I don't know if it was right or not, but that led to Gary leaving the house. He would have to stay at our neighbor's house. I don't know what happened, but Aunt Cislyn was at our home. She wanted to talk to our dad. It was interesting. I didn't know what was going on, but our aunts were at each other's throats. When Dad came home, he didn't know what to do. Aunt Cislyn told him the treatment we were getting, and I watched his face change with unbelief; I looked at him with pity. The poor man never knew what we were going through, he looked at me, and I felt his pain to know that he had trusted his own sister and to think that she would hurt his children like that.

The same night, Dad's sister left the house, and Aunt Cislyn too; it seemed as if Mother found out what was going on and made a call to her sister, who came and fixed everything. That night, Dad was mad at me because I didn't tell him. I told him that it was his sister. She should have known better; he never said another word. That weekend, he didn't go to his games, which was no fun. We had to stay inside the house.

Dad would play his records, like The Platters, The Temptations, The Drifters, etc. I knew most of these songs. When he wasn't singing, he was whistling. I couldn't whistle, so I sang along with him. It was fun having Dad home with us, but he was interfering with our adventures.

We had Marlene taking care of us until Mother came home. I knew she was coming soon; everyone was busy cleaning up the place. I helped Edson with whitewashing the walls; we didn't have money to buy paint, so we used what we had just to let the place look good for Mother. Dad, too, was excited that Mom was coming home; we all did what we had to do.

For some reason, I thought that she was coming the following weekend; to my surprise, she came three weeks after. The day came for our mother to come home, and everyone was excited. We waited patiently for her, and Dad left with one of his friends to the airport. It was the longest wait ever; I went inside the house, so Edson was on guard. Then he gave out the sound; Mom was home. I ran so fast to the front of the yard. As I watched her come out of the vehicle, I just stood there and stared at her. I couldn't believe that my mother was really home.

She looked so different and beautiful; no wonder these people hated her so much. I looked at Dad, and he was smiling inside out. She didn't greet Beddy like our dad did; she greeted her kids, and she hugged me so tight. *Man, I missed this woman so much!* Not before long, Mother and Althea left the house to go and get Gary. He was still at our neighbor's house; I knew that Dad felt bad, but he didn't know that his sister was treating us like that. Mother went and got her son and took him home. Gary didn't like our dad one bit, so he didn't want to come back home at all without Mother being in the house.

I was so happy that we were all okay, Mother was home, and all was well; of course, I had to sleep with my sibling that night. The next day, Mother was packing out our things; I got a nice doll and pretty dresses and outfits. I was really happy. Edson got cars and clothes too. We were so pleased; she knew what we had need of; Althea and Karen had almost the same thing, and Marlene and Oliver were happy too, not to mention Gary, her pet. As I watched everyone looking at their gifts, I kept thinking, *What if Mother didn't come home? What would have happened to us?* It was a scary thought; I didn't need to go there.

As always, Dad went to work and came home on the weekend. Mother was making her second trip to the USA; it seemed she was getting tired of us, or she loved what the US had to offer. Dad didn't like it at all; he thought that she should stay home and take care of us, but my sisters and brothers loved the fact of getting new stuff. I loved new things too, but it took my joy away.

Mother was getting ready to leave us again as she made her plans; Marlene and Gary were to take care of us. Dad was more in the dark, so he did what he did best. He went to his sister and back home; she didn't care for us at all; after all, she told us that we were killing her brother. We had gotten used to our lives, and we knew what to do. When we didn't have food, we would make *gongola*. Sometimes, we didn't go to school because of lunch money. We didn't dare let Dad know that. After all, everyone was having the time of their lives.

As always, the months went by really fast, and Mother was home; at this time, we found out that Marlene was pregnant again. Dad didn't say another word; he just let Mother have her way. It seemed as if it wasn't working out too well for her. She had stopped talking to the man Christ Jesus; she was doing a lot of her own thing, which didn't make sense at all.

Everyone was growing up fast, and a lot was changing, even myself. I didn't like what I'd become. I was skinny and ugly, with a lot of pimples, and everyone would make fun of me. I didn't stay around Edson too much because of his friends. They were older boys, and I knew I wasn't welcome with his friends at all. My neighbor next door was all grown up, so I didn't have any friends at all. So I made a doll out of paper and made her some clothes that I took to Marlene. She told me to wait until she got some markers my dad had. She borrowed them and colored the dresses for me. They were pretty, and I loved them, not knowing it would cause an argument. Our dad came home and noticed that we had used his markers. He got so upset and yelled a lot while cursing bad words. I felt really bad because it was my fault. Then he took the markers and broke them up. I just looked at him with tears in my eyes; he could have given them to me. I just looked at him and walked away; my heart was full.

I didn't know what was happening to my parents, but they weren't the same people I once knew. Marlene came over to me and said to stop crying because she got one of the markers that Dad didn't find. Then my eldest sister started to sing a song that she made up on the spot: "You got my brother, but you didn't get me; I was hiding in the left breast." I started to laugh because I didn't know what in the world she was singing.

My paper dolls were now my best friends; I played with them and sang too. One day, Edson's friend came over to the house to play with him; he would tell me how ugly I was and show his genitals to me; he told me that he would put it on me. I ran and hid. At this point, I was afraid of this boy; whenever he came over to the house to play with Edson, he would threaten me a lot. This young man didn't know I would put up with it for a while, but he didn't get me out; I guess he didn't know.

One day, he came to visit my brother, but Edson was busy making me a dollhouse with a large box. The young boy knew that it would take some time. He looked at me and said that he was going to put his friend on me (talking about his genitals). I just took up the knife that Edson was using and threw it right toward him. I didn't wait to see where it landed, but I knew he got hit because he was screaming like a little girl.

I got up and ran; I knew he wasn't dead because he was making a lot of noise. Mother came looking for me; I knew that I was dead myself. When my mother found me, I was under the bed, hiding. She asked me what had happened; I told her he had shown me his penis and wanted to show me again. She just laughed at me; I started to laugh too, but she gave me a nice piece of whipping. Mother dressed the young man's wound over his eyes and took him home to his mother. I heard that his mother beat him too. When Mother came home, she told me what I did was wrong and that I could have hurt the young boy really badly. I just stood there and listened to her. I knew that Dad was going to hear about this.

When I was finished with my punishment, I went outside the next day; our neighbors had heard what I did. Now I was the bad girl in town. I would pick fights I had no business with; I remembered what my dad always told me: never to be afraid of anyone.

Some fights I got in, I won, and some... I learned how to run. They say in Jamaica, those who fight and run away will fight another day. So I did just that; I didn't like to trouble people, but if they messed with me, I would help myself. Sometimes, I would win the fights, and sometimes, I really had to run away. This went on for a while, and then I was back with my paper dolls again.

Life seemed the same as always; Dad would come home on the weekend, and everyone was unhappy because he would act up and curse a lot. Mother was his number one target; I would just look at him really well and walk away; after all, he told me not to be afraid of anyone. I tried not to let all this get to me because if you don't think about it, you'll be fine.

At school, I was talking to my friends; they were telling me about their lives at home with their stepparents. I asked one of them what had happened, if they had "stepped" on their parents. Man, they laughed at me so hard; I didn't know what being a stepmother and stepfather meant. No one taught me these things. I knew about Mom and Dad; that was all I knew. When I got home, I asked Karen what being a "stepdad" meant. She told me it was like our brother Gary; he wasn't our dad's son. He had another father, but our dad didn't treat him any differently from us. Gary was our oldest brother, and that was how we grew—one happy family—I guessed.

Chapter 5

One day, our aunt came to visit us; she was looking for our mother. The only problem was, my mother had left to visit our aunt in the country. What was really going on? We were all crying and curious to know where our mother was. Marlene told us that she was fine, and then she went into the room with our aunt. "You're a child," they said, "you should not ask or say anything." Marlene told me not to mention this to Dad; after all, he was my best friend, and I thought he needed to know whether Mother was missing or not.

Everyone seemed to know everything but me; no wonder they call me a dunce. When Mother came home the next day, she greeted her sister as if she didn't see her in a while. I asked her where she was and added that her sister, to whose house she had left, came looking for her. She looked at me with a look I'd never seen before, as to say, "Don't you ever dare question me!" I didn't know if I should stay in her presence or not; I just walked away. My family treated me like I didn't have much sense and couldn't do anything for myself. When Dad came home, everyone was happy and talking; Dad wasn't cursing at all. He was making jokes with our aunt. She was the one Marlene was staying with when she was pregnant with Oliver. There was something about this woman my spirit didn't like; I didn't dare tell them. Mother seemed happy, after all, so I was happy too. Our family was the same as always; one minute, they were happy, and the next, they were sad. I got so used to it. I tried not to let it get the best of me. One thing I knew, my grades were not looking too good. Mother, on the other hand, didn't help at all. She would curse and tell me that I was not going to turn out to be anything; this really hurt a lot as a child. Some parents have their favorite child, and I knew I wasn't hers. As time passed on, I started to believe her, and now my grades were bad.

I really didn't care at all because, as my mother told me, I was going to sell in the market. Karen and Althea were her favorite children; Marlene had two kids already. Edson was her pet, not to mention Gary.

I was a nobody in their eyes except Dad; I don't know what he saw in me, but he would let me feel safe and loved. No one could do me any harm and get away with it. I tried to stay away from everyone at this time. I played with my paper dolls and kept really far. Mother, on the other hand, was going out at the neighborhood bar a lot; it seemed as if she forgot about the man Christ Jesus. She didn't talk to him much, and I didn't have much to say to him either. He never seemed to answer me when I looked up.

It seemed our family was getting crazy because Marlene and Althea were fighting over boys while Gary was fighting too. This home was chaos, and when Dad came home, it wasn't any better. I got used to this life, which was either you ignored them or acted like them. I ignored them; who would have known me to ignore them? It kept me out of trouble, which I'd learned.

I didn't study at all; after all, I was dumb, and no one took the time out to help me with schoolwork. Now I was dropped down to a lower class; this was where all the dumb kids went. I was happy to see my cousin in the same class. All of my friends didn't talk to me because I wasn't in their class, so I stuck to where I belonged. My cousin and I were best friends now; every day, I would go to her house, and we would pick fruits from her mother's tree. My mom knew where I was at all times because she was always on the phone with my cousin's mom. When it was time for me to go home, she would call my mom and let her know that I was on my way.

School was always fun with my cousin. We would play a lot and make jokes; sometimes, we made fun of people. Life couldn't get any better. Now exams were coming up, and everyone was studying; I didn't because I didn't know what I was doing anyway. Mother didn't have the money for me to get extra lessons, and some of the teachers in Jamaica didn't want to waste their time with you if they didn't see any potential. So I just prayed to Mom's friend that night to help me; I only hoped he did. Now they would know that I wasn't as dumb as how they thought.

As the days went by, I still came and waited for Dad at the corner of the street. His face sometimes seemed as if he was tired of me, but I still went and got my peanuts. Beddy always made me look bad; after all, he couldn't eat nuts. He was just happy that Dad was home, unlike everyone else. Meanwhile, Mother was still visiting our aunt even more often than before. One day, she brought home a new puppy. This puppy was very beautiful! Edson was so in love that Beddy got jealous. Whenever the puppy went near him, he would bark at him. When our dad came home that weekend and saw the dog, he was a little bit mad. Mother didn't tell him at all; we were happy for a new face to play with. Our dad and Beddy were not. The new puppy was a lot of fun and work, but he didn't know about Beddy's and my routine on Friday evening. I would look into Beddy's eyes and see that he was sad; that was the same way I felt when Oliver got in the picture. I told him he would get over it. It seemed he understood me; then his tail started to move; I knew Dad was near.

On Saturday midday, our cousin came to visit. She was the one that had Marlene at her house when she ran away; we were all happy to see her, but she had another appointment to make. She gave my mother a letter from my dad's sister in the US. As Mom was reading the letter, she was crying and yelling; she went over to Dad with tears in her eyes and asked him what his sister was talking about. He said nothing to her; then she kept asking him what she meant by it, but he still didn't say a word. Then I saw her run to the kitchen and grab a knife and go towards Dad. He didn't move or say anything but shook his legs; good thing Althea was close by to grab the knife from her.

It was so crazy to see all of that coming from the same woman who told me that knives were dangerous. The house was in an up roll, everyone was crying, and Dad was just sitting there. It seemed as if he didn't care at all. I'd never seen my mother so hurt; this was the second time I saw her that way. The first time was when my dad's mother died. I kept looking at Dad to see if he was going to tell her he was sorry. No, not Jamaican man. Dad didn't show any affection or love; I was so sorry for both of them. That day my heart fell.

I was hurting inside out; I didn't know what was in the letter, but I knew that Mother was devastated. I remember my mother holding her hand up to God and saying that she couldn't take it anymore. Then my dad turned to her and said, "If you can't take it, leave it." It seemed as if he spoke the magic words; she just shook her head and said, "Yes, Winston." I only thanked God that Gary wasn't there because I knew he would have hurt Dad. At this time, Mother was packing up her things. She was going to our aunt in the country.

She left us and took the bus to her sister. I kept wondering why our cousin didn't stay home with the letter; now our family was in real trouble. I had no one to talk to; my heart was hurting really bad. The only place I had was school. I didn't let what was happening at the house get to me. I put all my trust in my cousin, but she had something else up her sleeves. I could not believe my ears what she was telling my classmate; she told them that my parents were breaking up and that I was moving to the country. Not to mention I had a stepdad; my heart dropped.

I couldn't believe what I was hearing; how could this be? I knew that we were not the perfect kids, but how could Mother do this to Dad? I didn't know if I should tell my siblings or ask my mom. I knew that my heart was hurting really bad. I was going out of my mind. I would fight my cousin at school so that she would keep her mouth shut about this thing, but she kept on talking.

Her mother told my mom what I was doing at school, so Mother gave me a fine whipping; I took it and then went to school and took it out on her all over again. When I wasn't fighting, I was selling bottles to buy cigarettes to smoke; I didn't know what I was doing; after all, my brother Gary did it.

One day, Althea's boyfriend caught me smoking and asked what I was doing; I knew he saw me with the cigarettes. Then he told me not to do it again and started to give me the whole lecture about what it could do to me. Then he let me promise him. Of course, I told him yes; I didn't even tell Edson what was going on, and no one would believe me anyways.

One day, Edson and I were looking through Dad's things, and that was when we saw the Bible. Our dad had a big Bible with pictures in it; I couldn't read well enough to know what it was saying. So I looked at the pictures. I saw the man Christ Jesus Mother talked to; he was looking at the young boy who was smoking, and he was upset.

He had his finger pointing at the boy; I told Edson that he was upset with the kid. As we looked through the big book, we got scared. He put the Bible back, but I took it out and showed Althea's boyfriend; that's when he told me Jesus didn't like it. I kept wondering why my brother Gary smoked if Jesus didn't like it. They didn't read Jesus's book at all in my house. Mother prayed a lot, not as much as before. I knew Dad didn't pray at all, even if he did. I didn't see him doing it. As time went by, I forgot about what my cousin was saying; whenever Dad came home, Mother slept in the living room with my brother Gary.

I still slept with Dad; he didn't bother or ask me anything. I just went to sleep; the weekend went by so fast. It was a new week, and I was about to find out if I had passed my exam; of course not. I didn't hear the end of it; I was told that I was going to sell in the market. I was really hurt to hear this thing coming from my mother. I wanted to give her a piece of my mouth, but I knew I would be dead. She was acting as if every one of us passed these exams, even Karen or Althea. Gary was the only one who did, but he didn't care at all. I couldn't wait for summer to come and for the kids to leave me alone about this thing about my parents, but I should be careful what I wish for.

Summer was here, and our mother was packing up everything; she was moving, after all. I started to talk to Jesus, for him to stop all this nightmare, but he didn't hear me at all. She had made up her mind, and that was final; when Dad came home that weekend, he didn't say anything at all; he just picked up his cricket thing and went to his game. I was so mad at everyone; I couldn't think straight; at this time, everyone was crying. I didn't want to go away to my aunt's house; I didn't like her at all because she cursed and smoked a lot of weed.

Chapter 6

There was something about her I would get angry inside of me. I only wished Dad could have told Mother that he was sorry and they would make it up. I kept looking to see if Jesus would stop her, but she was on a mission, and even if Jesus was talking to her, she wasn't listening at all. Althea and Karen ran over to our neighbor's house; they didn't want to go either. Edson was crying too because he was leaving Beddy, his best friend, behind. My heart was just aching.

Mother took her dog with us and left Beddy behind; as the truck rolled out of the yard, I could see Beddy barking and following us. When he couldn't follow us anymore, he stopped. I cried more; no more Beddy to follow me to meet my dad. I didn't know what to think; my heart was too full. I didn't know when I fell asleep; the next thing I felt was Mother waking me up.

We were at our aunt's house; she loved the fact that we were there; my aunt just looked at me while I did the same. Gary and Marlene were happy that they were gone from Dad; Edson, on the other hand, didn't let it bother him at all, if it did. He didn't let anyone know; he missed Beddy, without a doubt. Althea and Karen were still crying, not over Dad but their boyfriends. I watched them pack out the truck; I remember Gary yelling at me to help them. He told me that my father wasn't here to help me now; I didn't pay him any attention. I just did what I had to do. Then my cousin came over toward me. She told me that she was going to the neighbor's house. She wanted me to follow her.

My aunt had two daughters; one was Edson's age, and the other one, I was two years older than her. She took me around the place to show me off to her friends; the country wasn't anything like the city. The only thing I was doing was comparing; their bathroom was outside, and the kitchen didn't have running water. Whenever you had to do a number two, you would really have to watch out for bugs, and it had a horrible smell. I just stared at everyone while they were talking and laughing; my mind was on Beddy and Dad. I didn't know if he was crying or happy because how could you let this woman walk out of your life with your kids?

That night, my dad was the number one topic; they talked about him so much. I had to speak up; I told them that all of them should leave Sammy alone. My mother stared at me, then Gary came over to me with one hit in the back and told me to shut up. Marlene was going on and on about how he'd made her feel while Gary was cursing his bad words. Mother was telling everyone how unhappy she was. I didn't want to hear it at all; I looked at the rest of my siblings to see if they had anything to say, but they kept quiet.

I was hurting inside out; my heart was racing so fast. I could hardly breathe. No one talked about my parents; even when I was around my dad's sister, she spoke bad things about Mom. I looked at her really badly and walked away while my sisters laughed. I hated every moment of this; I couldn't handle this at all. My life was really in a bad situation; this time, I didn't know what to do or who to talk with. That night, I went to bed crying. I was heartbroken.

The following day, this man came over to our aunt's house; my mother called me over to introduce me to him. I just looked at him because I knew just who he was. He told her that I looked just like her, then she told him that she wasn't ugly like that. Everything this man said, Mother was laughing like a young teenager. Althea and Karen didn't come at all to be introduced; my aunt was just watching us react to this man. Edson didn't let anyone get the best of him at all; he knew how to ride the waves. That night, Mother went away with this man; I was so mad. He took me away from Dad to live with these siblings, who didn't like me at all. I cried more that night.

The week went by so fast, no sign of Dad. I saw my mother's boyfriend more than anyone whenever he came around. I would go next door to see my cousin's neighbor, even though I didn't know him. I just wanted to get out of their sight; I guessed this man noticed it because he told my mother that he thought I didn't like him. He guessed right—no one was going to take the place of my dad. Mother spent more of her time with this man while I was trying to adjust to my surroundings. I tried, but it wasn't working at all.

As the days went by, so did the weeks. It was summer, and we didn't have anywhere to go or anything to do. I was bored out of my wits. Now Mother came to us with the most dreadful news; she was about to take her trip to America. I was dead, and I knew it; why would she take me away from Dad and leave me with these people? I knew my dad's sister didn't like me, but I knew to stay away from her. Now I didn't know if I could handle this at all because Gary was my number one enemy. I didn't know if I should cry or die.

The day came as always, and Mother was packing up to leave again; my aunt and Althea took her to the airport. That night, I was going out of my mind; no Mother and Father around me. Edson had new friends, while Karen and Althea were more of our aunt's pets. I played with my cousin most of the time, but I still missed Dad. My cousin would take me into the church that was in the yard; they said that my great-granduncle built it. It was a church of God of Prophecy. We would play in God's house, and no one would tell us to stop. Our aunt didn't respect God at all because when she cursed bad words, our dad could not compare to her; she was number one.

I didn't talk to God at all; after all, he didn't answer me whenever I called him. My cousin was just like her mother; she cursed a lot of bad words. One day, I told her to stop cursing in God's house; she got upset and told my aunt. That day, I noticed everything was changing a lot. My aunt's true color was showing now; she wasn't the same person they thought she was. I didn't know what it was, but I knew it all along. Every morning, she would get up and curse everyone. She didn't have to beat you; just her words would do more danger than ever. *Why did Mother put us in this situation?*

This time, my mother was sending money for the bills and to buy food for us, but we weren't getting any at all. My aunt loved to entertain her friends with my mother's money. She would cook big pots of food and have a feast; then, the rest of the week nothing for us to eat. Marlene didn't stay around too much because she was a competition for my aunt. I was a nobody; I was too skinny and ugly. No one noticed me at all; for Althea and Karen, they were all that. I wasn't jealous at all because I knew what that meant in Jamaica.

I didn't have anyone to play with because I told my cousin she cursed too much. She didn't play too much with me; I stayed with Oliver and his sister, Kim. I took care of them whenever Marlene went out. My aunt would send me to the shop to buy food for her, and when she cooked, she would tell me that it couldn't be shared. I would wait for Marlene to come home because I knew that I was going to get something to eat. Whenever my aunt cooked, she told my brother Gary to let me wash the dishes. I tell you, I had to wash the dishes in a big pot of water in the yard all by myself. I did this in the morning and at dinner time. These were my daily chores, sometimes in the burning sun.

I remember one day, I got upset and told them that I wasn't going to wash any plates; it was best that I kept that thought to myself; the beating that I got from my brother Gary wasn't pretty at all. He beat me like a man. When he was finished, I still had to wash them up without any food. I put the big pot and filled it up with water and washed all of them out. My heart was so bitter toward them, how I hated everyone. I hated my mother for having an affair with Dad; I hated my dad because he didn't even come once to see if I was okay or not.

I hated my auntie from the get-go; she had some evil spirit in her. I hated that man my mother bought into my life. I hated my life itself because I didn't see where I was going at all. I was full of hatred and envy. I started to keep to myself most of the time; sometimes, I even had daydreams. I would take myself to places in my mind just to escape from the abuse that surrounded me. In my aunt's house, there were a lot of men, all kinds of them. She sold weed; of course, it was obvious a lot of men were around. She loved to show off my sisters a lot, and with me, I was what you would call a maga dog. They broke every self-esteem in me that you could think of.

After a while, I stopped crying and believed them. I would sometimes answer them when they called me bones. This was my everyday life; whenever I tried to fight back, my aunt would send my brother Gary to deal with me. She had him wrap up with the weed. He knew where to get his fix, and she loved this. Marlene was leaving her kids a lot, and my aunt spoke to her about it, but nothing changed.

One weekend, Marlene took Edson and me to see Dad. I couldn't believe it at all. She told us not to mention the treatment we were getting. Even though Edson wasn't being abused, he told me because of my mouth, I should do what he did. How could you be quiet when things are not right? When we reached Dad's house, Beddy was outside; when he saw Edson, he was just barking as if his best friend was home.

Edson went over to Beddy and hugged him so tight, but he was hurt. Beddy got a lot of dog bites; Edson was crying because he wasn't there to help him. Then Dad came out, and he was just smiling. I just ran into his arms and hugged him as if I didn't want to let him go. I wanted to let him know what I was going through, but I didn't want my mother to look bad. Our dad's sister was there, I didn't want Marlene to leave, but she had to get back home for her kids.

The next day, Dad was home with us; he didn't play cricket at all. He went to the store and got things he didn't get before. He made breakfast, which I didn't even know that he could cook. He told Marlene that she should come home and take care of us, but she didn't want to hurt my mother's feelings.

He even went to our neighbor's to see if she would keep us, but she told him no. Dad didn't want to leave us with his sister at all. I don't think she wanted that responsibility. I knew he tried because I was with him. He couldn't leave us by ourselves. He had to work. I remember he looked at me and said, "Bubup, I don't know what to do." I told him that I would ask Althea if she would take care of us. After all, she didn't want to leave our aunt's house.

Marlene came for us that Sunday evening; we told our dad the next week. He gave us bus fare to come back and see him. When I left, I was so happy to know that he still loved us and that he cared so much.

I didn't care at all what people were doing to me or calling me. The following weekend, Marlene didn't take us to see Dad; I was upset, but Marlene had to use the money for food for us. This time, things were getting worse; we weren't getting food at all because my aunt thought that her friends were more important than us, even though it was our mother's money that was being spent. We couldn't say anything at all; I missed Dad.

One day, my mother's friend came over to visit us; he brought us milk from the farm he worked at and a large loaf of bread. He even gave Marlene money to buy food for us and gave her bus fare for Edson and me to visit our dad. When he left the house, my aunt dogged him and my mother out in front of Edson, Althea, and Karen, not to mention her friends.

She let my mother look so bad; I could not believe this woman. She was one of them who encouraged our mom to leave Dad. I looked at my sisters and just shook my head; they never said anything to defend our parents at all; when it was my dad's sister making fun of Mom, they would laugh. When they talked bad things about Dad, no one said anything.

Now my aunt was dogging my mother out; I just walked away from them. This made my aunt really mad, one thing with Gary. No one messed with his mother; Marlene was in the room with her kids. She didn't hear her at all; it seemed as if Althea and Karen were brainwashed; as I said, Edson didn't care one bit. That Friday, we went to see Dad; he left the key with our neighbor just in case we came. Marlene told us not to go outside without Dad being there; before she left, our dad's sister came. She was cursing us so badly. "I don't want you, kids, coming around my brother and hurting him the way your mother did. He was looking for you, kids, for two weeks and no sign at all." Marlene told her what had happened, but she didn't care at all.

When Marlene left, Dad came home. He was so happy to see us; he asked me what had happened. I told him that we used his bus fare to buy food; he asked what our mother was doing. I didn't dare answer that. We were told not to tell him too much because we would hurt our mother a lot.

This went on for a while, we would visit, and then sometime we couldn't visit. At this time, summer was over, and our aunt didn't get us registered for school; she said we weren't her children. Mother's boyfriend came by to see if we needed lunch money, but to his surprise, Edson and I were not even registered for school. Althea and Karen got into school, which our mother had paid for. Edson and I had to wait.

It seemed as if my mother's friend just came by and found out; he got so upset with my aunt. He knew that she was getting our mother's money, and she wasn't doing what she was supposed to do. This made our aunt really mad; she was having a field day with him, and he gave Marlene money to get us registered for school. Our aunt had to give her money for our uniform; that was how we got into school. This wasn't good now because the money wasn't lasting. After all, we had to go to school now. Our aunt cursed most of the time whenever we got money. We had to buy food to eat, so we weren't going to school regularly at all.

Our family was divided; Althea, Karen, Edson, and Gary were our aunt's favorites; as for me and Marlene, we were the outcast. This time, she would cook and not leave any at all for us. Marlene went out at night and would bring us food to eat. One day, she left and didn't come home that night; we didn't go to school either. I was hungry, and so were Marlene's kids. I took it upon myself and told my cousin that I was going to play a game. I told her that I was the husband and she was the wife, my aunt's friends' kids were supposed to be our children. I told them that I was going to cook some food. So I told my cousin to get some flour for us to cook, then her friend's son told me he could climb the banana tree and get some for us to cook. That night, I ate it with butter; I was full, and the kids were too. When Marlene came home, she bought us food to eat.

The following day, my aunt woke up and found that we had picked her bananas; she turned into a witch; she called me out of all the kids and put me in the middle of them. She told me I was a thief and deserved to be punished; while she was talking and everyone was looking at me, I blocked them all out; her mouth was moving, but I didn't hear one thing she was saying. I didn't know when she dismissed me; I was still standing there in the middle of them.

I looked at my sister's face; they looked ashamed of me. Gary, of course, grabbed me and hit me; I took his beating as always. I went to the back of the yard with the tears just rolling down my cheeks. Then Althea came behind me, asking why I took her bananas without asking her. Then Gary came to curse me more. I got so mad that I just told them I was hungry, so if I had to get something to eat, I did what I had to do. I would do just that. I told them they didn't care if my aunt wasn't feeding me at all. They were okay because they had food. When they came from school, they got their meal; I didn't. "So beat me all you can; I don't really care at all." Gary just looked at me and walked away; Althea went to Marlene, and they were both talking.

I was the problem child at this time; I wasn't used to all of this. I was the baby that had to survive. I had to grow up really fast at the age of time. I was left on my own. I couldn't tell Mother anything, and it was forbidden to even mention Dad's name. Now, whenever anything happened in my aunt's house, I would fix it before my aunt saw it. I tried to keep Marlene's kids in the room, out of my aunt's way, because my sister wasn't there much.

One Sunday morning, I was in bed, with my thoughts all over the place, and not before long, the rain came down suddenly. I heard a voice like my dad's. "The rain just came down and wet me up." After all, I knew that it wasn't my dad because he wasn't coming for us at all. Then Althea called us; it was my dad, after all; how the heavens had opened up for a child's cry. I couldn't believe my eyes; it was Dad. He had come to save us from this place; Dad was upset about the condition of the place. He was mad at our mother. I just looked at him as he went on. Gary didn't like the fact that my dad was there.

I just looked at him with my heart full. Dad told Althea to come back to the house. She told him she was going to school. I didn't get it; why no one wanted to go back home? I guess I was the only one who was living in madness. When he left, he gave her money for food and lunch money; not to mention bus fare for us. I couldn't wait that weekend to come so that we could see Dad. We got there late, so Dad had left; he thought that we were not coming. Marlene went over to our neighbor's house to see if she had the keys. She didn't want us to get it, but Marlene got upset and told her a piece of her mind; then she gave her the key.

We went in, and then she left. Beddy was happy as always; when Dad came in and saw us, he was smiling all over. I was happy as always to see him. I only wished I was old enough to take care of the kids and myself. This went on for some time; we would go to school for two days, and the rest of the week, we couldn't. It was really hard how I had to suffer for everyone else while they were having fun; my sisters were having the time of their lives; they were going to school and parties while my aunt cooked for them. They were okay while Gary was getting what he loved. His weed.

Chapter 7

They didn't care if I was getting all this abuse from my aunt. Marlene helped when she wanted, but she, too, wanted her freedom. They never took me to call Mother in the US; it was always Althea and Karen who went. The only thing I heard was Mother said hi. I couldn't spell that well to even write her a letter; after all, I didn't know where she was. No one cared at all. I should just live in sin with everyone else; this was everyday life for me.

Whatever my cousin wanted, she got. She slept in the same bed with us, and sometimes, she wet the bed and got up crying; then my brother, who was to look after his baby sister, would tell me to sleep in the wet urine bed. It was cold, and the smell stank. I didn't dare open my mouth; after all, it was her mother's house. I learned to take the good with the bad; every time I thought about Mother and what she did. Mother felt she was saving us from Dad, but she was only saving the ones that mattered to her the most, the ones that did what was right in their eyes, while the others had to pay the price. I didn't ask for this life that I was living at all.

There was no way out for me; I was back into a corner and no way out; I didn't want to live this way at all. I couldn't run away because I didn't know where to go. My life was a mess; if I ran away, I could be killed or even raped. I stayed because I didn't want either one. My sister Marlene wasn't at my aunt's house as much because she didn't like her at all. Her kids missed her a lot. I did my best to keep them away from these people. Whenever Marlene was around, it was a problem for my aunt.

One day, my aunt told my sister that she and her kids had to leave her house. I was devastated about what I'd heard and couldn't believe that. I saw the tears come out of Marlene's eyes. She heard these words again; she didn't want to go back to Dad's house. What in the world was wrong with these people? I couldn't understand why; Dad would do everything for us to come back home and be with him. I remember asking my sister if I could come with her, and she told me no.

Marlene didn't want to get in any trouble with my aunt, but I did. My cousin was there and heard when I asked Marlene if I could come with her; she went and told her mother. The next thing I knew, my aunt was calling me; she loved to embarrass me a lot in front of her friends. While Marlene was packing up her things, my aunt asked me who my mother left me with. "I don't know," I told her. She got mad and told me to get out of her sight; I did just that. I really didn't know who my mother had left me with because this woman didn't care about me one bit. When she cooked, she told me it couldn't be shared; she didn't care if I went to school or not. She even made sure that my brother Gary disciplined me well. Sometimes, I had to go to the shop and get things she needed and wash their dirty dishes whenever she cooked. Then she would give my brother weed to smoke, which made him listen to her.

I went outside and watched Marlene pack her things in Mother's boyfriend's van. Marlene had told this man everything but was scared to let our dad even know what was going on. My heart was beating so fast; I couldn't let her leave me all alone; I didn't know where I got the courage from.

I just jumped the gate and ran into the van; I didn't look back. I didn't pack anything at all. I left my aunt's house with the street clothes I had on. Marlene didn't put me out of the van; she told the driver to keep on driving. I felt relief; I didn't know what I was going into, but I would have done everything possible to get away from that house.

When I got to my mother's boyfriend's house, he was cooking up a storm. He told his friend to come for Marlene and the kids. He didn't know that I was coming; heck, I didn't know that I was going. When we reached his home, I just looked at him while Marlene poured out her heart. I really felt sorry for her; the only thing pondering in my head was if I'd made the right choice.

Mother's boyfriend was really upset to know that my mother's own sister would treat us like that. This man knew how to cook, unlike my dad. When I was finished with dinner, he washed the dishes too. I offered to, but he told me to rest. I asked Marlene if she had anything that I could put on. She gave me one of Oliver's T-shirts; it was a little bit small. This was the least of my problem; that night, I had a piece over my soul. No one to curse me or beat me. Even my niece, Kim, and nephew, Oliver, were okay. That night, I didn't know when I fell asleep.

The next day, this man cooked a pot of cornmeal porridge; I'd never had this before. It was so good. He really knew how to cook. Mother's boyfriend lived on a farm with all kinds of animals and fruit trees. This was a different experience for me; I didn't have any clothes at all, so I couldn't go anywhere. I would wear my sister's clothes that were too big for me; I wasn't going to school at all either; most of all, I was looking at the animals, and when I got bored, I picked mangoes.

Marlene wasn't allowed to go back to my aunt's house at all. One thing I could say, I really missed my dad; he probably thought that we didn't want to see him at all. I knew that his sister was happy that we stayed away.

One day, Edson came to visit me after school, and Mother's boyfriend took him to the house. I was happy to see him; I asked Edson why he didn't bring my clothes. He looked at me and said if I was crazy, he didn't want to get in any trouble with my aunt. After all, she hated me a lot, he told me. Even though I knew that she hated me, it still hurt. As the months went by, I wasn't going to school at all. No one cared one bit. Marlene didn't even tell my mother what had happened. She didn't want to worry her; then she would have to get back home.

I was fine and getting food to eat; the most interesting thing to me was the animals. I loved the peacocks; they were a noisy bunch but beautiful. Then the ducks, now they were messy; I just looked at all these animals. They all needed someone to love them and take care of them too. This man did a great job; I had my morning routine, and when I was finished with breakfast, I would help with the dishes; then I would talk to the animals, who would sometimes talk back to me, especially the peacocks. They occasionally turned their backs on me and showed off their beautiful feathers. The pigs and goats were in their own world. When I was finished with the animals, I went into the field and just meditated. I would look up into the sky and ask God if he was real and why he didn't answer me when I cried. I was just pouring out my heart to this man.

I told him all that was bothering me; I let him know that I was happy with my mother's boyfriend's house, but I needed to go to school. My heart was so full of all the things I'd been through. When I was finished talking to him, I felt a piece inside my soul. Now this was my everyday thing, talking to the animals and God; my new life was interesting. I would do this daily, and I got a sense of happiness; just God and the animals and me.

One day, I was in the field talking to God; when I saw my brother Gary coming, my heart was racing so fast, I was so nervous. I thought he was coming to take me back to that evil place. I ran and hid myself, but he didn't stay too long. He had brought my clothes, even my uniform, so that I could go to school. I was so happy that I went and told God, my new friend, about what had happened. I told him that my brother had come by and brought my clothes; it seemed as if my aunt put him out as well. The two people that Mother had let us leave Dad's house for. He went to stay with his friends in the city; I was sorry for him; it seemed as if I was the only one that saw this woman's evil deeds.

It seemed as if our aunt didn't have anyone to blame, so she started on my brother Gary. I just wanted to thank God for the things that my brother Gary had brought to me so that I could go to school. I didn't waste any time. I was getting things ready for school the next week, but Marlene told me to wait for her. She had to take me to school so that she could explain to the teachers what had happened.

I didn't know what she told them, but I knew I was back in my school, and there was a lot of work, and the children would make fun of me. I didn't let that bother me one bit. I did the best I could; for some reason, I felt something inside me letting me know I was going to be someone great. I just believed this feeling; no one or anything was going to keep me down.

Whenever I went to school, my mother's boyfriend would take me to school on the tractor that he used on the farm. I was the only one on a tractor for a car; I didn't feel anything at all because where he lived was really far. I loved all the attention I was getting; everyone was just looking at me. After school, Edson and I would go to the farm. We would get something to eat while Gilbert milked the cows; this was his other job. He worked on a dairy farm, which was fun too; we got to see him milk the cows with the machine. He always told me not to go near the cows because they would kick me. School was good every day; sometimes, it was a drama, but what was I to complain about? I was happier than ever before.

One day, Edson didn't come to school, so I had to walk to the dairy farm by myself. I didn't know what had happened, but these groups of boys were bothering me. They told me that they were going to rape me and what they would do with me. I just cried as I walked to the farm; I didn't know that Gilbert was watching me; he saw the boys behind me.

When I got to the dairy farm, out came Gilbert. He asked me if those boys were bothering me; I had tears rolling down my face and said yes; I was so afraid of these young men. They were big boys, and the words that were coming out of their mouths were sad. The only thing I knew was Gilbert ran on the tractor and drove the boys down. He didn't ask me what had happened; he just told me that they wouldn't be bothering me anymore. When he was finished milking the cows, he took me back to the house. I told Marlene what had happened; I was so afraid of school. I still went the following day.

At school, I saw one of the boys that had troubled me; when this kid saw me, he ran as if he saw a ghost. I just stood there and wondered what in the world Gilbert did to him. I felt so safe; I looked up and told God thank you. When lunchtime came, Gilbert brought lunch for Edson and me. He told Edson to watch over me at school, which he always did. After school, we walked to the dairy.

When we got there, one of the young men was there with his father. He told him what Gilbert had done to him; Gilbert told him he was lying and needed to speak the truth, but he didn't. Gilbert hit the young man across his face in front of his dad. I was shocked; the young man was shocked even more because Gilbert hit him right there in front of his father. His dad got upset, so Gilbert asked him if he wanted a fight. He told them that it was not okay for anyone to trouble his daughter; I started to cry because I never saw anyone defending me like that before, and to top it off, he called me his daughter. I was touched to know that someone, who wasn't my real dad, cared for me.

My heart was so full of love; I just hugged him and told him thanks while the tears rolled down my cheeks. Gilbert had driven down the boys that were bullying me; one of them he threw into the gully, and the other one got a lot of hits; then he told them if anything ever happened to me, he would find them. I was protected on both hands; not only they couldn't trouble me, but if anyone else tried to. These boys were there to see to it that I was safe. Gilbert told me not to be afraid of anyone, and he told Edson to watch over me; he spoke the same words Dad would tell us.

I had so much fun at Gilbert's house. Edson would come over on the weekend. We had fun the same way when we used to live at Dad's house. We were all over the place; Edson even made friends with one of Gilbert's friends. He worked with this white lady; she lived on a hill near Gilbert's house. I wasn't a friendly person; I always stayed to myself. Edson told me to come with him, but Gilbert told us that he didn't like us going to people's houses. This man was just like our dad, the same things Dad would say, but Edson still went. I followed him, of course; we were just having fun. Edson would come every weekend.

Marlene was in a contest where she modeled. She taught me how to wear high heels, which I did well; whenever she wasn't looking, I would put on her lipstick and act as if I was a movie star. On Saturday night, I would watch my niece and nephew while their mother went out to practice for her contest. I was not afraid at all, Gilbert was there, and I was in the room with the kids. We were safe, after all.

One day, Gilbert went to work. To my surprise, Althea and my aunt came to the house; they came for me. It seemed as if they called my mother and told her I was with Marlene, so they came and took me back to her house. They told us that Mother wanted me back at my aunt's house.

As I watched Marlene let them take me, my heart fell. Gilbert was not there; I knew he would have saved me from them. On my way to my aunt's house, we passed Gilbert's workplace; how I wanted to cry out and tell him to save me! I couldn't... Tears rolled down my face. I was just talking to God to help me when we got to her house; I felt like an outcast. Everyone was looking at me strangely.

I felt really bad when I went into the room where I used to sleep. My cousin told me that the bed was taken; she said my sister Karen and her mother's friends slept there. It seemed as if everyone had a boyfriend; I asked Edson if he had a girlfriend too. He just laughed at me. I couldn't understand why she came and got me if everyone was okay. Every day was the same; I was in the same room with this girl and her new love; no wonder they didn't want to go back home to Dad. Everyone was happy; I felt really bad. I had to hear all these kinds of sounds; no wonder she got rid of Gary. I wanted to run away, but where could I have gone? My aunt would have found me. I was so depressed I cried most of the time.

Every day was the same; I would do my daily chores. I could hardly do my homework; everyone was too busy to help. One day at school, one of our teachers came into the classroom selling tickets for a fair. I knew I wasn't able to go to events like those, so I hissed my teeth. I should have known better that you don't do that in Jamaica. The teacher asked who did that; the girl next to me just looked at me and didn't say anything. I did the same; I kept my mouth shut. The teacher was so upset; he said that it was disrespectful and rude. I knew if he found out, I would be in a lot of trouble. While I was sitting in class, I heard a voice telling me to apologize to this teacher. I kept telling the voice that it was crazy because this teacher, Mr. Brown, could deal with me really well.

I couldn't shake the feeling, so I went over to the young girl and told her thanks. The feeling was getting stronger than ever, I couldn't contain myself, so I had to go to the teacher after school. I did what I was told; I went to the teacher, not knowing what to expect. I told him that I was the one that had hissed my teeth; I told him that I was really sorry. Mr. Brown just shook his head without saying anything. I couldn't wait for school to be dismissed, even though I was going into that crazy house. It was the weekend after school; Edson and I went to visit Marlene and the kids. I wanted to tell her what my aunt was doing, but I dared not open my mouth.

I thanked God I was skinny and ugly, so no one looked at me at all. Karen's boyfriend would make fun of me; then my aunt would say that Karen was the best-looking one of all of us, then they would look at me and laugh. I didn't have much self-esteem; they took it away. I didn't feel jealous of them because they were beautiful, and I wasn't. As the weekend went by, I could hardly wait on Monday to go to school.

In life, you should be careful about what you ask for. On Monday mornings in Jamaica, we always had morning devotion. This was when all the students came and worshiped the Lord our Savior, Jesus Christ. All the teachers and the principal had to attend as well.

To my knowledge, Mr. Brown was leading the morning prayer. At this time, I was shaking all over; my mind was telling me all kinds of things. I was told that Mr. Brown was going to embarrass me in front of the whole entire school; I wanted to run, but my legs wouldn't move at all. Mr. Brown kept looking at me, so I moved beside one of the students so that he could not see me at all. I kept asking God to let him talk about something else, or what he did for the weekend, etc. He didn't; he spoke about what took place on Friday; as I put my head down, waiting to be called out by him the same way my aunt would do to embarrass me. I was so shocked when he started to tell them the whole event of what took place.

Then he said the student came and apologized to him; the student didn't have to do what they did because no one had confessed. "I'm telling you, students, that you can all learn from this child; I can see that this child is coming from a good home." I was so shocked he didn't embarrass me, and he didn't even tell them that I was a girl!

Mr. Brown hid my identity from everyone; my heart felt relieved. I just said to myself, "Thank you, Jesus." If only this man knew where I come from. My aunt sold weed; the house was infested by all kinds of men, from murderers to thieves and rapists and drug dealers. She had them in the house; I didn't know if Mother knew this, but I always wondered why she took us from Dad to live in this kind of environment. The things parents do to get back at each other, they don't think about how it will affect the children. They wanted revenge, and that was final. I looked at Mr. Brown differently; I kind of respected him. He could have embarrassed me, but he didn't.

The week went by so slowly; it felt like I was just dragging myself each day; finally, the week was over, and I went to visit Marlene and the kids. I could only stop by on weekends; the walk to the house was really far. When I saw Marlene, I wanted to tell her what I'd seen about Karen and her boyfriend. I kept pondering in the back of my head, *Man, I can't hold this anymore.* I sang like a patriot.

Marlene was so upset; she was beyond herself. Gary wasn't there to watch them, and no one to tell them it was not okay; there was nothing that she could have done. These girls were all grown up, and no one could talk to them; my aunt had them like a pimp. Marlene told me not to say anything to anyone; I just looked at her as if there was anyone I could talk to. I did what I was told; I heard nothing and saw nothing. This was a new thing for me because I always let you know what was on my mind.

I learned a lot of things; I knew how to wash my own clothes and how to take care of myself. I wore big clothes so that these men didn't notice me, which I didn't have too much anyway. At this time, everyone was acting funny; I noticed Karen's boyfriend wasn't coming often as he would. My aunt was being nice to me, and they were fixing the house up.

One day, I went to Althea and asked her if Mother was coming home; she told me no! I knew just where to go; I went to my cousin. This girl knew everything; she even told me the time and date. I don't know if my sister thought that I was that dumb. Whenever these people clean up and get the place in order, not saying it was a mess. You had to think like them at times; I played the game they wanted. The week went by, and my mother was coming home; I didn't say much. I was so happy and relieved that she was coming home.

This was the day Mother was coming home. Edson and I went to school. I didn't tell him at all; he probably knew. I was so excited to know that all of my pain was over with; my mother was coming, and all would be well. When we got home, I took a shower and got ready for Mom. I loved that lady so much; no one could let me hate her. I waited and waited, but no sign of this lady; I got so tired of waiting that I fell asleep. I felt Edson hitting me on my foot to wake up because Mother was home. I jumped and ran to the front of the house; Edson went and got his hug, and so did Karen. I looked at her; she was so beautiful; she looked at me with a smile. I'd never seen that look before, then she stretched out her hand, and that was when I ran so fast and hugged her. I didn't want to let her go. Then she told me that she had a bone to pick with me. This woman could have let me have my moment. When everyone was greeted with kisses and hugs, it was time to get down and dirty. They told my mother all lies; she believed everything my aunt and sister had told her.

Gary, Marlene, and I were the bad ones. I didn't understand it at all; I did run away with Marlene for three to four months. This woman didn't want me around because she could have come and gotten me. She waited until she knew Mother was coming home. I felt hurt. There was nothing I could do or say; I was in a den of lions. Edson and Karen were the best kids, not to mention Althea. I was the mistake; I knew that Mother wanted another boy.

I guess I was born for a reason, and that was it. I couldn't understand all of this, but I knew I had to talk to God about this. I was told to apologize to my aunt, as always. I did it out of respect, even though it was killing me. That night, Mother didn't go to Gilbert's house; she stayed with us. The next day, we went to school and to see Marlene and the kids; we were told to meet her at Gilbert's house.

When we got to Gilbert's home, Mother seemed as if she was a different person. I didn't know what they told her; she seemed as if she was in another world. That weekend, we stayed with her at Gilbert's house while the girls were with my aunt.

Mother and Althea went to town to visit. Mother wanted to know where Gary was. It seemed as if she was always looking for him whenever she went to America. When they came back, both of them were crying. I knew that something was wrong; then she asked for Edson.

Chapter 8

His dog Beddy was dead; he was my friend too. Then she told us that our dad got sick and they took him to the hospital. It seemed as if his sickness came back on him, this time even worse than before. Mother had made arrangements to go get a vehicle to take us to see our dad. That Friday evening, he went and got Oliver; it was a sad day. Oliver almost died because he ran right into the back of the van. The poor driver didn't see him but thank God someone saw him and shouted out. He only got a couple of bruises and cuts; he was lucky. Mother decided to take Karen and Althea with her; I felt really bad because I was here feeling sorry for myself, and my dad, all this time, was sick and all by himself. I couldn't handle all of this hurting.

When they got back that night, they couldn't find him. The next day, Mother and Althea went to town and looked for Dad. They went all over the place; they went to the hospital and even the morgue, but still no sign of him.

Mother called one of Dad's friends, and he told her where he was. My dad's sister took him to a witch doctor, and when Mother got to Dad, he was in a terrible condition. She took him from that place and took him to the hospital. When she came home, she was tired. She took a shower outside at night and then went to bed.

The next day, she told us that we were going to see Dad on the weekend; she didn't want to take us out of school. I could hardly wait for the weekend to come; when we got to the hospital, Mother was arguing with the staff at the hospital. Dad was filthy and dirty; it seemed as if he was fighting the nurses and doctors. They tied him up and left him; Mother didn't waste any time. She and Althea cleaned Dad up as I watched them through the window; I kept thinking that these two people hated each other so much, and now look at them.

When they were finished with Dad, we went into the room. He didn't even recognize me at all; he was all over the place. I was just crying as Mother tried to explain to Dad who we were. My best friend didn't know who I was; I had failed him so badly. As I watched her attend to him, my heart gave way. I felt really sorry for Gilbert because Mother was so affectionate and loving towards Dad; if I had to choose between the two, Dad would be my choice, no doubt; I could see the love was still there.

Christmas came and went; we were back and forth from the hospital. It was taking a toll on Mother; she didn't have so much money for bus fare for all of us. We had to visit him whenever she could; he didn't know who we were anyways.

This thing went on for some time; the doctors couldn't tell her what was wrong with Dad. She did the next thing she knew how. Mother called my dad's brother once more and told him the situation. She was happy that she had spoken to him; they were going to send him back to the US for help.

Dad's friends got involved once more; he was off for treatment again, I didn't get to see him leave, but I was told what took place. When all of this was over, Mother was focused on us again. Gilbert didn't say much because Mother focused more on our dad getting better.

One day, our brother Gary came to visit Mother; she was so hurt when he started to tell her about what had taken place at our aunt's house. Marlene told her about Althea's and Karen's boyfriends. Mother went crazy; she took up her things and went for her girls. When they got back, everyone was crying; I just stood there and looked at them. The house was chaos, and Althea was crying that she wanted to go back to our aunt's house because she didn't like Gilbert one bit.

Karen, on the other hand, was just crying over her love; she didn't care at all for anyone else but who she loved. I did not like Gilbert at all until I got to know him. He treated me like his own child, even more than Dad sometimes. My sisters were spoiled, and that was all it was; anything they wanted, they got. If only they got to know this man... But our aunt had spoiled their minds on him. My poor mother went through it with these girls. They were in love, and nothing was going to stop them. After school, they would meet these guys and go out. She couldn't control them at all.

Althea even cursed Gilbert out when she was ready; they didn't have any respect at all. If Gilbert put us out of his house, we didn't have anywhere to go, but they didn't see that. They were all thinking about themselves. Every day was an argument between Gilbert and those girls. Mother would cry a lot; that wasn't helping the situation at all.

In some way, I felt sorry for her; she was trying to save us, but it was not working at all. I remember living at Gilbert's house; it was so peaceful and calm; now it was a mad house. The devil had gotten in, and it was through my sisters. The house was heavy and dull; you could hardly want to be there. This went on almost every day, the cursing and argument. Mother did the best thing she knew how—she went and rented a house with three bedrooms. One for the boys, one for Althea and Marlene with her children—they had the big room—and I shared with Karen; Marlene had a queen-size bed for her and her kids. Everyone was happy until the bad news came again.

Mother had to go to America once more; she had to get a job for us. We had no Dad to help us, and the girls didn't want Gilbert around them at all. She did what she had to, and it wasn't easy, but I guess that was what she had to do to help us. As the weeks went by, Mother was in the US; she was working three jobs, I was told. The girls went to private school, which she had to pay for, while I had to follow Edson wherever he went. I didn't know what graduation felt like because I had to follow my brother at all times. I didn't have much of a life; I was always told to shut up or look the other way.

One thing I knew kept me was talking to God. Of course, Gary started beating me again. I thought he got over that; my dad wasn't around, but he got pleasure with it. No one told him to stop. I got so used to it when he couldn't find a good place to hit me, he just got tired and stopped. My tears didn't mean a thing at all. I got so used to being beaten; my body got numb.

It wasn't a month since Mother left; the girls' boyfriends were back, this time for good. It seemed as if they moved in. The bed I shared with my sister Karen couldn't hold that man and me.

He would make fun of me, calling me all kinds of names. I couldn't handle it at all. I just got up and went to the couch. That was my new bed; I had to sleep and watch myself. I was living in fear with everyone as I went to bed with tears in my eyes. I went into my own little world; that's where I found peace. I didn't have anyone to love me; I was an embarrassment to God's world.

Whenever my sisters went to parties and got drunk, I slept on the couch; I didn't want to interfere with them. Everyone had fun, and my brother Gary made sure I didn't have any friends at all. He didn't tell my sisters what they were doing was wrong; I was his number one target. Marlene was in charge of the house, buying things for her kids and hiding them from us. I didn't know what was wrong with people with money; it seemed they changed a lot. She bought the good things for her kids; you would be lucky if you got the things they got. Things were going on so well; Marlene was pregnant with her third child, and Althea was pregnant too.

They all looked at me as if I was next; no one even saw me to even look at me. Marlene was hiding her pregnancy really well; I didn't know until she was near to giving birth. She was feeling pain that night when it happened. Gary, Althea, and her boyfriend went to call a nurse; we were all left with her. It seemed as if this child couldn't wait at all.

Karen had to help her deliver this baby; Edson and I had to sterilize the scissors we used around the house. The children were crying because they thought Karen was hurting their mother. I had to be back and forth with everything they needed. Marlene told Karen what to do and where to cut the umbilical cord. She did, then washed the baby off in cold water. The baby screamed so loud. She was a beautiful baby girl with black eyes. I was a bit afraid of her at first. Then she put clothes on the baby; Marlene had bought up all she needed and hid it well.

Then she told Karen to help her with the afterbirth; she was crying as if she was having another child. When Karen was all done with Marlene, Althea and the rest of them came with the nurse. The nurse was a bit upset because Karen did a good job. That night was a night to remember, thanks to Marlene. Edson and I had to go to school the following day; I was so tired. No one could understand what I'd been through that night. We went on with our lives as always; we had to try to survive all by ourselves.

Althea's boyfriend was leaving for the US; he wanted to help her and the baby. She was really sad that her true love was going away. Now she was close to Marlene; they both had something in common, they talked a lot. Althea was really hurting; she thought that with their first child, her boyfriend would be with them. He wasn't at all; she had to go throw all of this on her own; Marlene was used to this by now. I guess that was why Althea talked to her a lot.

When I thought things wouldn't get any worse, I was told that Mother wasn't coming home anytime soon. Then we got noticed by the landlord. She said that we had too many people living in the house. This was crazy; no one would rent us their place with all these kids. Marlene searched and searched until she found a place. It was more like a mansion, so we had to move again. This time, it was a four-bedroom house, so beautiful. Althea got the best room, as always; I don't know if they were afraid of her or what.

When Mother sent a barrel for her and the baby, it was the best. Of course, Karen and I had to share a room with her boyfriend. I could not take this guy for nothing. When we got settled in the new house, no one had ever lived there before. Marlene always went for the big things; no one knew it wasn't our house. We didn't know anyone in the neighborhood; we were there and hungry. It seemed as if she had used all the money she had to get this place; we had no food for three days. I was so hungry I couldn't move. The kids were crying most of the time; Karen's boyfriend had left for a job. Althea, too, was pregnant, to top it off.

When you are hungry, you cannot think straight. I think we had too much pride because we were living in this big house. We were afraid to ask for food, to stop the hungry pain. I slept most of the time.

When Karen's boyfriend came back from his job, he gave Edson money to visit Gilbert. He came and was so upset to know that we were living like that. Now Mother had to find another job just to maintain our lifestyle. Gilbert came with a large bread and milk from the dairy; then he gave Marlene money to buy food. I could hardly get up to eat what they provided. I was so weak.

Gilbert gave her enough to take us over the next week until Mother sent the money for us. He came by the next day to see if we were all right; at this time, Mother wasn't talking to Gilbert at all. We couldn't go to school most of the time; we had to catch up on life itself.

As I watched, the year went by, and normally, Mother would be home. That was only something I would wish for. My body was changing a lot; I didn't like it one bit. I started my menstruation. I didn't let them know; I would use Karen's things and hide it from them. I knew what they would do and say; this went on for a while, and Karen thought that Marlene was using her things. She hid them from Marlene. I didn't know what to do, so I made my own pad with toilet paper; this thing wasn't keeping me safe.

So I went and told Marlene, then she told Althea, then she told Karen, who didn't have any right to tell her boyfriend. Then he told my brother Gary, who grabbed me and told me if he saw me with anyone, he would kill me. Marlene took me into a room and told me what could happen to me. I kept thinking that she should have taken her own advice.

She was the one who had three kids without a father around; I felt so bad and dirty. I remember cursing my body; soon, Marlene took me to the telephone booth. We didn't have a phone at the house to call Mom. When Marlene spoke to our mother, she gave me the phone; my heart was full as I spoke to Mom; she told me the same thing Marlene told me about my body and what to expect, which I'd already known. I watched my sisters a lot; I was fun of Althea because she did things really well.

I was just crying to hear Mother's voice; I dared not tell her what I was going through with my siblings. I wanted to tell her I had to sleep on the couch because Karen's boyfriend was sleeping with us on the bed. I couldn't sleep in the room with them because that boy gave me the creeps. Then I got the biggest news of my life; that she wasn't coming back home as yet. She had found someone, and she was getting married. "How can this be? What is happening? What about Gilbert?" I asked her. Mom told me that she had to help herself so that she could help us.

My dad was nowhere to be found; it seemed as if he had forgotten about us. I didn't know if this was good news or not; I was shaking all over. When we went back home, Marlene broke the news to the others. Some took it well, while some didn't like it one bit.

Lying on the bed, I kept thinking about what Mother had told me; I thought about Dad. He never wrote once at all; we didn't know if he was alive or well. I was fourteen now, and life was the same; we would go to school when we had money. Marlene didn't know how to budget the money at all. She was going out a lot with Karen, while Althea was left home with us. She was almost ready to have her baby.

At night, I would hear my niece crying, but no one looked at her. The only thing Gary did was close the door. I went in that night to find them alone in the room; the bed was all wet. I also woke up the other two and changed them; Marlene was doing this every night.

She would leave the children and go to parties and come home the next day. I didn't get much sleep for school. I chose to get up and change the kids every night cause no one cared about them. Althea and Gary told her to stay away from the children because she didn't care at all. One day, I tried to ignore their cries like everyone else, but I couldn't. I got up and changed them night after night. This was a regular thing with her every night. When I went to school, I could hardly function.

Althea had her baby, she didn't know much about babies, so she went back to our aunt's house, who she loved. Karen didn't care about anyone but herself. Edson was in love with the next-door girl. The house was a mess, and Marlene was getting out of control with her lifestyle.

She would party all week long; sometimes, she took the money Mother had sent for her friends and enjoyed themselves. We sometimes didn't have food as always. We got used to this kind of life now; I had to do the best I could for these kids.

One night, Gary and Marlene got into a fight; he told her if she left these kids, he would put them outside the house. I thought she understood what he had said; of course, she left them. It seemed as if Gary had left the house for a while when he came back and didn't see her. He got mad. He took the three babies and put them outside in the wet grass. I couldn't let him do this to the babies; they were all crying.

He stood at the door and cursed all kinds of bad words for me to come inside the house. Even though I knew he could have killed me that night, he was so full of so much anger. Edson begged me to come inside the house and leave the kids outside, but how could I have done that? Karen, too, came and told me to get inside the house, but I still refused. I just sat down and sang to them; the neighbor told us to come over to her house. My brother told her to leave us alone, and just then, Marlene came home.

I didn't know what had happened, why she came back. She was so upset to see her babies on the wet grass. They both started to fight; I just held the children; I thought the neighbor was going to call the police, but she stayed out of it. When they were finished fighting, Gary left the house. He had ripped the clothes off Marlene; she went inside and put the kids to bed and left the house once more. You would think that she knew better, but apparently not. Marlene left the kids that same night again.

That night, I was signed over to those kids; now, she was gone every night, and she would come back the next day. Sometimes, it was too late for me to go to school. My brother made sure I took care of those kids. Now she was gone for days... that turned into weeks.

It was my fault; I should have gone inside when he told me to; sometimes, I found myself beating them the same way my brother did to me. I had to wash their clothes and bathe them. I was their mother now; at this time, Marlene was nowhere to be found.

She was gone for months; she would take the money Mother had sent and spend it on her friends. The sad thing about this, she was working and used our mother's money on her friends. She wasn't paying the bills at all; now, we had gotten notice once more.

Gary had left the house a couple of days and went to town to visit his father; Karen, too, was gone with her boyfriend. I was left with the kids and Edson. We had nothing to eat, so I sold bottles, bought flour, and cooked for the kids. I didn't know too much about cooking. I learned a lot about baking because I used to watch Marlene a lot. Whenever Gary came back from his two-day tour, he would bring food for us; sometimes, he would cook, and when he was gone, I would have to take up the job.

For peace of mind, I would go into the yard and look up at the stars and just sing my heart out. I thought I was Whitney Houston. Then I would talk to God and just laugh. I didn't know if people thought I was mad; living with these people would make anyone insane.

Gary came back home and bought some groceries for us; it seemed as if he spoke to our mother, and she had sent a barrel for us with food and things. Then Althea and her son came back home too, and Karen and even Marlene came back home. I kept wondering whenever I spoke to God, things happened.

It seemed as if Althea was in charge of the money now. Marlene only came back because she had no money to spend. We got the barrel with the food and everything. I was happy that I didn't have to take care of these kids as I watched them embrace their mother. I just wished I had my mother to hold me like them. That Sunday, Karen and I washed the carpet in the house, then we were told that a hurricane was heading to Jamaica.

I told her that it would dry in no time; she laughed. I was right; the breeze was unbelievable. We didn't know how serious this storm was; we were doing our daily chores. I washed most of my clothes that day, and so did my sisters. So we had food and clean clothes. We just wanted to see what Hurricane Gilbert was going to do. That night, the hurricane made a lot of noise. The wind was getting stronger and stronger. The next day, Edson went outside to watch the storm; as the wind lifted roofs from people's houses, he was outside laughing and making fun. I was in one of the rooms upstairs; I kept hearing a funny sound. I got up and went into Marlene's room. I saw the roof lifting up, and the baby was sleeping; I grabbed Fiona and ran downstairs to tell them.

This time, everyone was grabbing furniture and moving everything downstairs. They all worked as a team. Edson, on the other hand, was quiet at this time. We were all scared because this was our first experience with something like this. They told me to stay with the children while they got the furniture on stone just to keep them from getting wet. As I watched them working so hard together, I kept thinking about the day we were moving in. They were all complaining that it was too much work, but now they made it seem so easy. We didn't know what to expect because another side of the roof was gone, and water was coming in like a flood.

Marlene went and asked our neighbor if Althea and I, with the kids, could stay with them until the storm went by. She didn't think twice; that night, no one got any sleep at all. The wind made noise; then, it went quiet for a while. I thought that the storm was over, and then it came with more wind and even more horrible noise. I just prayed to God that night more than before; the kids went to sleep.

Althea was worried about our brothers and sisters that were left in the house. I didn't know when I fell asleep; our neighbor asked us if we were okay. We were; it was still raining. Marlene came over with food for us and told us that the roof was gone and that they had moved downstairs most of our things.

Thank God she had rented a two-family house, so we had to move to the first floor. The next two days after the hurricane, we saw the damage that Gilbert had done. Thank God we were alive and well; we were out of electricity and water. Edson and I had to go far and get water for the house; I sometimes bathed with my clothes on because I didn't want men to look at me. We didn't have any vehicle to take us to any water areas, so Edson made a wagon with roller skates.

Then we would put bottles on it, and he would pull them. We did this for a week or two; then Gilbert came to visit us. He took us to his house, where we got water to take a bath and wash our clothes. We couldn't stay at his house anymore because Mother and Gilbert were no more friends.

We didn't get by really well without the water; we could live without electricity for a while. Water and food were the most essential thing for us at that time. For a couple of months, we got our light back. A lot was happening in the house, Karen was now pregnant, and everyone was upset. I could never forget her crying because Althea and Marlene wanted her to have an abortion; her boyfriend stood up and cursed them out. He wanted his child, and so did Karen.

Althea was more concerned about our mother because she had spent a lot of money on her for school and everything. My mother had invested in Althea and Karen a lot. When Althea got pregnant, then Karen was the one to make her proud. Now it seemed as if everyone had failed her, as for me. I was a nobody in their eyes; I didn't go to a special school, not even special classes to help me in school.

Now the house was in an up roll; this time, Gary had moved in with his baby's mother and the child, Althea with her son, Marlene had her three kids, and now Karen was pregnant. I remember Gary coming over to me and telling me if he saw me with a man or even near one, he would kill me because Mother couldn't deal with other mouths to feed. I just looked at him while the tears rolled down my face. Marlene didn't know how to tell Mother what was taking place, but she did, after all.

The house was a mess; every day, Gary and his girlfriend would fight. I thanked God she came around because he was off my case. The next problem I had to face now was Althea; she was beating her baby boy too much. It seemed his father wasn't coming back to marry her; she was heartbroken. Whenever her son cried, she would beat him well; I couldn't deal with it; I took up the knife and told her that if she put her hands on him once more, I would really use it. She just looked at me and walked away. The poor child followed her; he didn't even know the danger he was in. Children just love their parents so much. Gary, on the other hand, gave me the shock of my life. He was a different person with his daughter; not even flies could come near her. He was so overprotective of her;

I guess that's love. We all were in a two-bedroom house, which Mother had to pay for; everyone had their own life to live. Karen had a son named Leon. She loved that child so much; she didn't care for anything else.

Now I had to take care of myself and be very careful. I remember one day taking a shower. To my surprise, Karen's boyfriend was looking at me through the bathroom window. We didn't have any shower curtains at all; the only thing I heard was this man telling me that I had nothing and was just laughing at me. I felt so embarrassed; I looked at my body and shook my head. I didn't say anything to them because they didn't care what happened to me at all. I just stayed far from this man; I knew he wasn't up to any good.

One day, Marlene came home and told us that Mother's boyfriend was coming to Jamaica to visit us; we all didn't know what to expect when this man came. I always thought that Mother had hit her head with these guys; Gilbert wasn't bad, but he could not walk next to Dad. This one was even worse than Gilbert; when this man came, I just couldn't stand him at all. He seemed proud and boastful; he looked down at us. Karen was told to hide her son, Leon; after all, she was the daughter that Mother spoke about. No one dared know that she had a child. I didn't even think that our dad knew; Mother had spoken to him. He was well, and he was staying with a friend for a while in California. One day out of the blue, I got a birthday card from him with five dollars in it, which meant the whole world to me. I showed it to everyone, even Gary. He changed a lot with his new baby girl; I was happy for him because she made him into someone I didn't even know.

We stayed at this place for more than a year and some months. Althea was going through a lot, and I knew it. She had gotten involved with another guy, and she was smiling a lot these days; of course, Marlene was gone again. I got so used to my responsibility with these kids. I did what I had to do and went to school. Althea helped out a lot with the kids; she would cook when Mother sent money. Whenever we were out of food, the new boyfriend would bring food from his mother's house. She would share it with the kids and us.

We had gotten noticed before, but we had to stay due to the hurricane and most of the homes being damaged. Now everyone had to find their way out; Gary and his family left, and so did Karen and her boyfriend. We didn't know where to go; Marlene came back. I didn't know what she discussed with Althea. I was told that we were moving back to our aunt's house. Marlene had tried to get somewhere, but too many kids... No one wanted that many people in their houses. I didn't want to go back to my aunt's house, but I had no choice at all.

Marlene and Althea had helped with packing up all our things, so we had to leave that life behind us. We knew who our aunt was, so we tried to stay out of her way. Althea gave her money towards bills and so on, but she bought food for us and cooked.

Chapter 9

Marlene didn't stay too long with us as always, so I had to take care of my kids. I got so used to my life; I didn't complain at all. I just did what I had to do. Althea did the cooking and cleaning for the house while I washed and bathed the kids. I washed the dishes that we used, and Althea did her best and kept the house clean because our aunt didn't want her daughter doing any work at all. My other cousin went to Canada to live with her dad.

In life, I did what I had to do to survive; I just went into my own little world; I would go deep in my thoughts. My mind would take me to places I didn't need to be, and sometimes, I wanted to escape reality; this was the only way out for me.

Our aunt would curse a lot, as always; nothing that we weren't used to. I knew that our aunt loved Althea, so I knew I was safe in some ways. My brother Gary wasn't around for me to get any beating at all; life was good. This time, my life was changing really fast; I was in the lion's den, and my aunt's house was changed a lot too. She didn't have many males coming around a lot, only a few. She had only one male friend, which seemed good to everyone. He rode a bike whenever he came by; everyone seemed happy. I didn't know much about him until I watched him and got to know him really well. He sold weed, which was the lifeline at my aunt's house. If it wasn't one thing, it was the other. I didn't complain at all; I got a summer job with him.

I would cut up the bags that he sold his weed into; I did this for a while, then I would get paid. It helped me a lot because I didn't have to ask anyone for money to buy things I needed. I was doing good for myself; I still didn't try to run away at all. I went to school and came home. I took care of my kids. We were all growing up; I was in a new school, and so was Edson. Wherever he went, I had to follow him. The new school was much different; we were around grown-ups. I was already a mother with three kids, so this wasn't new to me.

I remember one day when I was cutting up some bags for my aunt's friend, he asked me if I had a boyfriend; I told him that I wasn't allowed to have one. He asked why. I didn't know myself; then he started to talk to me like a sister; he told me if a boy really likes you, he won't pressure you into things you don't like. He told me to always respect myself so that people would do the same. This conversation was going well; he didn't speak to me the way my brother did, with vile words and threatening words.

I felt really good after that talk; he even told me to do my best in school and be somebody. Words like that you don't hear often coming from a drug dealer. I took his advice, went to school, and did my best; no one troubled me. I had found a new friend; we only hung out at school; I couldn't take her to my aunt's house. I could hardly wait for Monday to go to school, just to find out what my friend did. She was always talking and telling me about her mom in the US. I told her that my mom and dad were there too. She asked me when I was going to be with them; I said, "I really don't know yet. Only God knows if that is ever possible."

The days went by as always; we did what we had to do. I could hardly wait for Monday again; at this time, my friend told me that there was a young guy at school who had his eyes on me; I just laughed at her. Now who in the world could love someone like me? I was told that I was ugly and a dunce. I believed that all those years, so why now this guy had his eyes on me? I felt really good when she told me. I didn't know that someone could like me at all. At this time, I was at school even if I didn't have lunch money. Once I had bus fare, I was fine; I did my best at school. I was good at maths; I didn't know where I got all that knowledge from. For the fact that I wasn't going to school regularly as other children were. I liked to write stories sometimes, but spelling was my weak spot. This would be my downfall because to write stories, you must know how to spell. Who was I kidding? Overall, school was fun.

One day in my maths class, the teacher told me to go to another maths class to talk to one of the teachers. He gave me one problem to work out, and I did. Then he asked me how I got the answer. "I don't know myself; I just know." Then he gave me another one to work on, which I did; I got it right, and then I was told to get back to my class. I didn't know what these maths teachers were doing.

I knew that I didn't get the same work as some of the kids did; I got more challenging work to do. I remember one day while in class, our math teachers came over to my friend and me and asked when we were going to America. He knew that both of our parents were living there; my friend told him in November. He looked at me and asked, "Davis, when are you leaving?" I just looked at him and, with lying lips, said, "In March."

My friend was so excited that she was all over the place; I knew that I was lying and that one day, it was going to catch up on me, but who cared? She didn't stay long; before I knew it, November was here, and she was gone. Now everyone was waiting for me to leave; at school, I got to see the young man who had liked me. I didn't know what I was feeling, but it felt really good to know that someone liked me a lot. I only talked to my new friend at school; I didn't dare take him home to meet my aunt. I was a little embarrassed about the house; I still think that my aunt's house was the only one that had an outside bathroom. I was okay with that, but I dared not invite anyone there.

There were a lot of changes in school; we had teachers who looked as young as we were, and I couldn't understand it at all. I took up electrical engineering in my studies. Althea loved that subject a lot; out of all my sisters, she was the one who was my role model. I noticed that one of the new teachers was very bright with young females; he had an office and would call each of them into that room. Whenever they came out, they had a smile on their faces. I didn't play up with these teachers at all; before I knew it, I was called to go into that room.

Without thinking, I told the teacher that I was not going into the room with him by myself for him to touch me. He asked me to repeat myself. I told him the same thing. Then he told me to get out of his class. At this time, I was a troublemaker. I went to other classes and was told to leave; before I knew it, I was suspended from school;

I didn't know how to tell Althea, and my aunt didn't care if I went to school or not. I didn't feel safe, and I knew that I had to go back to this teacher because he was the one who was the head of electrical classes. I knew that I was doomed, so I stayed home. I always found an excuse not to go to school. This went on for almost two and a half weeks. I was home, trying to find a way out of my situation. Althea wasn't good at these things like Marlene. She would know exactly what to say or do; she was a natural with things like these. The following day, I got the surprise of my life; it was Marlene. It seems as if when you think of people, they seem to appear out of the blue. She came with the news that I didn't even believe her. Marlene made lying sound real; I guess this was her gift.

She told us that she had spoken to our dad, and he told her that we were going to America to live with him. His sister had filed his papers over some ten years now, and they got through. The only problem was that only Edson, Karen, and I were on the paper with Mother. She and Althea were too old, so they would have to file all over again. I didn't know what to think; I looked Marlene in the eyes and asked her if she was playing with me. She said no; I looked at Althea and told her to call Mother just to make sure that this one didn't have something up her sleeves; after all, this was coming from Marlene.

Then she told us that she had to go find Karen and let her know. Althea didn't waste any time; she went and called Mother. I just watched Marlene as she talked and talked; I wasn't going to believe her until my other sister came back. When Althea came to our aunt's house, she told us that she was telling the truth for once in her life. I couldn't believe what I was hearing at all! My mom and dad were coming home for Christmas. We were going to America; I still could not believe this at all.

Edson was in another world himself; it seemed as if dreams did come through after all. I knew Althea and Marlene felt bad, they wanted to come too, but they had to wait until Mother or Dad filed their papers. My aunt was happy too; she started treating me really nicely; I could not believe it at all. What a Christmas gift we got from God—our parents were coming home for us.

I was told Dad was coming first, then Mother later; I didn't mind at all. I had a lot to catch up with this man. I wanted to know if he was well and what had happened to him and why he didn't write as much. I had a lot to ask him. I was more happy for my mother; now she didn't have to marry that man for her papers.

The week went by really fast; we didn't go to school at all. I didn't mind because I was suspended from school. The week wasn't long; we were getting things ready for Dad. Marlene had left the house once more; she said she had to get Karen and tell her the good news. She left and didn't come back until the next day later. She couldn't find her at all; Marlene and Althea took all of us to see Dad at his sister's house.

When I saw my dad, I just ran into his arms as if I was holding on for dear life. I didn't want to let him go. He hugged Edson and then Althea. He looked at all the grandkids that he had. He was just smiling all over. Althea was in the kitchen with my aunt while Marlene was telling Dad all of what we had gone through. I didn't leave Dad at all; I could not have asked for a better gift than this. The kids were happy, and I was out of words. Dad asked for Karen, then Marlene told him she was at the house of one of her friends. She told Dad that she was going to get her the next day; Marlene told us that Dad wasn't to know about Karen's baby. I just looked at her and nodded my head.

They still couldn't understand this at all; the following day, Marlene left to go find Karen. Dad was concerned about us, and now he was asking me about my mother. He told me that we were going to stay with him in America. It seemed as if each family member was going to take one of us. I just stood there as he talked; he made us sound like cats that people gave away. I didn't know what to say to him; I just waited until my mother came to Jamaica to find out what the arrangement was in this place called America.

I knew my dad's family didn't like me and for me to live with them. I just didn't know at all what I was getting into. We gave Dad two days with us, and he was still cursing a lot like before. I didn't know if it was too many children that were around him. Althea didn't want to stay with us too long, but she had to. On Monday morning, Karen and Marlene still weren't there, so Dad took Edson and me to town and finished most of our papers. He was mad that Karen wasn't there, which meant he had to do this all over again. While we were walking into the park in downtown Kingston, he was at the top of his voice, yelling and cursing bad words; Edson just walked fast as if he didn't know us.

Dad told me, "If she is pregnant, she can't come to America; this will mess all of us up." I was so sick and tired of all this. I just told him as it was: "I'm sick and tired of you cursing bad words and being loud! She's not pregnant, but she has the baby."

He stopped right there in his tracks; I didn't know if he was shocked about what I told him or how I told him. Edson was out of sight; I didn't know if he had run or what. Dad just looked at me. Then he asked me what kind of baby she had. I told him that it was a boy and his name was Leon. He looked at me and said, "Only you and Edson left..." I wasn't thinking about children at all, if anything. I wanted to run far from children. They were too much responsibility and always needed their parents' love. He didn't say another word at all; Edson was on the other side of the road, and he was so afraid of Dad. I wasn't afraid of him at all; he told me not to be afraid of anyone.

When we got to the house, Karen and Marlene were inside talking to Althea. When I got inside, I asked Karen where Leon was; they all looked at me as to say I must keep quiet. I told them that Dad already knew about the baby. They all looked at me as if I had gone mad, but I was so tired of the lies and the secrets I'd been through. That evening, I just sat down and watched all of my dad's children and grandkids with him. I knew this was killing my dad's sister because we were at her house now. Dad had rented out the house to someone.

I wasn't afraid of all of them anymore. Althea couldn't stay with us because Mother was coming home in three days. She went back to our mother's sister's house to help her. Everything was falling into place; we left the house each morning to get things in order for our interview. Dad got our passports ready; then, we had to wait for my mother to do our medical for the big day. That weekend, Karen's baby's father came with Leon; he was getting so big; Dad was having real fun of him. He looked at me and just smiled; I didn't know what he was thinking. At that time, I didn't care.

When all of our paperwork was done, our dad's sister couldn't wait for us to leave her house. I didn't mind at all because my mother was coming home. When we told Dad goodbye and left, we were going for our next gift, and that was to see Mother. I had missed this woman so much; she didn't curse like Dad. They both had something about them, which you had to deal with. When we got to our aunt's house, my brother Gary was there. He was happy to see all of us. I asked him about his daughter; he said she was fine. Then he told me that he was happy for us and he only hoped that I didn't forget about him. How could I forget about him? After all, he taught me. Then Edson made the sound out that Mother was home; I felt my heart was just pounding. When I went outside to meet her, I watched everyone greet her. I just looked at her as she greeted everyone, then she looked at me and hugged me. She said that I was tall; after all, I was fifteen. I wasn't that twelve-year-old that she had left; I think I had grown up too fast with a lot of experience I'd gotten from my sibling.

As I watched everyone talking and making fun, Mother told us that we had to choose who we were going to stay with; I told her that I wasn't going with Dad. He told me that one of his nieces was going to take me; I knew they didn't like me at all because I looked like her.

The following day, Mother told us that she had to go back to work; she had only taken off three weeks from her job. It seemed as if things were going too fast. She took out what we had to wear at the embassy and made sure she had all of her paperwork. Dad had ours; I guess he didn't trust us at all. I didn't blame him. Mother told Karen that Leon couldn't come to America with her; she would have to file for him when she was filing the rest of their papers. I knew this was killing her; she had to say goodbye to the love of her life and her baby boy. Althea was listening to our mother as she told her about her son's dad. She was so upset with that man.

Sunday was here, and we had to go to bed early because we had to take four buses to reach our destination. On Monday morning, we got up around four o'clock, and we took our shower in the cold water outside. Then we got dressed and had breakfast; we were on our way again. When we reached town, we were a bit late, and Dad was cursing all the way. I looked at him, and he asked me if I was okay; I told him I was fine. He looked at all of us as we waited in line. We got our number and were waiting to be called. I just looked at Dad; he was shaking like a leaf. Where was the one that told me not to be afraid of people?

Mother was handling this thing well. When the interviewer asked Dad a question, he couldn't answer. Then Mother told him not to be nervous; it seemed as if Dad had missed one of his paperwork. Everything else was in order except one thing. Now they gave him six weeks to get it done. Mother, on the other hand, was upset. She couldn't let the interviewer see that she was mad. We left the window and came outside; then, she said she wouldn't have a job when she got back.

I knew that Karen was happy, and Dad was too. He had more time to fix some things in the house. Edson didn't care at all; I, on the other hand, had to deal with school now. Things were not looking up, but we were still going to America, only a little delay. We told Dad bye and went with Mother; she wasn't happy at all. She didn't say much; it seemed as if she was in a different world. When I heard Mother telling our aunt that Dad had forgotten his police record from the US, I didn't mind at all; we were still going to America, and nothing or no one was going to stop us. It was a minor delay, which I could always wait on.

We had three months to stay in Jamaica, so I knew I had to go back to school. I thought I would have gotten over this school business, but I guessed I had to make things right. I had to apologize to the teacher that I had disrespected; then, I had to get all my grades in so that my transcript didn't look that bad. There was a lot I didn't know about life; I had to put pride aside and do what I had to do. Now, I was faced with another situation: how to tell my dad that I was not going to live with his niece.

Karen was going to stay with a cousin, while Edson and Dad would stay at our aunt's house. Then I would stay with another cousin; I wanted to know why. I asked my mother, but she had no say in the situation. I told her that I wasn't going to another cousin and aunt's house; I wanted to stay with her. Mom told me to let my dad know because she was afraid of telling him. I wasn't; it didn't go too well.

My dad was mad at me, even to the point of not talking to his baby. He thought I was putting Mom over him, but I wasn't. I just wanted to get away from people that hated me. This went on for a while; whenever I went to visit Dad, he didn't say much; I just wanted to know if he was going to buy my plane fare or not because my mother didn't have much money to do so. There were a lot of things going on in my mind. Dad thought I didn't love him enough because I chose Mother over him, but that wasn't the point.

My dad had a lot of profanity words; I needed a break from that. I really loved this man, but I needed a break from it all. To have your parents separate is a hard thing for a child. If you stay with one, the other one gets upset. I wasn't going to stay with him; he was sending me to a cousin who didn't like Mom at all, not to mention I looked just like my mother. It would have been Mother being in their faces at all times; I had my share of that with my aunt in the country.

Chapter 10

Mother was with us now; she didn't go to see Mr. Gilbert. He had gone on with his life, and so did Mother; now we had her all by ourselves. Mother even got a taste of our aunt's behavior; this woman would get up and curse all of us, even Mother. She would cry a lot and wish that the three months would pass by really fast. This time, Karen was happy because she had time to make arrangements to leave her son because she couldn't take him with her. She didn't know where she was going to stay when she came to America. Dad, on the other hand, was more interested in fixing the house in Jamaica. He told Althea to go back to the house, but she refused once more.

When I went back to school, it seemed as if I didn't miss anything at all; the young man that I was told liked me now was making it really clear. He was one of my classmates; I talked to this guy every day at school, and he never once told me. He was a popular guy at school; he could dance and sing. He was really good at what he did; most school girls were all over him or wanted him. When I was told that he liked me, I was shocked because, to my understanding, I wasn't all that. He could have gotten any girl he wanted, girls that looked like women, who had everything going on for them.

I was a disgrace to look at, not to mention low self-esteem. I could not believe it at all; I didn't think about too much because my brother Gary once told me if he saw me talking to boys, he would kill me. I was so afraid of a boyfriend; whenever he came around, I would keep quiet. I guess that everyone knew because I talked whenever I wanted. He would wait for me at lunchtime and after school. I wasn't used to all of this attention. It was new to me, but it felt good. I felt different for once in my life, to know that I wasn't all that and someone saw me differently.

One day, he came up to me and asked if I would be his girlfriend. I knew I was going away in one month. I told him yes; what I had to lose? His name was Hurbert. I didn't know why these men in the country had this "bert" at the end of their names. We called him Blue. I could work with that. He was such fun to be around; he made me laugh. Whenever he was singing, he would mention my name in his songs. I was on cloud nine, and everyone knew who I was. I wanted to go to school every day, even on the weekend, but of course, that was impossible. I didn't dare tell anyone anything about him; it was forbidden for me to have a boyfriend. I was told once I had a boyfriend, I would get pregnant, so I just left it the way it was. When Mother didn't have lunch money for us, I walked to school just to see him, things we do for love. I was getting to like this guy a lot; now I knew what my sisters were feeling.

When you are a kid, you do kid stuff, like playing and doing a lot of adventurous things. When you are a teenager, it is a new ball game, your hormones are running wild, and your feelings for the opposite sex are different and unique. The feelings I had for Blue were so different. It wasn't like the way I felt for my family. It was more about me and how I saw myself; I wasn't Daddy's girl.

I knew I didn't have much time left with this guy; I wished I had more time with him. The days were going fast. I was hurting and wanted to stay in Jamaica; I guess reality kicked in. I was really leaving Jamaica. I wasn't going to see my nieces and nephews for a long time. I knew what they were going to face because their mother wasn't around at all. I knew my sister Althea couldn't handle them that well; my aunt was in her evil mood most of the time. My world was changing once more; the scary thing was, I didn't know if it was for the better or worse. I knew my life was a roller-coaster ride; I didn't know when the ride was going to be, but I had to buckle up and prepare myself for it.

The week before I left, I told Blue that I was leaving soon, which he didn't want to think about. I was heartbroken about it. He asked me to go out with him to the movies; I told him that I had to ask my mother first. I was only fifteen, and I would be sixteen within two weeks. Mother told me that it was okay; of course, Blue had his entourage with him. We went to the movie, and he put his arms around my neck. I was nervous. He didn't kiss me at all because too many of his friends were with us.

After the movie, he walked me home with two of his friends while the others went their way. We held hands, and he sang to me while we walked; it was good.

I never felt this way before. When we got to my aunt's house, he stayed there for a while, and then they left. I went inside the house; my aunt was the most loving person now. The things that America does to people; now everyone was coming by to say goodbye to Mother and me. My heart was feeling the pressure now. I was really on my way in two days. Blue didn't miss a day; he was always there to see me off. I remember telling him that I would come back for him one day. He started to cry; I cried too. I didn't know what I was feeling for this guy, but it was real.

We both heard a song at one of the shops while we were walking home. It was "Right Here Waiting" by Richard Marx. He told me that it would be our song; it was so depressing. The words were so right; I cried like a young chick. As I told Blue goodbye and good night, I felt my heart break. The song that he dedicated to me wasn't helping one bit.

The day came, and I was so nervous; my first time on an airplane. I could hardly breathe; we said goodbye to everyone. They were all crying; I don't think I handled this thing well. Mother was used to this, and she was happy that she was going to see her love.

Althea came with us to the airport; I was so unhappy that I was going to say goodbye to my sister. My brother Edson and sister Karen were coming up with Dad in May. I told Edson I would see him soon. As we left our aunt's house, it felt like déjà vu. It felt like the day Mother took us away from Dad; everyone was crying. I fell asleep in the car, as always.

When we got to the airport, I hugged Althea and told her to take care of the kids; she just shook her head as tears rolled down her cheeks. Mother embraced her and told her that she was going to work on her papers as soon as possible. I knew I was going to miss her because she was always working hard, and that son of hers was a handful.

My other sister Marlene was in and out of those children's lives. Now I was gone; I didn't know what would happen to them. They were my babies, and now I was leaving them. It really broke my heart. I didn't know if anyone would take care of them the way I did. I knew that they needed love from anything or anyone. Their dad wasn't around to teach them that, and neither was their mother.

Mother told me that it was time to check in; we told Althea bye again and went inside the airport. I always wondered what it looked like in this building. Everyone was busy talking and searching; as I stood close to Mother, she did all the necessary things. She knew what she was doing. While we waited in an area for a while, she told me it was time to board the airplane. I just followed her; she told me to wave goodbye to Althea. Then we went and boarded the airplane. As I watched the air hostess, I always wanted to be one, but my aunt told me I was too dense to be one. I would have to speak different languages to become one; they all looked professional but spoke English. The plane took off; I was nervous. But no one knew; the only problem I had was my ears. They were killing me to the point that I was crying. Mother told me to chew gum and blow; that was not working at all.

The flight took us almost four hours, which seemed forever. The plane landed, and Mother took us to the immigration window, where they stamped out our passports and told us, "Welcome to the United States of America!" Mother smiled and told me to come; that was one of the happiest days for her. We got our luggage and went outside the airport. It was March the third. Cold was not the word; it was something different for me.

As we stood inside the airport waiting for my mother's boyfriend, he called her name. Her face lit up; she was all over him like a teenager in love. She wasn't afraid to let him know how much she missed him. He didn't hug me at all, as if I cared. He gave us jackets to wear in the cold; of course, the one I got was too big. When we got into the vehicle, his brother-in-law was driving. I sat at the front with him while Mother and Mr. Tucker were in the back seat. She wasn't acting like my mother at all; they were acting like teenagers, all kissing and going on.

I didn't say much; then, his brother-in-law asked me how I liked the places so far. I told him I didn't know. Mr. Tucker explained that I was from the country and wouldn't know anything good at all. I still didn't say anything to him at this time.

When we got to the house, Mother took me to introduce Mr. Tucker's sister. She looked at me and said I looked just like Mom; Mother was trying to be funny. Then she said that she wasn't ugly like that. I told her hi, and then I was all around being introduced to everyone in the house. She had four sons; I met three of them. Mr. Tucker's daughter and son were there. To my luck, his daughter and I were the same age. I just watched everyone's movement; then, Mother took me to the attic of the house. That was where she was staying with this man; it had everything. A living room, one bedroom, and a bathroom.

I asked my mother where her kitchen was; she told me that she shared the one downstairs. I didn't see another bedroom, so I knew that the couch was my bed for now. Mother went back downstairs to get something for me to eat.

Mr. Tucker told me to go downstairs and help my mother in the kitchen. His brother-in-law told him that I was new to the place and that my mother would bring up my food. His reply was that the kitchen was big enough for me to find it, then his daughter started to laugh. I just went as he said because it was really cold to be outside at this time. I was used to people like that; now I knew what I was in for.

When I was finished eating, Mother told me to take a shower; she showed me how to turn on the hot water and cold one, and Mr. Tucker made fun of that too. He kept saying that I was from the country and wasn't used to anything good. I didn't talk much. I just looked and watched; his daughter didn't say much to me at all. She only laughed when her father tried to put me down. When Mother was all done, she took a shower and told me to sleep on the bed while she and Mr. Tucker slept on the floor. That night, I didn't sleep. The tears were just rolling down. As I listened to them as they made out, I kept thinking about my sister Karen and her boyfriend. Mr. Tucker's daughter had the couch. I didn't know when I fell asleep. I just blocked them out of my head.

The next day, I went outside the house without a jacket. Mr. Tucker's nephew told me that I needed a jacket to wear because it was too cold. I told him that I was fine. I only stayed outside for one minute. The cold went through me like nothing; what was I trying to prove? I ran inside, and Mother started to laugh at me. Then she went inside her closet and gave me a jacket to wear. It was not big like the one Mr. Tucker had brought at the airport. She told me that she was going to the grocery store, and she asked me if I wanted to come. I went with her; at this time, fashion was not working for me. I was more concerned about being warm. While at the store, Mother showed me the famous American apple. She brought some grapes and potato chips; then she picked up things she had needed for the house. When we got back, she put away the things downstairs. She knew where to put them because she shared the kitchen with Mr. Tucker's sister.

She didn't let me stay downstairs too much. Mother was that kind of person. She didn't want people to get tired of me. When I went into the den, I turned on the TV. Their den was more their living room. I was happy that Mr. Tucker was at work, so I could spend a lot of time with my mother. Whenever he got home, it was all about him. He was the king in the attic, Mother was his slave, and now I was a peasant in his eyes. I would just laugh at him when he talked.

This man was an arrogant person, full of pride and self-conceit; whenever he talked to you, he would let you feel as if you were nothing. I couldn't understand why Mother put up with this man at all. He was ugly and not to mention his daughter.

I guess love is blind, really blind. I knew what to do when he got home; he always went to the couch. Then he would send his slave girl to get what he needed. He had me going down and up the stairs for things he needed. His princess had gone home; she only came to visit him on the weekend. I only did what he told me to do for a quiet life. Mother wasn't working, and if he told us to leave, where would we go? After all, I could handle him; it was better for me to keep my mouth shut than to be in the cold. My aunt was my number one professor who taught me how evil people can be, so I could handle this piece of cockroach.

The next day, Mother took me to the social security office so that we could get our numbers. I asked my mother what this number was for. She told me it was to let the government know about you. "This number holds everything; you will need it for school, a job, etc."

We went in line and took a number. Then we waited to be called; there were a lot of people there. When they called our number, Mother gave the man at the window our paperwork, and he looked over every document and gave us each a number on a paper. I asked her if that was our number, and she told me that we would get a card in the mail with our own numbers on it. "Now, you can register for school, and I can get a job."

She was so excited. The job she was doing had gone due to the fact she had to stay in Jamaica for those three months. As we walked out of the building, she couldn't stop laughing and thanking Jesus; it had been a while since she called his name. I just smiled at her. Mom took me to the famous Jamaica Avenue in Queens, New York. I had died and gone to heaven. When I saw all of the stores and the styles, my heart was beating fast. Then, she took me into the store; I knew she had no money to buy anything. She said that we were window-shopping, whatever that meant. It seemed as if we were gone all day; when we got to the house, she started cooking and got everything ready for King Cockroach. I knew my place when he got home. I went into their bedroom and waited for Mother to serve him dinner; then, I could wash out his plate. I did what I was told, just for a peaceful life.

That same night, Mother's friend came over to visit her; they were all laughing and talking. I just went inside the room. Mother's girlfriend wanted to see me, so I came out and introduced myself to her; then she said that I looked like Mother. She always made jokes like she wasn't ugly like that; then Mr. Cockroach got upset because they were not talking about him. He told me to go get the ice bucket and get him some ice. I asked him what was an ice bucket. He called me a fool in front of their friends and said I was an old country gal. I looked at my mother to see what she would have said. She told me to go get the ice for him.

I was so embarrassed. I didn't cry in front of them; his brother-in-law was there, and they just looked at me. I asked him if he needed anything else. He waved his hands and told me to just go. I walked away like a little puppy; I was really hurt. I didn't need this at all; I thought living with my mother would be all right, but I was feeling the same way with my aunt. Mother was afraid of this man, and I wasn't. She always wanted to please people. I went into the bathroom and cried my heart out; I didn't like embarrassment.

I waited until they left, then I came to my bed, the couch. As I lay down, the tears just came out; I couldn't control them. I cried like a baby; my heart was full.

Chapter 11

The following day, my mother took me with her to Manhattan, the city, to meet up with her girlfriend. She took us to her job; she was a nanny. She took care of a white baby, and she was so cute; I was just playing with the child, then her boss saw me, and I introduced myself as always. She asked my mother if I had anything to wear, and of course, Mother told her yes. This white lady went inside her closet and gave me a couple of her suits. I loved them; I was thankful for anything at this time because I needed clothes for school.

This wasn't Jamaica, where I would wear a uniform. I would have to change each day. Mother's friend was nice. She told Mother that she would take me shopping one day. When we got home, Mr. Tucker was there. He was so mad that his dinner wasn't ready yet. He was arguing that he went to work and when he got home, his meal should be ready.

She didn't say a word, she got his meal ready, and when he was finished, he told me to wash his dishes. Mother took them from me, and the look he gave me was pure evil. I just walked away. The tension was really sharp; I went into my address book and went through it. I saw Blue's address. I needed to write to him; I really missed this guy. While I was going through the book, I saw my friend Pam's address.

Pam, the young girl I went to school with in Jamaica, had come up early in November. She had left for the US five months before me, and her address was Queens, New York. I took it to my mother and asked her how far this address was; she told me Queens was a big place. I didn't have a phone number for her; that was my downfall.

I waited until Ryan, Mr. Tucker's nephew, came home from school. He told me he might have an idea, but we had to wait until the weekend. I didn't mind at all. The following day, Mother and I were on the road again. This time, we went to the Bronx to see my uncle. He was the one who came and got my dad when he was sick; he gave Mother one hundred dollars to buy me a jacket for school. When we left, she went right to the store and bought me one and a couple of tops and two pairs of jeans. I knew I was going to work really soon. The things I liked, Mother wasn't going to buy them, and moreover, she had to send money back home for our family. I was so thankful for what I'd gotten; Mother was always doing her best, but she wouldn't get a job. She had no degree but child care.

I watched her as she tried to budget the little money she got because this man was only paying the bills now. He didn't even offer to buy me anything. This week, we did a lot, then the following week, she took me to get me registered for school. This was a really big building; I was a bit nervous. Children were in the hallway making noise, and it was just loud. Then we went into the office, and she gave them all my paperwork.

I was just looking at everything around me; things were so much different. On my report card from Jamaica, the grades were not good, so they thought I was slow. My mother told me I needed to study hard; I was just looking at a student that came into the office and made noise. My eyes were all over the place; when we left, I was a bit afraid of everything I saw. Mother told me I would be okay; I just looked at her.

That weekend, Ryan and I went searching for my friend Pam; this guy had me walking all over the place. I was eager to find her, but no luck. Ryan showed me the school I would attend; then, he showed me a couple more high schools. It was a good walk.

When we got home, I was so tired. I told Mother—no luck. She told me I would find new friends when I went to school. I knew in my heart that I was going to find Pam one day, but for now, I had a lot to focus on. The weekend went by, and I was getting ready for school. Ryan walked with me to school on the first day. He knew all the shortcuts; he told me that I should wait for him because his school was nearby.

I didn't think so; what he called near was a long walk. I told Mother I was leaving for school, and she was leaving also. She was going on a job interview. Before Edson and Karen came to America, she wanted to get them clothes and things they would need for the summer and winter.

Mother was glad it wasn't winter, so she didn't have to focus on getting jackets for them right now. Her thought was back home on Althea with the kids; I wished I could help her because that man she had would not help her at all. I told my mother bye and went with Ryan; he walked through a couple of neighborhoods. This young man knew his way around well. I was so nervous; he didn't leave until I got into the school building. I wanted to run back outside, but I had to be brave. This school was like a maze; I knew I asked a lot of questions to find my way around.

When I got to my first class, I gave the teacher my program card, and he told me where to go. When he read my name, it was another story; he asked me if my name was really Angela Davis. I said yes, and he asked me who named me Angela Davis. I looked at him and said, "My dad. Why?" I wanted to know.

This man went on and on about Angela Davis; he told me that she was a murderer, kidnapper, and the list went on and on. At this time, most of the children in the class were laughing and talking. I didn't think I needed to hear all that, but I did.

When I went into all my classes, most of my teachers didn't have anything good to say about the person I was named after. I didn't listen to them one bit. I knew my dad wasn't going to name me after someone bad. He would most likely name me after someone who stood up for what she believed in. In every class I went in, the teachers gave me tests, they were all easy, and I was finished in no time. While on my way to the next class, I was focussing on the program card. Then I heard my name being called; when I turned around, I could not believe it. It was my friend Pam, the one that I was searching for! I just ran and embraced her; we were both talking at the same time. Then I stopped and let her go first. She took my program card and looked at it. Then she told me I was in the same homeroom with her and a couple more classes as well. She looked so different; she had makeup on and all the works. She was even talking like an American. I could hardly understand her myself; I was just looking at her to see how she changed in five months. She introduced me to some of the girls in the class.

With all the makeup and the language, I was in another world. I just looked at all of them while they were talking at the same time. The teacher was talking as well as the children. In Jamaica, you would have gotten beaten for that. I just sat back and watched all of them. They were so noisy; I couldn't wait to get out of this class.

Pam told me where my next class was and that we had lunch at the same time. She told me where to meet up, which I did. The lunchroom was another story. The children didn't have any behavior. The noise was even louder than in the classroom. I knew I could not handle this; after lunch, we went into different classes once more. I introduced myself to the whole class, then I heard about Angela Davis again. After school, I told Pam bye, and she gave me her mom's number. I didn't know the number at the house. When I came out of school, surely enough, Ryan was waiting for me. I told him I had found my friend Pam and how happy I was. I wasn't afraid of going back to school. When I got home, I told Mother all about my day.

She even got good news. Mom had gotten the job; we were both happy! I went and did my homework, ate dinner, and took a shower for the night. Mr. Tucker was watching TV, so I had to wait until he was finished before I went to bed.

This went on almost every day; I would go to school and hear how Angela Davis was an evil person. When I got home, Mr. Tucker was on my case; if I wasn't a fool, I was stupid. I didn't let all of that get into my head; I would block them out.

One day at school, I asked Pam if I could go into the library, and she told me I would have to do it on my lunch break.

The following day, I went to the library and showed the librarian teacher my program card, and she let me in. She asked me how she could assist me. I told her I wanted a book on Angela Davis. She asked me if I was doing a paper on her. I told her it was more about me. She looked at me; then I excused myself. She gave me a couple of books; of course, I took the smallest one. I read all about what they said about her and what really went down. I knew in my heart that she must have been a good woman because my dad named me after her. Now I could hold my ground whenever these teachers had anything negative to say; I told the lady thanks and went to my other class. When I did my quiz, I got good grades; the children would call me a nerd.

I'm from Jamaica; what in the world was a nerd? I did find out what a nerd was; I could not believe these children were calling me a nerd. All my life in Jamaica, I was called a dunce, and now a nerd. I loved this place called America. When I was in Jamaica, the men didn't like skinny girls at all. They said they wanted a woman with meat on their body; now, Americans wanted bones. I didn't get it at all, but it was working for me.

As the days went by, I was doing the same thing over and over again. Whenever I was home, Mr. Tucker tried to put me down. I just ignored that son of a baker and his daughter whenever she came over. He would have a field day with me. One thing I didn't like about Mother, she didn't say anything to him when he talked bad things about me, but I let it roll down like water on a duck's back. After all, my aunt back home was the number one villain; she cursed me. She starved me and even tried to deprive me of my education.

One thing she didn't do was hit me, but her words alone could kill. Now I was dealing with Mr. Tucker's words; I blocked him out most of the time, and to top it off, his daughter wasn't any princess either. Looks were all gone. She looked just like her father. Everyone was telling me that my mother was beautiful and I looked just like her. I needed to start thinking that way; I wasn't all that, but I wasn't bad looking, after all.

One night, I was sleeping on the couch, and I always rocked myself to bed. I didn't know what had happened, but there was Mr. Tucker's brother-in-law over me. I jumped up and asked him what it was that he wanted; he said that he thought I was sick or something. I just looked at him and said, "I'm fine." Then he went back down the stairs. From that night on, I slept with one eye open just to protect myself. Who would believe me? Mother was too in love with that man. I knew that my dad would not want me back in his life; after all, I chose my mother over him.

I made my bed, and now I had to lay in it. Every day was the same for all of us. Mother would tell me that I was bathing too much because Mr. Tucker's brother-in-law was complaining about his water bill. I only bathed twice a day, which was normal, and once on weekends. I had to bathe only once. Anything I did was a problem with these people; I was really getting fed up. Whenever I came home late from school, the brother-in-law was on my case, as if I didn't have Tucker to deal with. I didn't want to be the only female in the house.

I would go by Pam's house and wait until I knew Mother or even Mr. Tucker's sister was almost home. This was America now, and these men liked the young and skinny. I wasn't going to set up myself like that. After all, it would have been my words over theirs.

One evening, I went by Pam's house; she lived with her aunt and sister. Her mother had a job; she was my friend, so I went and stayed for two hours. When I got home, the brother-in-law gave me a piece of his mind. He told me that my mother thought that I was a saint, but I wasn't. I went upstairs; then the Angela Davis in me went back downstairs and asked him what he meant by saying that. He looked at me and laughed; he said nothing. I went back upstairs and was just thinking about what nerve this man had. After all, I caught him over me; I wasn't buying that for one minute.

He thought that I was sick—as if I looked stupid. The only person who was acting stupid was my mother, to not notice what was going on. Karen's baby's father was the same way; my gut was telling me something was up. That evening when Mr. Tucker came home, I didn't know what he told him. He was furious with me, and to top it off, Mother started yelling at me.

I started to cry because she never called Pam's house to find out. Mr. Tucker wanted her to punish me more, but she didn't. When he saw that she did not hit me, he called me all kinds of things; at this time, his words hurt my soul. I just wept that I felt pain in my belly. Living with this man was getting to me; now, he was letting my aunt look like a saint, and that wasn't possible.

I did what I knew best: I went to school and made the grades, then came home and got verbal abuse from these men. Thank God, not sexually. I knew that I would have died; who was there to save me? Not Mother. She was too much in love; he wasn't like Gilbert at all. He was pure evil, and I was his number one target; he totally forgot that he had a child too.

Mother told me that she heard from Althea; she told her that my dad and the rest of my siblings were coming up within a week. I didn't know if I should be happy or not. I knew that my dad was upset with me right now. I didn't know how to explain that I had made a mistake by living with my mother; I didn't know the circumstances with him either. Dad's family also didn't like me. I was stuck between two worlds, which way to go. The week went by, and Mother took me to see them; she had saved up some money, and she went and got them a couple of outfits for the summer. She was so happy to see my sister and brother; I was happy too.

When we got to the Bronx, Mother stayed downstairs and told me where to go. They buzzed me in, and I went inside to see them; this was a different setting. We lived in a house, and they were staying in an apartment; it was cool and nice. When I got to the door, I rang the bell, and my dad came and opened the door. The man didn't say anything to me. He just yelled for them to come to the door and see me. I went in and greeted my aunt and cousin. Then Mother started to buzz us to get downstairs; she wanted to catch the stores before they closed.

I told my dad bye; he didn't say anything at all. While we were going to the elevator, I told them to go ahead and that I would catch up with them. When they left, I went back and rang the doorbell, and my dad opened the door. I told him as it was, "I know that you are upset with me right now, but I still love you, no matter what." Then, I kissed him on his forehead and walked away. Dad didn't say anything, but he made a funny sound. I ran and met up with the rest of them. Of course, Mother was upset. I did what needed to be done; I didn't know what Dad was feeling, but I loved that man so much; he had to know it. Sometimes as a child, you have to let the grown-up feel like a kid.

We left with our mother and went to the store to get things for my siblings. Mother was so happy that more of her children were here. I watched my sister Karen open up her eyes the same way I did. I knew that she was going to get a job soon, and she had her son to think about as well.

Chapter 12

Mother told us that Mr. Tucker and his family were having a cookout, and she wanted us to look good. They saw and liked it and then bought it. When we were finished, we went to the house. This was another story; they were introduced to his family. Mother told Karen not to mention her son, Leon, to Mr. Tucker and his family; for some reason, Leon was a secret, and that was final.

I didn't like it one bit, and neither did Karen. I didn't know what the big problem was with this man; after all, he wasn't our dad. She did as she was told, a secret. The day at the party, I saw the true Mr. Tucker. He was an alcoholic, and it seemed as if the whole world knew. I just looked at him and held my guide; Mother was in love and could not see a thing. I knew that I had to be extra careful around him.

The party came, and it went well; now it was Sunday, and we had to take Karen and Edson back to the Bronx; it was a long ride. As the weekend went by, we did the usual things. Then the weekend was here again; Mother got my siblings. This went on every weekend; it seemed as if Mr. Brother-in-Law was getting upset that there were too many people in his house, and now his water bills were getting higher. Mr. Tucker told my mother that we could not stay at the house anymore. So that summer, I stayed at my dad's in the Bronx.

I got to meet up with cousins I never saw before and ones that I'd not seen in years; we had so much fun. We went to Fun Land, out of state, where we had a barbecue in the park, and we went to the pool. Dad was enjoying himself as well. Mother, on the other hand, was searching for an apartment for us to live in; I loved the idea that she was doing that, but now I wouldn't feel the way I did. The summer with Dad and my family was the best time ever; I got to express myself once more. I felt safe and sound to know that I was the baby again, and I didn't have to protect myself from anyone or anything.

The weeks went by so fast; then Mother called me one day to let me know that she had found a two-bedroom house. She had asked Esdon if he wanted to come, but he told her no. She went and took the house because it had more space for all of us. School was almost ready to open. Now she had to get clothes and back-to-school stuff for all of us, even the grandkids in Jamaica. She had it really hard; our dad was not working to help her, and she didn't even ask him for help.

She did what she knew best so that everyone had something new for school. I was happy that we had moved from that house because that brother-in-law was a handful, and knowing me, I would have lost it. I knew how to handle Mr. Tucker, but two of them were driving me mad. I knew we had to go back to Queens and help Mother with the new apartment, which would be really fun.

One week left for school to be open; Mother wanted us back in Queens to help her with the new apartment; she had a surprise as well. It was our aunt that we didn't know. She came from England; she was staying with my mother, sister, and Aunt Cislyn. She, too, was in America. It seemed as if it was a family reunion; she had two of her sisters with her; the only difference was that they lived in Brooklyn.

My aunt from England sounded nothing like an English; she sounded more Jamaican than ever. I asked my mother if she was in the country part of England, and they all laughed. We did what we had to do to get the place ready because those people wanted us out of their house. Dad was happy that Mother had taken Karen with us, he noticed that people didn't live up to their words, and he was not working to help with the bills due to his sickness.

Mother had gotten Karen into a school as well so that she could get her GED. She even got her a job at Burger King. I wanted one, but I was only sixteen and had to wait, but my chores were to get dinner ready during the week and clean the apartment up, which included everything. I remember getting a letter from Blue back home in Jamaica; he told me how much he had missed me and that he couldn't wait to see me. My heart was just hurting for him; I missed him so much. He had always put a smile on my face, and that was the best feeling ever.

I didn't know what it was or if it was love, but I knew in my heart that something was real for this man. I wrote him back and expressed my feelings for him and let him know that he would be the only one in my life forever. Our relationship was a long-distance one. We would write to each other, and sometimes, Blue would call me, and I had to deny the call. I wasn't working to pay the bill, and if Mr. Tucker knew, I would really get it.

Karen and I were roommates; she did what she had to do, and each of us had our chores. Karen went to work and school while I had to do the housework. Mother didn't give me any time to idle if I was working at home. I had to bring in the grades; I was competing with Mr. Tucker's daughter; this girl was really smart, and Mother wanted me to get higher grades than hers. Nothing I did was good enough for her; if I got 95 on my test, that wasn't good enough for her; it had to be 100 or more. I was so stressed out I would have a migraine headache. Whenever it happened, I would have to stay home from school. I felt nauseous, and I could not handle the light very well.

It always lasted for three days, so I had to let it take its course. Being under stress was no fun when it came to mother; on the weekend, Karen and I had to go and do the laundry, which was no fun either. Mother had shown me how to do it, but one thing that killed me was when we had to wash Mr. Tucker's underwear. It was full of mess most of the time; I didn't know if he did it on purpose.

I had to get home from school, cook dinner before he got home, and do my homework in the meantime. I didn't have time for myself at all. On Saturday, the house had to be cleaned, as well as the bathroom. I really had it bad.

The thing I hated most was when I cooked; Mr. Tucker would tell me that the food tasted terrible; sometimes, I took it with a smile and thought about how to improve; this man knew how to get to me. I would just break down and cry, I tried not to let this man get the best of me, but it depended on the mood that I was in.

I always felt sorry for myself and got depressed most of the time. I would cry a lot, and then I tried to focus on my life. There wasn't anything I could do for Mother to see my point of view. I would watch this man eat around the dinner table and leave everything in the same place: bones and plate. I was his slave, and no one saw it at all. Even when his daughter came to visit, he still called me to get him what he needed, and if I bought the wrong thing, I was called a fool, which made her laugh.

One evening when Mr. Tucker came home from work, I was taking a shower; when he came into the bathroom, pulled back the shower curtain, and looked at me, he just kissed his teeth and closed it back. I felt so defiled; I didn't dare let Mother know because she wouldn't believe me at all. I just cried; it seemed as if Karen's baby's father was living with us once more.

I thank God for the day I met Aunt Audrey. I spent most of my time with her; she had moved to Queens as well. Aunt Audrey was a wild card. So she moved and came to Queens with her boyfriend, whom she married later.

It seemed as if I couldn't get through to my mother; she was always on my case. I was not allowed to go anywhere at all because Mr. Tucker wouldn't allow it. I was only good for keeping the house clean and washing dirty plates and the bathroom, not to mention dirty clothes. I had to make sure my grade was in place. This was no fun, and if I complained, I would get it really good. It's not that I could not be rude to my mother, but God said to honor your mother and father, and your days will be longer. I didn't know a lot about God as much; I knew that I talked to him most of the time.

I didn't read the Bible that much because some of the words I could not pronounce. I went with Psalms and Proverbs. We didn't go to church on Sunday because we had to go to the laundromat. I was back at school on Monday. I didn't mind school at all; once you got good grades, you were fine with the teachers. All you had to do was study a lot; one class I didn't like was Spanish; I couldn't spell it, not to mention read it.

I still passed with a 75, which was good enough for me, but tell my mother that. I still did the same thing I did in Jamaica. Each morning, I would say my prayer to God. I didn't let this place change me one bit.

Now that I had Aunty Audrey around, I didn't let what Mother and that man had to say about me. Karen was in her own little world. She missed her son very much, and she could not mention him at all in the house, not even a picture of him in our bedroom. This should not have happened; that man didn't need to know who Leon was. I often asked her if she missed him, then she asked me what I thought. She still didn't answer my question... Regardless of what our mother thought, my child's picture would be in the room.

I didn't let them get to me at all; whenever I got A's on my report card, I would call Aunt Audrey and tell her. She would make me feel as if I was the brightest kid in the world. She encouraged me a lot, which made a difference in my life. I just did what I had to do.

My dad and I would talk a lot at night; I didn't let him know what was going on in my life. He asked if I was going to college or the army. I told him college, but he wanted me to fight in the army. I didn't like the idea of killing and fighting after all I'd been through. I was more looking for peace. Then Dad would ask about Mother and her boyfriend; I told him, "Leave her alone. She is in love or something. I know that love didn't hurt you but your kids." Then I asked him about Angela Davis and why he named me after her. He told me she was a bad cookie; when he came to America for his cricket games, she was doing her thing in the seventies. I listened to him as he went on about her. I just laughed at him.

I didn't know her at all to even say she was my role model, but I did a little research about her myself. It seemed as if every class I went in was a problem for the teachers, and most of them were white. I told him what the teachers were telling me about her, and he hissed his teeth and told me not to listen to them because they were pagans. I just laughed and told Dad good night. I spoke to God as always and thanked him for the day.

My life was about the same; Pam would call me and tell me about her boyfriend, then she asked about Blue. I told her that I had written to him the other day, and she was laughing, telling me that I needed to hear his voice. This girl must be crazy; I needed money to call him, not to mention to pay for the call. This was basically my life; I would do what I was told to do.

One day, Pam and I went to Karen's workplace just to say hi; we went on Jamaica Avenue to see what was in fashion as well. When we got there, a lot of guys were looking at us, mostly Pam. She didn't mind at all; then, there was this Guyanese guy talking to me. I didn't look at him at all. Then Karen told him that I was her sister; Pam then told him that I had a boyfriend already and I didn't need any more. I didn't say anything at all; I kept thinking about Blue. We left my sister's job because I had to get home and get dinner ready before Mr. Tucker came home. I told Pam later, got off the bus, and ran so fast home to start dinner.

It was a mess, of course, and I got yelled at, but it put a smile on my face to know that someone else liked me other than Blue. Pam called me as she got home, then the big question came up. She asked me if I was a virgin. I told her yes. I knew she wasn't because of what she told me. She told me that it was the best feeling ever. I was told by my brother Gary that if I had a man, he would kill me. So fear was my number one thing, and I stayed away from that. I told her I was waiting on Blue, and she was quiet for a while. I told her that I was going to get my homework done for school; when I hung up the phone, I was just smiling. When Karen got home, she started telling me about this guy; I just listened to her as she told me about him. I didn't let Pam know that he was inquiring about me. I thought it was cute.

I would go to school and do what I did best; it was Pam and I, as always, friends from Jamaica and now friends in America. We dressed alike as if we were twins; if she saw something on Jamaica Avenue, she told me. Sometimes, I asked my dad for money to buy it or just waited until my mother or aunt gave it to me. Pam would wait until I got my outfit, then we would wear it together. I knew I needed a job to keep up with this fashion thing.

My aunt would give me some dresses she wore in England; I liked them. Pam thought they were too old for me. I loved them, so I wore them. I loved to look different from other kids at school.

One day, a teacher came up to me and said that he never saw me before and asked what class I taught. I looked at him and told him I was a student, then he looked at me and walked away. I went to Pam and asked her if I looked that old. She asked what I meant by. I told her what the teacher said. She explained that most students wore jeans and sneakers while I wore dresses, stockings, and shoes. I loved to look different from everyone else; in Jamaica, we had to wear uniforms like everyone. I took what that teacher said as a compliment.

I didn't have to look like everyone else; I loved putting on my mother's gowns and taking pictures; this was who I was, apart from looking like twins with Pam. Whenever Karan came home, she would tell me about her co-worker and how he would like to see me again. My mind was far from him.

One day, Pam called and told me she had some bad news for me. It was about Blue. I didn't want to hear this at all because when she had bad news, it was bad. She told me the most hurting pain. My true love was seeing someone else. This girl was also pregnant. It was like my heart was ripped out of my body. I felt numb and hurt as the tears rolled down my face. I could not speak.

Pam told me everything I needed to know. My mind was so confused; how could he lie to me like that? I thought that he loved me and we were to be together. I needed someone to talk to other than Pam; she was telling me to leave him for a long time, but I didn't listen at all. My life didn't make sense at this time; I wanted to just hide myself. It seemed as if my life had ended, but she reassured me that it would get better. She told me that I didn't love him at all until we made love. There she went again with that sex thing.

I finally got the courage and told Karen about my Blue. She told me that life would get better because she was dating one of her co-workers. She totally forgot about her baby's father. I couldn't believe this girl. I asked her about Eddie, and she said that he didn't love her at all. Then I asked about this guy she was dating. "I will know later, not now." I totally forgot that she was more experienced than Pam and I. She told me that I would be okay and that it was Blue's loss. If he had loved me, he could have waited for me, but he wanted to fool around.

I guess everything comes with a price, and so does love. I didn't feel 100 percent happy, but I felt a little better. Whenever I heard our song, I would cry, then I would get mad. Karen kept telling me about her co-worker. I finally got the courage to tell Pam about him, and she told me to test the water. It wasn't that I was going to marry the guy; I told Karen that I would talk to him. I didn't know what to talk about; I was shy and afraid. All my life, I had fears about boys and what might happen. He was from another island with a different culture and different lifestyle of living. I didn't talk a lot, but I would listen to him.

He was the only son of his parents; he had two sisters, whom he adored. While I spoke to him, I was so afraid of Mr. Tucker picking up the phone and hearing us talking; this boyfriend thing was getting me so nervous whenever Tucker picked up the phone. I would give it to Karen. She laughed at me so hard; then, I would call Pam and tell her everything. Karen told me not to mention everything to her, something I should just keep between myself and this guy, but how could you not tell?

We were dating for four to six months now, and the sex thing came up. He told me that he could not believe I was a virgin. He said that the girl today was not; of course, I called Pam, and she told me it was true. I knew that Karen was going to tell me the same thing, now I was only seventeen, and everyone I spoke to thought I was waiting a long time. I heard that Mr. Right was having fun himself. I needed to know what I would have before I got married.

I knew in my heart that this thing wasn't right; I didn't feel anything for this guy. I was more nervous than anything else. This guy was pressuring me a lot; most of our conversation was now based on sex. Most of the time, I wanted to hang up the phone, but I kept listening to him go on and on. One day, he gave me an ultimatum: I should choose if I wanted him or if I was still waiting on Blue. I was still in love with Blue, but he hurt me once. I didn't know if he would do it again.

Chapter 13

I knew this guy could get anyone he wanted because he wasn't bad looking, but I still didn't think it was right. I called Pam and told her this was the wrong thing to do; she told me to fight for my man. These girls wouldn't play at all, so I took her advice and decided to give up my gift just to make this guy happy.

That day, everything was planned; Karen even took the day off from work. Pam was excited, and I was nervous. I stayed in the room while he came in; my heart was beating so fast. He asked me if I was fine, and I told him yes. I watched him undress. I was just shaking. Then he told me to relax; he took off my underwear. I watched him as he put on the condom; this was no fun. I lay down like a dead corpse; he was just having his way with me. I wanted to push him off, but I didn't want to upset him. I felt so dirty and ashamed. When he got up, he looked in the mirror as if he was the man, and I felt so disgusted with myself. I didn't even dare look up to God because I knew I'd done wrong. When he left, Karen asked me if I was fine.

I just shook my head; then Pam called to hear what had happened. I told her that I would talk to her; nothing she told me about was so magical. I was ashamed of myself, and I had let down God. I wasn't a Christian but talked to God a lot, and now I couldn't dare look up at him. I felt so dirty and ashamed.

The next day at school, Pam asked me how I was feeling, and I told her dirty. She looked at me and said maybe he wasn't the right one for me. It was too late. He took my most precious gift. This guy wanted more of me; I told him to just wait because I wasn't feeling good about myself. He didn't care at all; he wanted it when he wanted. He was a man in need, and he could get any girls he wanted. I was more disgusted with him and myself. We didn't last long because my grades were going down, and Mother told me I had to bring them up or else. I told him that I had to take some time out to study, but as always, he had to make an ultimatum.

I chose school because being with this guy wasn't anything great. I felt more guilty and dirty than ever. I got rid of this guy. Then he started calling me a female dog. I could not understand him; he took my virginity and called me a whore. I could not understand him at all. When I thought about this guy, he wasn't good for me at all. He would tell me to cut school just to meet him, and now I had to make up summer school for him. It was not worth it at all, but I'd learned the hard way.

Life for me was no fun in the park; I did what I did best, schoolwork. Pam and I were best friends; sometimes, she didn't give me the best information at all. She was there when three girls jumped me at school; she took one and left the others on me. We had to go into the principal office for protection. According to the dean, those girls were troublemakers and had boyfriends with guns. So they called our parents. My mother and Pam's mom came as well. When I went home, I called my dad and told him what had happened; he asked me who won the fight. I told him that the girls did; he was disappointed.

I told him that it was two big girls and, after all, I was a little thing. Then he said size didn't matter; well, he could think that. I was hurting all over; those girls did a number on me.

Now, whenever Pam was seen, I was there unless when she had typing class. I had drafting class; my major in school was to become an architect. I loved this class; as always, I was the only female in my class.

This was no fun at all; every day, the guys would make fun of me, and they told me this wasn't a place for women. They let me have it most of the time, but I wasn't afraid of them. I laughed most of the time. One semester, we had another girl; she didn't last long. Those guys made her cry; she gave up.

I wasn't going to let anyone run me out of what I wanted; I remember one day at school, I wore a nice colorful outfit. It was my birthday, and I wanted to look cute. These boys had a field day with me; they told me I came into the class looking like a bag of Skittles, then they went on asking me what flavor I was. I had to laugh because they were right. School was fun as you know it, one day a senior student came and asked me to help him with his maths work.

Our maths teacher told him that he needed to pass the class or he would not play on the football team or even graduate. I had a job after school to help this guy with his maths. I loved that subject a lot, so I had no problem helping him. I did all I could do just to help the children. Who would have thought that I could do that? High school was a big challenge; students you had to deal with—you knew the work, and they didn't. I was not ashamed of being called a nerd because, back home, that was a good thing. The only problem I had was these white teachers had a problem with my name. They would judge me before they knew me, but I still lived up to the name Angela Davis.

I remember one day, I totally forgot to pray, so I closed my eyes in class. I said my prayer in my mind. When I was finished, I made the sign of the cross. Good thing I did that because when I opened my eyes, the teacher was looking at me, then he asked me if I was finished; I just shook my head. I could not wait for school to be out. Whenever we were in the hallway at school, one teacher called us immigrants and said we needed to go back to our country. There weren't any dull moments with these teachers at all.

This time summer was coming up, and my brother and I had gotten work at Burger King; Karen's manager told us to come to the city, and he would get us jobs. I didn't think twice; I didn't wait on Mother to help me. I went and did what I had to do—I worked all summer, Edson and I.

I remember our first paycheck; we took out our fare for work and went into Conway and shopped. It felt really good when you didn't have to depend on your parents, and I knew they were happy too. I bought things I needed for school and other stuff. Pam went to Jamaica for her vacation that summer. I had to work; I couldn't afford to buy the plane ticket to go to Jamaica at all.

I was having the time of my life, I saved some of my hard-earned money, but I spent more on clothes and shoes. I loved to dress up and look good. The summer came and gone, and we were back in school.

This time, we were all seniors, and our school schedule was changed; we got in late sometime and left early most of the time. Everyone was having fun; I think that this got the best of us; we had all idle our time at school. Most of our grades were dropping significantly. Our teacher would warn us to keep our grades up, but we were seniors. I had one maths teacher we didn't get along at all.

I had swimming class before his, so I would get to his class late most of the time. I would explain to him that it was totally impossible to get there on time. The man would close the door in my face and send me to the dean's office. I always went, but that still didn't do much because I could not drop one class since I needed both to graduate. He told me that he was going to make sure I didn't. I had to have one. I told him that it was not for him to decide; I still could not win with him.

I just stopped running to his class after swimming. I was too tired to even bother. He told me he was going to fail me, which he did. I knew that I would have to go to summer school, but because my other grades were good, he could not stop me at all.

Pam told me I needed a man for my prom date; she didn't think I was capable of finding one for myself. I was more into passing my class, and she was talking about a man in a time like this. I asked this guy at work, but he was too much into himself. Edson didn't have many friends, and the one he knew wasn't my type. Pam did come through; she introduced me to a nice-looking guy; he wasn't a Jamaican at all. His name was Cleveland Johnson. He was the type you brought home to meet your mother. She told him as it was, I was her best friend, and she hoped he didn't hurt me like the rest. I looked at him with my mouth open. He just looked at me and laughed; I was so embarrassed. I just said, "Hi! I'm Angela." She told him everything that he needed to know about me. Then she walked away with her boyfriend. She even told him that I needed a date for the prom. I should have dropped dead. He told me he couldn't take me to the prom because he had other plans, but that was fine with me.

Pam was just crazy and wanted me to be happy, so during the rest of the school years, we were dating as a couple. It was a lot of fun. I took my sister Karen as my date. Pam went with her boyfriend. Edson was dating my friend, and some of our classmates went without a date too. That day, I got ready as if I was getting married; my dad came over to take pictures of us. I didn't leave him out at all; his three kids were going to the prom. We didn't take a limo because it was too expensive for the three of us, but Karen had a friend who drove a taxi, which we all fit well.

We took Dad to the train station when he was finished taking our pictures. Mother was happy that I had my sister and brother with me. Aunt Audrey was there too; she helped Mother get us dressed up. We were all looking lovely as always. Dad looked so proud, as well as Mother. I didn't have a date, but that was the best day of my life. Man, we had fun! They didn't have a King and Queen Day, but we had a contest for the best dress for men. Edson won that contest because we were all screaming for him. Pam told me to yell for her man, and I did, but my brother won, and his girlfriend was happy. It was a night to remember. The school year went by so fast; we were graduating already.

Cleveland had bought me a bouquet of flowers. This time, everyone was at my graduation except my dad. It would have been too late for him to take the train home, so he gave Edson his video to tape the entire thing. Mr. Tucker was there, and so was my aunt.

The gift I gave Cleveland was a bit childish; that was how I felt when I was around him. All my life, I had to grow up to help my niece and nephew; at that time, I felt like a kid. Mother loved Cleveland so much; it seemed as if he was the son she wanted. Cleveland loved when I baked bread pudding.

That summer, we went to summer school and movies; we went all over the place. Pam's boyfriend had a car, so we didn't have a problem with transportation. As the summer came, my love had gone. It was only a summer thing. I really got hurt this time because this guy knew my family. I was really hurt because I let down my guide. I could not eat at all; my heart was broken. Every time I watched the weather, I would cry when the state of Cleveland came up.

I kept thinking I should not hold out on sex with this guy; maybe he would still be with me. He told me his mother didn't like the gift that I gave him. Then he told me that his girlfriend was pregnant with his child, and he wanted to be with her. All this time, he was with her; no wonder he never asked for sex. I was trying to be loved after all I'd been through. It wasn't meant to be. At the time when you are going through all the pains in life, it seems as if the world will end, but it gets better.

I was busy that summer. I finally went and took the test for the army; after all, I had nothing to lose. My dad wanted me in the army like my cousin. While Mother was upset because she wanted me to go to college, I was between two worlds. How can you make either parent happy? I didn't know what to do; if only they could come together and understand what a child was going through. I didn't pass the test at all; I didn't know what had happened. In some way, I was not disappointed at all; maybe Dad was.

In all of this, no one cared about what children were going through with divorced parents; it was like they had ripped your life apart and expected that you should put it back together yourself. I hated the whole situation. If only Mother didn't cheat, or if only Dad were good to her. Moreover, if they only got over their differences. I was broken into many pieces and didn't know who I was or who I wanted to be. I took some time off from school. I had to find out what I wanted in life; at this time, the architect wasn't cutting it.

One day, Pam called me and asked if I wanted to go with her and her mother and sister to Canada. Of course, who wouldn't want to? I asked my mother, and she spoke with Pam's mother; it was a done deal. Mother knew that I needed a break from everything and everyone. Mr. Tucker tried to stop me, but this time, she told him I was old enough to know right from wrong. I was surprised to hear that; I didn't know if my aunt had spoken to her about the way that man treated me and that his daughter could do anything she wanted. I just needed a break from everything.

While in the van, Pam's mother asked her what she was going to do. She wanted to know if she was coming with her to her brother's house or Pam's sister's home. She told her mother that she was going to stay with her sister; then her mother asked me if I wanted to stay with them or come with her. I was a teenager. I went with Pam to her sister's house.

When her mother dropped us off, a lot of what I thought wasn't what I expected. Her sister was pregnant and was living with her boyfriend; the home that we were staying at was not her sister's but her best friend's home, and she was living with her boyfriend and her son. I looked at Pam and asked her what was going on; she told me that she didn't know that her sister had done this to her. I just watched out all the plans they had made. We got the bedroom, the three of us, while her sister's friends and the child with the father stayed in the living room. I had the chance to call Pam's mom to come and get me, but I didn't. The boyfriend of her sister's friend took us out to the store and roundabout. Canada is a beautiful and nice place; even the atmosphere was clean. When we got back to the house, we cooked and were just having fun; the young lady was more of a good person.

She didn't drink or smoke; she just wanted us to enjoy ourselves. We were all planning to go to Caribana; it's like a festival where you go and have fun. It's almost like Caribbean culture. Little did I know that Pam had told her ex-boyfriend about her plans.

He came with his friend too; now the house had too many guests; I just sat and watched everyone. Her boyfriend I knew well and his friend too; they wanted the cheaper way out like everyone else. They just came for the festival that weekend; we took the train and went all over the place. We were just having fun; I took pictures everywhere I went. I went up to the police officers and took pictures with them as well.

That night after the festival, we got home, dressed again, and went to a party. This time, it was the four of us. The others were at home because of the baby. The boyfriend of Pam's sister took us to a club and left us there. He told us to call him when we were ready. We had to use the pay phone. I didn't take the number, which wasn't wise because I was with my best friend, after all. At the party, we were all tired because of walking in the sun all day. I saw one of the young men that was at the house with us, but I couldn't find Pam. I kept searching and walking; still no sign of this girl.

I was so tired; I couldn't think straight. So I left the party and was just walking; I didn't know where I was and didn't know where I was going. I was just cursing out this girl. She knew that it was my first time in Canada; I didn't know the place that well. If only she had come and told me she would be back soon, but not a word. While I was walking, a van pulled over, and the door was open. There were a lot of men in that van; it was the holiday, and Canada had a lot of visitors from all over the world. Then I heard the young man at the house calling me; when they saw him, they just drove off. He looked at me and asked me if I was crazy or what; I was in a different country, didn't know the place, and was walking home alone. He said if he wasn't around, maybe those guys would rape and kill me.

He was right; I asked him how he knew where I was. He said that he was sleeping, then just got up and was looking for anyone he knew; then he saw me walking. I just thanked him, and we both walked together. He asked me if I knew where I was going or if I had the phone number for the lady's house; I told him no. While we were walking, Pam came up in a car with a man I didn't know; then, she had the nerve to tell me to get in. I didn't curse that much before, but she and the guy drove off; then the young man said there went our ride. We just walked until I saw the building, then I said we made it. Pam was waiting in the car until she saw us getting into the building.

I went upstairs and couldn't wait to call her mother to get me, but I didn't. The next day, we went to another club; we thought we were in New York. The clubs in Canada closed really early. While we were there, Pam's other sister came with us; we had only one hour there. This almost turned into a nightmare; her little sister accidentally stepped on someone's shoes and didn't tell him that she was sorry. This guy was all in her face; I had to go over to him and tell him she didn't have much sense. "So please see with her; she was just looking." And Pam didn't say anything at all.

That night, I had it with this crowd; I knew that if I kept hanging around them, I was going to get into trouble. The week went by, and I couldn't wait to get back home; Pam's mom asked me if I had enjoyed myself. I told her it was interesting. We hit the highway, and I went to sleep. Then we stopped for the restroom and a bite. When I got home, Mother asked me if I had fun; I told her yes. After all, I did have fun, but I also learned that no matter how much you think you know a person, just think again.

Pam was my best friend, but she put my life in jeopardy. I trusted her to keep me safe, but she was only thinking of herself. When we got home to New York, we were still friends. I would go out with her only if my sister and brother were with me. My brother drove, so we had no problem getting around. That was my life. We would party all weekend. On Monday morning, I was broke; this went on for a while. I had gotten involved again with my sister's friend; he was running and gave a lot of jokes. The only issue he had was another woman. I was the side girl; I had to act as if I was just a friend.

I would get to see him but only at a distance; we would fool around, but no one knew but Karen. It was really hard being the second woman when you wanted him; he was home with her, or you couldn't call him at all. It was putting a toll on me; I started to think that I wasn't good enough to be number one. The same guy friend wanted to date me as well, but I told him that I couldn't date the same friend. He, too, told me that I was crazy if I thought that he would have left his child's mother for me. He told me like it was that this guy was only using me for sex and that I needed someone to love me better.

It was really hard to face the truth, but he was right. It seemed as if Pam found out and asked me; I denied everything just to protect this guy. It seemed as if he wanted to be Mr. Big Shot; he told his friends everything. I didn't like all this drama, so I just walked away. It really hurt me a lot because I really had feelings for him. He didn't have any at all because he was just using me like this friend had told me. I cried, and I got over it, I thought. Life went on, I guessed.

One day while I was at home, I got a call from a man. I didn't know how he got my number and name. He asked me if I was interested in a job, and I knew that Burger King was only a summer thing, so I said yes. He gave me information and told me where to meet him in Manhattan. I got up the next day and got dressed up for a job interview. When I got there, it was a new beginning for me.

He told me to sit in a room full of people; then he gave me a test to do. I sat down and took the exam; then, he told us to wait for the results. Of course, my name was called. He told me that I had gotten a high grade and that I was to go over to the financial aid office to get registered. I asked the young man what he was talking about. He said I had taken a placement test for school.

I said to him I thought this was a place for me to get a job. He said, "Yes. When you are finished with the course, we'll place you into the job you want instead of going to college and still not knowing what you want."

I just looked at him and went to the financial aid office; he took my information. He told me to bring in my parents' information and my high school diploma. I still couldn't believe what just happened; when I got home, I went to my mother and told her that I was going back to school. She looked at me and said that it was about time. I needed her income tax information, but I had to go to Mr. Tucker for that. He was filing taxes for Mother and me.

He gave me all I needed, and I took it to the school. When I went and gave the young man my information, he asked me if I was on welfare. I asked him what that was. He then asked me if I was an American. I told him no. Then he told me I had to take out a loan for school myself because the information I had couldn't help me at all. I signed the papers, and it went through; I told him to wait until I asked my mother about this, and he was fine with it. When I got home, Mother told me I was on my own with this loan; she wasn't going to sign it at all. She thought that I wasn't serious with school at all; she didn't give me a chance like how she gave Karen and the rest of them. I called the school and told him that I would take the loan; I was old enough to pay it back.

Burger King wasn't enough, but it was a start. So I went to school and signed all the papers I needed; then, he gave me a list of what classes to take. I didn't know anything about business class at all; I didn't know how to type at all. I took drafting in high school. That was all I knew and loved. When I came home, I called Pam and told her about the school; she took the information as well.

I took the afternoon classes. It wasn't like I was working in the morning. Pam finally got in school with me as well. Now this girl knew how to make friends. I, on the other hand, was antisocial; I kept to myself. After school, we took the train home; Pam had a male friend who took the train with us. He lived in Queens as well. We were all friends at this point; I took typing class. It didn't do too well.

Chapter 14

Spelling was not my number one thing either, so I didn't know what in the world I was doing in a business school. As I watched all the students go by with their typing, I was still looking at the keys on the typewriter. The teacher didn't like it one bit; she told me that this class wasn't for me; she didn't have to tell me that. I still went to school. I couldn't fail at this point because Mother would have said she was right. I passed the class, not with good grades, but I passed. The next semester, I took traveling and tourism.

There were a lot of older people; they didn't know my age at all. I was in a class that had grandparents in it. This was a good experience for me; I learned a lot from them. They didn't talk too much about sex and boyfriend; they spoke a lot, like paying bills and making sure the house was taken care of. This sounded like my kind of world. As I went to the bookstore to get one of my books for class, a man came up to me and said he liked my hat. I didn't know which hat I had on. I told him thanks and walked away.

When I went into the ladies' room, I looked at the hat and read what was on it; then, I smiled, not for what he said. More for what was written on the hat. That night, I met a lot more students; I met a young lady; she was married and had a son. She seemed very quiet, unlike Pam. I didn't see her in school at all. I had to call her when I got home. I took the train with the guy that lived in Queens. He got off at his stop; when I got home, I called Pam. She told me that she was not feeling well at all.

She then called me back and told me she was pregnant; I asked her for who. She told me about the guy she met in Canada; I knew it. I asked her if he was going to marry her, and she told me that he was married already. Now this was serious business; she told me she loved him, and he loved her too. I asked her about her mother and school, but Pam knew what she wanted. I told her that I would be there for her and the baby. I called Karen and told her about Pam's situation; she looked at me with guilt in her eyes. She, too, was pregnant. I could hardly control myself. I asked her if our mother knew; she said no, and that's when I knew that this girl was crazy.

I knew that this wasn't going well at all because if Mr. Tucker knew, all would break through. I just sat down and thought all my party girls were pregnant. I didn't know what to tell them, but I knew Karen and Pam had to let their mothers know. Karen was three months ahead of Pam because this was her second child; she knew how to hide it well. Pam, on the other hand, didn't know anything at all.

I didn't dare tell Mother about what I knew; it wasn't my place to talk. I was feeling happy in a way for both of them. I knew that Mother was going to kill Karen; I didn't know about Pam's mother. At school, everyone asked for her; I just told them she wasn't well.

One day at school, the man who liked my hat came over to me and told me to write ten things about myself. I asked him why, but he couldn't answer me. I didn't do it at all; he wasn't my English teacher. I thought to myself that he was odd. He then asked me my name the other time he saw me; I asked him if he was in my class and didn't know my name. He smiled and then asked me if I knew his name. I then smiled and said no!

He told me his name and was waiting for me to tell him mine; I just walked away. At the same time, my friend, with whom I took the train, came; then we left and got on the train together. I didn't have many friends at school. I was with the guy I took the train with each night. One day, I asked one of my classmates if she was a Christian; she asked why. She had a piece over her; she was always smiling and happy. I was always grumpy and didn't talk much, so now she told me who she was a Christian and what she was about. It seemed as if God wanted me as well, but I was not ready yet.

Every day, this man would smile at me and talk a lot. I started to look back at him, just to see if he was looking at me; of course, he was. One day, he caught me looking at him; he came over and said, "I see you."

Like a child, I looked away; one afternoon, he came over to me, and we were just talking. We talked for a long time, then my friend came to me and asked where I was. I told her that I was talking to that man in class; she didn't even know who I was talking about. I told her that I would see her later. I wouldn't wait for school the next day; I wanted to see this guy. After all, he had nice things to say.

It was Friday, and I wasn't going to see him until Monday; he came over to me and gave me his number. He said, "Don't be afraid to call me; I have no wife or girlfriend." He then smiled and walked away. I, too, smiled and walked away. I took the train home, and then I said bye to my friend Elaine. That Friday night, I told Karen about this guy; she asked if he had money; I just looked at her and walked away.

I called and checked up on Pam; she told me she had spoken to her mother. She was upset because her mother wanted her to have an abortion. I asked her what she was going to do. Pam said she was going to keep her baby because she loved this guy so much.

I took out the guy's number, but I didn't call him. I was so scared too; I didn't want him to think that I was desperate. I didn't call him that weekend. I wanted him to wait until I saw him in school. He came over and asked why I didn't call him. I told him I was busy, and he shook his head and walked away.

I went over to my friend and told her what had happened; she told me if I had liked this guy, she didn't see why I should wait to talk to him. He didn't have a wife or a girlfriend. I knew that I wasn't in high school, this was college, and this wasn't any kid thing. I was afraid of many things; I was afraid of getting hurt again. I was even afraid of hurting him. I didn't say anything to him at school for the whole week. That Friday night, he didn't come to one of his classes. I went home feeling sad about it; I still didn't call him.

When I came home Friday night from school, Karen told me that she had left the job at Burger King; at this point, Mother knew that she was pregnant, but Mr. Tucker didn't. I called Pam, and she told me her story. She was moving to Canada to be with her baby's father. She had one more good news; she was having twins; I almost passed out. She seemed so happy, unlike Karen. I finally got the courage to call the guy. We talked for almost three hours; I was blushing over the phone. He asked me my age; I told him that I was nineteen. He went quiet for a while; then, he asked me if I knew his age. I told him no. Then he told me, and I almost fell off the bed. I went and sat down on the floor. I could not believe he was thirty-nine years old. This wasn't any guy; this was a man who was half my age. What in the world was I thinking? He asked me if I was okay with that because age wasn't a problem with him. I still didn't say another word.

What in the world can I tell this man, and how can I be with him? I was afraid to even talk to him on the phone. I really liked him, but where could it go? There was no way I could bring him home to meet my mother. He wasn't a Cleveland; I really liked him, but his age was a little bit too much. That night, I couldn't wait to see him at school, but at the same time, I didn't want to know about his age.

When I got to school, he came over, kissed me on my forehead, and told me he would see me later. He then asked me what was the relationship between me and the guy at school. I told him that we were only friends; we only took the train together at night. He told me he would take me to the nearest point; so I wouldn't need to take the train home with my friend.

I didn't see Tom at all in class. Then I heard his voice. He seemed happy and jolly; then, he took me into an empty classroom and gave me a gift. He told me that it was a pre-Valentine gift; I didn't want to take it at all. I wasn't used to getting gifts from men; I only got beer when I went to party with them. He told me to not embarrass him; then he told me that I deserved the world. That night, he followed me on the train to Queens and then went back to catch his train to the Bronx.

When I got home, I hid the gift from my mother and opened it with Karen. It was a perfume set he got me from Elizabeth Taylor, White Diamonds. I was still wearing my Avon ones; Karen asked me again if he was loaded. I told her I didn't know; he didn't work at Burger King like me. He was an accountant; that was all I knew.

That night, I called him to see if he got home safe, then Mr. Tucker came on the phone and told me to get off. He told me that I wasn't paying any bills in the house. Thank God he didn't understand him at all; I told him I would see him the next day.

How I hated that man! It was so embarrassing. When I got off the phone, I went and talked to the baby in my sister's stomach. I asked her what she was going to name the baby if it was a boy; she didn't know. I told her Kunta Kinte. We both laughed. Every night when I came home from school, I would make breakfast for her at 2:00 a.m. in the morning while Mother and that man were sleeping. She wanted a boy, after all, so I would sing to Kunta. I didn't know if she had forgotten about her son back home; Karen didn't talk much about him anymore, which was sad.

This time, I was happy about this guy at school; he asked me if I would be his girlfriend. I told him yes; age was just a number. He was the happiest thing ever. He would take me home halfway and then jump on his train for home. I knew this was getting to him, the things we do for love. After all, he didn't want my friend to follow me anymore. He said I was his lady, and he didn't want anyone around me. He even told me to leave my weekend job at Burger King as he couldn't get to see me more because I was always working. He was my man, and if I was in need of anything, I should ask him; all this was new to me.

I didn't have a man taking care of me before. I asked him if he had children; he told me three. Now I was a stepmother; he didn't talk too much about them. He didn't like their mother, and I tried to find out what it was. He just didn't want to talk about them at all. I guessed when he was ready to talk about them, he would let me know.

I was still afraid of my mother knowing about him, but I think she knew. Even my boyfriend kept asking me when he was going to meet my family. He had spoken to Karen, which I thought was good enough. How in the world could I let him meet Mother, not to mention Mr. Tucker? This man was permissive about everything, while I was afraid about the whole situation.

One day at school, I saw him with a red rose. I asked him who was the secret admirer, and he told me about one of his exes. I looked at him and said, "Really?" He told me I had nothing to worry about. I said I hoped so and walked away; the week went by, and it was soon Valentine's Day.

This time, he came over to me and told me that he had a gift for me; I looked at him and said, "You don't have to give me a gift for me to like you." He said that he knew that, but if he had it all. I would be on top; as he walked away, I asked God to make me love him the way I should. I didn't want to hurt him at all; after all, he was way too old for me.

Tom had left again while I was in class; I noticed he wasn't there. I looked, and I didn't see him at all. He came back later with a pair of gold earrings and a rose. I just looked at him, and then he walked away. I kept thinking that he was showering me with gifts, but I wasn't used to it at all. I worked for what I wanted. To have this man treating me this way was something new. He told me to quit my job and that he would take care of me. He wanted to take me out, but I was too scared of my mother and Mr. Tucker; I told him no. He got so upset that he walked away. I knew he wasn't a young man; he was old and needed someone mature. I knew that my mother listened to everything that Mr. Tucker told her. I knew if Karen was not going, I would have to stay home.

That whole weekend I called him; he didn't answer me until Sunday night. I told him that I was really sorry about that, but he didn't understand me at all. He told me that he was a big man and could not handle childish things at all; he had fallen in love with me. I didn't say anything else. He was just pouring out himself to me. I kept thinking that it was too soon for him to love me.

I went to God and asked him if this was for real; I was doing most of the talking. I remember asking God to put it into my heart to love him. I didn't want to hurt him the way I always did.

I called him back and told him that I would have made it up to him. Monday evening at school, he came over to me and told me that he was sorry. I asked him about what; then, I was faced with the most embarrassing situation. This older woman came up to me, yelling and screaming. She was his girlfriend; it seemed as if he was afraid of her. She wanted to embarrass me, which she did. Now everyone in the school was just looking at me; she even knew my age.

She told me that I couldn't be the woman he wanted. She didn't know if I was still in diapers, and now I wanted a man. She told me that she was going to call my mother on me; I watched this woman talk me down. I kept looking at him to see if he would rescue me from her cruel words.

If only the ground could have opened up and taken me in. I was too ashamed to move or say anything; as she went on and on, I just blocked them out. Then she kept hitting him in the face and back; he just stood there. Then Elaine came over and asked me if I was all right; I told her yes and asked if she could bring my book bag for me. When she did, I told her that I would call her later.

I just walked away from the both of them; he ran towards me, trying to hold my hands. That was when she got mad and told me he didn't want me; he only wanted to control women. I didn't want to go home too early because Mother would ask me why I was home. That night, I went into the back of the yard and cried my heart out. I cried to God and asked him what was wrong with me. I asked him why it was so hard for me to find someone to love. I stood an hour and a half talking to God in the cold. One of the times, I fell asleep in the cold. My heart was full of hurt and shame. I didn't know if I wanted to go back to school anymore. When I finally woke up, I went inside the house, and my heart was heavy. Karen asked me if I went to school or not. I asked her why, and she told me that Tom and Elaine kept calling to see if I was home. I couldn't hold back the tears; I just told her what had happened.

This girl didn't tell me how sorry she was to hear what took place; she told me that the woman was old and jealous of me; no wonder he left her. Then she asked if she had long braids in her hair; I said yes and asked why. She told me that the old woman didn't have anything on me; she was old and finished with it. My boyfriend wanted young meat and a pretty girl, and that was me. "Fight for your man! After all, he is taking care of you." I stopped crying and just looked at her. I thought to myself, *This girl is heartless.* The following day, I went back to school. I was not thinking about all the embarrassment that I went through last night. I thought about what my sister had told me after all.

When I walked into class, all the girls were looking at me, and some of them were even pointing and laughing and talking. I didn't care one bit; I just went over to him and kissed him in front of all of them. I didn't think I had it in me to do that; I was sick and tired of people pushing me around. I had reached the point in my life to fight back. This was a risk I had to take, and I had to fight for it.

He was so shocked he took me into a classroom and was crying; then he started apologizing to me. He thought that I was never coming back to school after last night. He told me that he didn't know if he was going to see me again. I looked at him and told him I never ran from problems.

I went to class, and some of the girls were still making fun of me. As my sister told me, I needed to just be cute. They saw they could not break me; now, the joke was on them. Tom told me that his ex-girlfriend wanted to kill herself; I felt sorry for her. She came to let me look small and tried to embarrass me in front of the whole school. She didn't care if she hurt me at all. Everyone was laughing and pointing their fingers at me. Tom only stood there while she was hitting him in the face. He never told her to stop; she even knew my age. She even wanted to call my mother; I was really hurt, but I had to get even, as my sister told me to.

I was upset, of course, and mad, but I had asked God to let me love him; it seemed as if it was working. I told him to go and be with her; he looked at me as if I was crazy; after all, no one deserves to be hurt. If he were for me, he would come back.

Chapter 15

He called me when he got home and told me thanks for what I did because he never meant to hurt any one of us. I just wanted to know what in the world took place, why he lied to me and told me that he didn't have a woman. I told him I might be a child, but I was still a human being with feelings as well as anyone else.

I told him not to hurt me, and he did just that; I let him have it. I told him that it was over and that he should leave me alone, but he started to cry and told me not to break up with him. He said that he never saw a young lady so grow up; he didn't have words to tell me. I was still thinking on how to leave this man alone, but Karen was telling me that the dogs were all over the place. I knew what I had, so I should just keep it. I looked at her and asked her if she was having problems with her boyfriend, and she told me that she was fine.

As our love was growing, we were all over the place; we went to movies after class and had dinner sometimes. He took me to the store and got me a diamond necklace. He even put it on for me and said, "Only the best for my baby!" At this time, he didn't ask for sex; he told me that he was waiting for me to turn twenty. I laughed so hard because he didn't want the police to come looking for him. My birthday was in two weeks, and he was planning something special for me.

I asked my mother if I could go out with a friend, and she told me yes, so I was planning my date with Tom. On that very day, the doorbell rang; it was a bouquet of flowers. He had gotten me two dozen red roses for my birthday. Mother asked me where I got those from. I told her a friend; she asked if it was the same friend I was going out with. I told her yes; it seemed so strange to talk to her like this. The day came for my birthday. My dad called me and everyone else. Even Pam in Canada, I told her about this guy; she kept talking about how it was. She told me that she wasn't happy and that she was coming back home to have the twins because she could not get medical help at all due to the fact that he was married.

I told her I would help in any way possible; that evening, I did all of my chores because Karen was almost there. Then Mother told me that I couldn't go out with this guy; she told me she didn't know him and that she wanted to know him first.

My heart dropped. *Why would she do this to me?* I saw him at school almost every day, and I knew most things about him. She didn't care at all. She told me no, and that was final.

I didn't know how to call Tom and tell him that the date was canceled. He just hung up the phone, and then he called back. He sounded just like my dad with all the bad words. I sat down and just cried. He told me things that I didn't want to hear; he said he was not a teenager and that he was a man. He even told me that he could have gone back to his ex, but he loved me so much. I still didn't go. I was afraid of my mother, and that was all there was. He begged and pleaded with me; then he couldn't take it anymore, and he told me to _____. I deserved everything that he told me; I was too scared to meet him.

I listened to him as he screamed into the phone, and then he hung up. I just cried. I went and asked Mom why she did this to me; she said Mr. Tucker told her no. I looked at her with hate; it was my birthday, and I was in a lot of pain. I knew I had lost him this time. The next day, my mother called me. It was a man standing at the door with one dozen red roses again. It was from him again. I didn't know why he sent me roses twice; I just took them and went downstairs.

I called him and told him thanks; he was just crying. He told me all about the plans he had made and the reservation he had made for one of those restaurants in Manhattan. I told him how sorry I was and that it would never happen again. He said that he knew that we, Jamaicans, respect our parents so much, unlike Americans who don't care. Then I told him that my mother wanted to meet him the next day.

He was so happy that he asked me what he should wear. I just told him to look good; he called me back later that night and said he had gotten a pair of shoes. I just laughed at him once more; I told him that he would be fine. He said, "Anything for my baby!"

I told Karen that he was coming the next day to meet our mother; she was so happy because she wanted to see him as well. Sunday came, and I got up early and helped my mother with dinner. Mr. Tucker had gone out with his friend. Then Tom came; he bought something for my mother and me as well. I took him to meet Karen, and she told me that he was not bad-looking. He just smiled. Then Mother called me for dinner for him to eat. When he was finished, he went back into the living room and looked through pictures.

To our surprise, Mr. Tucker came home with his friend; when he saw Tom, he got so upset; he started to curse us. He told us that he didn't want any more men in his house and that we were a couple of female dogs. He knew that Karen was pregnant, and he didn't want her in the house with him. I told Tom it was time to leave; I was more than embarrassed. Thank God he didn't understand what he was saying. As we listened to this man classify us as female dogs, Mother just stood there and never said a word. I just cried with my sister.

We felt really bad and embarrassed at the same time; how I hated this man, I hated the fact that Mother kept letting him cheat us like dirt; there was no way she could have loved him so much that he hurt us so badly. Mother called one of her friends and told us to put on some clothes. She was looking for an apartment for Karen; I told her that I wanted to move as well. I would get a job and find me a place.

I had a lot of hate in my heart for that man. This reminded me of Marlene when she was pregnant, and my dad was upset with the idea. This alcoholic man didn't have anything good to say about us, and it just killed me that Mother let him talk to us like that. We had no luck at all; Karen's boyfriend wasn't there to help her as usual. He was home in his bed and was well warm.

It took us almost three weeks to find something, and when we did, it was a one-bedroom with a living and a kitchen together.

I knew that Karen was weak when it came to her boyfriend, and I knew that I wasn't going to face what I'd been through in Jamaica. I went on the phone, called my dad, and told him what had happened. He told me not to worry; he could get me a bedroom out of the living room and have space left over for a living room. When we got to the place, Mother told us that we had to help her with things. Karen got her bedroom set; I didn't get anything yet. My dad was still working on my room; when it was finished, I just smiled. He had gotten all I needed to part the room off; the only thing that was missing was a door. Dad told me when he got paid, he would buy me one.

I called Tom to let him know what was going on; he wanted to help with almost everything, but Mother told me to never let a man buy me a bed; at the end of the day, he couldn't take it back. I didn't understand what she was talking about, but he insisted on buying me a chest of draws. My room was not as big as Karen's, but it was just right. Mother was happy, and so were Karen and I.

We didn't hear how much of a whore we were; the only thing I was facing now was Tom. He wanted to see the place, and he wanted to come over. I told him that there was no door in the room, but he still insisted. I still didn't let him come.

He told me to meet him one evening after school; he wanted me to see his place. He had a one-bedroom place, where he shared a kitchen and bathroom. His room was spotless; he had gotten my favorite dish, and this man had set the mood so well. He had on Mariah Carey with soda; he knew that I did not drink. He gave me a small gift with a blue mountain card that said a lot. As I read the card, it was talking to me and telling me my innermost feelings. That night was magical; he didn't pressure me at all. He knew that I was his girl.

I was nervous, and he knew; he looked me in the eye and said that we could do this another time. As I watched him lie there and hold me in his arms, I could hear what his ex-girl had told him. This was the first time I'd ever told him I loved him. I told him that he was mine and I was his. I'd never made love with him before; he took me to a place I didn't know existed.

I just looked at him as the tears rolled down my face; he told me that I was safe and that he would make sure that no one or nothing happened to me. That night, I called Karen and told her I wasn't coming home; she covered for me very well.

That night was the first time having sex; we made love after love; we had to stop when we ran out of condoms. The next morning, I took a shower, and we went to have breakfast. He told me he would see me later at school, put me on the train, and went his way. When I went home, I was so tired I just went to bed. I woke up in time for school. When I saw him, my world had just begun. Whenever we were at school, he would get a bit jealous; he didn't want anyone looking at me. I thought that it was cute until I saw it was beginning to be too much. If we were on the train and someone looked at me, he would yell at the person. I was embarrassed most of the time. I told him I wasn't going anywhere, so it was all right for him to relax. I was so in love with him; I couldn't see straight.

He would come to my apartment, and I would go to his after school; we would make love; we were both addicted to each other. This went on until Karen gave birth. She had the cutest girl you ever saw. She even had dimples. We named her Angelique. Everyone thought I had named her because I was Angela, but no. She named her after a soap opera she loved.

My mother was at the house every night, and late too, so Tom had to stay at the white castle restaurant until she left. He told me he was fed up with the bull he was going through with my mother. He told me she needed to know how we felt about each other and that I was his woman. He yelled most nights and told me he wanted to sleep; when they left, I would make it up. I felt really sorry for him because he put up with a lot of things with me. I really needed to grow up, but I was so afraid of my mother.

One Saturday, my dad called me, and we were just talking; he asked me the big question. He wanted to know when I was going to have a baby before he died. I told him to stop talking like that. He had to be there when I got married; then, we would talk about babies.

It seemed as if Dad heard something bad from his doctor, so he wanted me to give him a grandchild before he died. I wasn't going to listen to him talk about death; I told him to change the subject because he didn't want to pay for my wedding. He was telling me that he was going to die; I told him that I loved him and he would be around long enough. That was the final talk I had with Dad about a baby. It seemed as if my dad knew something. Soon, I had missed my period. I was just watching to see if it was late; after all, I was having sex. It had been a while since I told Karen I had missed my period. She asked me if I was sure. I knew how my body was; she then told me to tell Tom about it. I was afraid to.

One day, Mother told me she had good news for us; it seemed as if my sister's son Derrick had gotten his papers to come to America. The good thing was that he was going to live with us because his father couldn't watch him. Derrick would have to stay with me, and that was final; I didn't have any say in the matter. Now I didn't know how to tell Tom that I would have a roommate and I was pregnant. I didn't know how he would handle this news, but I had to tell him. That night, he came to get me from school, and we took a cab to get home.

The cab took a different way home; he started to yell at the cab driver. I told him to let the cab driver do his thing. He never said a word to me until I came out of the cab. He called my name, and just as I turned around to answer him, he gave me one slap across my face; I was so frightened that I stood there with my mouth open. Then he told me how I dared to disrespect him. I still could not believe that he hit me. I didn't cry, but he did. He told me how sorry he was to have hit me, and it would never happen again. I was still in shock because only my brother hit me and my dad once. For this to come from my loved one, I was thinking a whole lot of things.

Should I tell him that I may be pregnant? I was so embarrassed that I didn't tell anyone about the hit; I just looked at him. That night, he told me that he loved me so much, and if I ever left him, he would find me and kill me. Now, this wasn't a good time to tell him that I was pregnant; I cried that night. I didn't know what I had gotten myself into; this man just turned into a monster... just like that.

I knew that my dad would be happy to hear, but I had to tell the father of the child first. That night, he came over; he was not himself. He was just moody and acting up. I went over to him and told him that I was pregnant; the look he gave me was not right. He looked at me with disgust; I started to cry, then he got a hold on himself and hugged me. He told me that everything would be all right; that night, I just slept in his arms. The following morning, he asked me if I was sure that I was pregnant. I told him yes; he said that he would buy a test to make sure I was. That day, he left; I didn't see him at school at all. I wasn't feeling well enough, so I came home early from class. Elaine asked me if I was okay; I told her I was fine. When I got home, Mother and Mr. Tucker were there once more. I didn't feel well enough to see them; she asked me why I was home so early. I just said my period was on me. She told me to have some dinner and take a pill.

I listened to her play with my niece. *How in the world can I tell her I am pregnant?* When they left, Karen asked me what had happened to Tom. I told her that he was acting differently; she reassured me that he was a bit nervous. I only hoped so; he didn't call me at all. I didn't see him until one week later. He told me that he had to clear his head. He asked me if I wanted the baby since I was going to school and my sister had just gotten a child. He had brought up my mother, "How will she handle it?" I told him that I thought about all these things, I knew about all that; I wanted my baby. He went quiet on the phone. Then he told me that he would see me the next day.

I didn't care at all what Mother had to say because my dad wanted a baby from me. That was fine with me; Tom would get over it. When he finally came over, he still didn't buy the test. He was a bit afraid. We would argue a lot, then the hitting came. He promised not to hurt me, but he was just doing that. I was so ashamed to let anyone know that my prince was hurting me. This went on. Whenever he saw me, he would pick a fight, and then he hit me really badly.

One night, he told me if I was really pregnant for him, there was no way I could leave him. The next time he saw me, he wanted me dead. One day, Karen went over to our mother's house with the kids; I knew that he was coming over, so I stayed home. That was the wrong thing I could have done; he beat me so badly. He kept hitting me in my back, and he hit me in my stomach. He told me that he wanted that piece of crap I was carrying to turn sideways in my stomach and just kill me. I went into the bathroom and just cried; how I wanted to die. I washed my face and went back into the room because Karen's baby's daddy was home. I still didn't want them to know that this guy was hurting me.

When I went into the room, he told me how he really felt about me and his baby. He said that he was too old to have a child right now, and he didn't think that I was ready for one too. I was a weak woman who didn't know how to take care of herself, much less his child. He told me all I didn't want to hear. He even brought up his ex-girlfriend. I just went blank as I watched him talk; I was in a trance. I kept hearing a voice telling me to end my life; the voice told me that I had nothing to live for; I was a fool like what Mr. Tucker called me. My brother called me an idiot, and the list went on.

That night, I was thinking of ways to kill this man; he told me that I could not leave him and if I did, he would find me and even kill my family too. The fear he put in me, I couldn't handle it. I didn't know where to go; I was trapped. I stayed with him because I had no choice. He wanted my baby dead and me as well; this voice stayed with me for some time. It wanted me to end my life so badly; it told me everything people did to me and how better I would be if I had ended my life. It reassured me that I would be better off.

One day, I got a call from my friend Pam; she didn't sound that well at all; she told me she was back home in America. Pam told me all she had been through; the kids' father wasn't treating her well. She was staying with her cousin until she gave birth. I didn't know how to tell her that my love wasn't any better. I just told her about all that I was going through; then, she asked me what I was going to do with the baby. I was so scared; I didn't know where to turn to. She told me that she would always help me with any decision I came to.

I wished I could help her, but I didn't know how to help myself. Tom overheard me telling her about the baby. When I got off the phone, he got mad and started beating me; he said that I was going around telling people I was carrying his child. He was not even sure it was his. He put on his clothes and left; I still did what I had to do. I cleaned up myself and went to school as always. He used to come and wait for me after class, but all of that was changed. It was the weekend once more, and Karen asked me if I could watch her boyfriend's nephew for her. I knew Tom was coming over that night, so I stayed and did just that until he got to the house.

When he came and saw the baby, he was upset; he asked whose baby it was. Then I told him. Tom told me I was putting ideas into my head, and then he accused me of sleeping with my sister's boyfriend.

Chapter 16

I just stayed in the room with the baby until the child's mother came. When I went back to the room, he held my hair and gave me one box across my face; just then, Karen's boyfriend came home. I was in the room while this man had me like a rag doll; I didn't know where I got the strength from. I turned around and hit him so hard that his glasses fell off his face. He could not believe it.

He kept saying, "You hit me! Motherlover, you hit me!" When he came over to me, I called Frank. He came into the room to see what was happening; when Tom saw him, he got scared. He didn't leave the house that night, but my mind was made up. I told him to leave the next day, and that was when he got crazy and told me that I was motherloving with my sister's man and that piece of crap wasn't his. He went outside the house and called me all kinds of names. Karen got afraid and called my mother. Mother then called the cops, and he started to stone the house. It was a mess; I begged him to leave because the police were coming. He still didn't leave. Tom went to the payphone and called me, telling me that I was dead and didn't even know it. The police came and took my information and report. They asked me how old he was; that was when my mother knew.

She looked at me with disgust and told me to pack my bag. She took us back to her place because she feared he would come back to hurt us. That night, she didn't want us to let Mr. Tucker know, but she did let me have it. Mother told us to stay that Monday evening until she got home from work. I didn't know what to say. She told me that I wasn't allowed to answer the phone or go near the door. She told me I could not go back to school, just in case he was there looking for me. I knew in my heart that I could not have told her about my baby; after all that went down, I was just hurting inside out. I didn't know how to face myself. My life wasn't worth it at all.

Tom called every day, sometimes five or six times. Karen was allowed to talk to him; she told him that I was with my dad. He didn't know his address. Whenever he called, he would cry and tell her how much he missed me. She asked me what I was going to do with my baby. I told her that if I kept it, our mother would kill me anyway. So she got the money and gave it to me. I called Pam, and she went with me. I didn't know what else to do; that night, I cried my heart out. Pam told me that everything would be okay.

I don't think that anyone understood what I was going through. I had just killed the only thing that could ever love me. I had to put on a mask that no one could see but me; I listened to Karen get fed up with Tom calling the house, and sometimes they made fun of him. I couldn't take it anymore; I was in prison. I couldn't go anywhere or be on the phone. My mother had so much control over me. She would be at work, and then she called the house and told me, "I know how to pick them." She would call me and let me know that I could have put their lives in danger.

The following day was something different; she was watching a talk show on TV about how the young lady's boyfriend killed her and her family. Then she told me that I could have put their lives at risk; this really made me feel guilty. Then she went on and on. The next subject was that she needed money to help pay the bills; I wasn't working at all. It was stress after stress; Mr. Tucker wasn't working at all, but she wanted me to call Dad for money. She didn't want me to work at all because of my life, or maybe because she wanted me to take care of Karen's baby and watch my nephew as well. I just wanted to die and get over all of this. I didn't see the point of living.

That summer, I had to stay in a hot house. I wasn't allowed to go outside. Frank's friends would come over and make fun of my room because it was in the living room. I just stayed in my little space; I cried most of my life, wondering if I would ever be happy. I would always be the topic for my sister's boyfriend's friends. They would laugh and talk about what took place. Karen was laughing too. While I listened to them, I felt really bad. After all, I still loved him. Looking at the four walls, I felt like I was in prison. I was in prison in my own mind and apartment.

I had to take care of my niece while my sister and her man went out. That was fine with Mother. That was my punishment; now, I couldn't talk to Karen at all. Everything was about her and the baby. She totally forgot about her son.

Pam was due anytime now, and I couldn't do anything to help her as my lonely life went on. I was getting by day after day, facing the shame of what I did. I was a murderer, and I didn't need to live. At this time, Mother was planning Angelique's christening. She invited everyone. At this time, Pam had her daughters. They looked so much like their mom; they were so small, but she was happy to hold her babies. I just watched everyone as they had fun; my dad and uncle came as well, and so did Edson with my friend from high school. Everyone was having a ball; I knew in my heart that this place wasn't for me; the guilt of not having my baby was unbearable, not to mention Tom.

At the christening, one of Frank's friends was there, watching me as always. I had no love for him; he was the one that told me I was wasting my time with the other guy. I was lost in time. I looked over at Dad; he was laughing because he was with his grandkids. If only I had told him that I was pregnant, I knew that he would be happy too. I didn't need my mother's approval; I knew he would have been happy. But to put so much shame on her was not right. After all, I was a harlot, according to her man. My aunts were there laughing and telling jokes. I was like a broken vessel. I knew that this was no place for Tom.

I had to forget about him, but how could I? After the party was over, I told Dad goodbye. Everyone was happy, and so was my mother. I told Pam that I would talk to her later. As I watched her put the babies in the car, she was so happy; now I had to help Mother clean up the place. After all, I was Cinderella. The party was a hit, and everyone talked about it. Mother was glad because she loved to make people talk; she was always a people pleaser. Mr. Tucker, too, was glad; he wanted my dad to feel small.

The following day, my dad called me to see how I was doing. I told him that I was fine as always; then he asked about my mother once more. He wanted to know if she was happy and if she could talk to him later. I knew what he wanted to ask her. I told him to just leave her alone and find someone that would make him happy; she had moved on, and I didn't think that she would come back.

He was silent for a while; then he came back on me with the baby thing. He told me that he was dying and wanted me to give him a grandchild before he left this place. My heart dropped; the tears just came out like a flood of water. I was talking to him, and he didn't know I was crying. I answered every question he asked and told him, "One day, Dad." At this time, I wanted to die. I had to get him off the phone by asking him for some money to pay my rent. He told me he wasn't making a lot, but he would see what he could do.

Mother knew that I wasn't working, but she wanted me to ask Dad for money to help with the rent. Karen and Frank were both working, and not one of them would give me a dime to watch my niece. I didn't understand this at all; I guess this was my payback for life. Of course, Tom didn't give up; he was still calling and talking to my sister. I listened to him on the other line while he was crying and telling her how much he loved and missed me. I was crying most of the time with him because I loved this man, and knowing what he did to me was really sad. It got to the point of him calling her so much that she got upset and told our mother; then, my mom called me once more to remind me of this crazy man I picked up. I couldn't deal with all of this, so I decided to call him. I knew it was forbidden to do. So, I had to tell him to stop calling the house and asking Karen about me.

"Hello, who is this?" I hesitated before I answered him. I told him that it was me; he couldn't believe it, he was just crying.

I told him I didn't call to talk to him too long but to tell him to stop calling my sister's phone. He asked me if I was okay and how the baby was. I told him that I wasn't pregnant; it was only an infection I had, and I was fine now. He wanted to know where I was and how I was doing. He told me that he went to the school every day just to see if I would show up, but I never did.

I told him that I was with my dad, and I just called him to tell him to move on with his life, I could not make him happy at all, and he deserved better. This man cried like a baby on the phone. He told me if I left him, he would kill himself. I told him that he should stop talking like that. I could not get him to stop crying; he told me that he would never find love again. Then I started to cry with him. I told him that I would call him another day; I had to go. Then I heard him begging me, "Please don't leave me!" I told him bye and hung the phone up; while the tears rolled down my face, my heart was beating fast. I knew I should not have called him, but I did what needed to be done.

He was so happy that I had called him; he called Karen and told her he had spoken to me. She was upset that I called him. I just let her know that he wouldn't be calling her anymore. "I had to stop the crazy from calling you," I told her. She was fine with it, but she didn't tell our mother at all. I knew I couldn't talk to my sister about him, so I called my friend Pam; she told me what I needed to hear.

I know it was wrong, but I didn't care at all. This man loved me, and I knew that he was my true love. I would call him every so often. He would ask me when he was going to see me. I knew he couldn't come to the house at all. I kept telling him one day. Then I called Pam to hear what I wanted to hear: "You love him—go for it," she told me. Whenever I called him, I would block the call so that he could not track the number to see where I was calling from.

I would call him every so often, and we would laugh and talk. I felt so guilty about my baby, but I didn't want to hurt him now. One day, I called him, and he told me he went to church and even told his mother about me. I was shocked about that; I told him that he didn't need to do that, but he insisted that if we were going to be together, we should not have secrets. I knew this man loved me so much, and I loved him too. I decided that I needed to see him. I missed him so much, and I knew he missed me too.

When I finally got to see him, he was just crying and holding me. I just held him, and we made love like never before; we both cried that night. The next day, I called my mother and told her that I was with Pam and the kids; she was my backup plan. My mother was upset because I wasn't home to take care of my niece. I didn't care at all. I was happy, and that was what mattered. We were seeing each other now for three weeks until one day he called me at the house.

Karen overheard us talking on the phone and came into my room; she asked me if I was crazy. I just looked at her as if I was. I knew that I would be in trouble if Mother found out. I knew that I was on my own if anything happened. I didn't care at all what she or Mother had to say. I called him, but no answer; I was so worried about him.

This went on for three days; no call, no show. I thought that something had happened to him. I couldn't take it anymore, so I called his mother. I was so embarrassed; the woman didn't know who I was. I asked her if her son was okay. She told me yes and asked who she was talking to. I hung up the phone and started to cry once more; I didn't know what had happened to him. I went to my bed, just crying as always.

I had a dream about him, that I was following him. When he came out of a lady's house, there were two young children with him. He kissed them and told them he'd see them the next day; I didn't hear from this man until the fifth day. When he called me, he was yelling and screaming with curse words. He wanted to know why I called his mother. I told him that I was worried. Then I told him about the dream I had. That's when he hit the roof; he called me all kinds of things, telling me I was following him.

I didn't know what he was talking about, but he didn't believe I had a dream about him. I sat on the phone while he cursed me so badly. I couldn't understand this man at all. I kept thinking that it was my fault; I should not have upset him at all. Then he told me that he was with his kids and that he needed time with them too.

Now this was an everyday thing with him; I called—no answer. When he did answer, he had bad things to tell me. Now a lot of things were going through my mind. *Why did I let this man back into my life?* I should have just left him and moved on. My life was empty; I was so ashamed to let anyone know what I was feeling. I still lied as if he was the perfect man in my life, but he was more the devil who had me wrapped up. I couldn't leave him because he told me he would kill himself; I didn't want that on my head.

One day, I called him, and he wasn't home. My finger hit a couple of numbers accidentally. To my surprise, it was his phone answering service. The phone was just giving me his messages all at once. I heard his ex-girlfriend thanking him for last night with the kids; how he made them feel happy. Then it was another woman. This one I didn't know at all; I was crying and shaking like a leaf. My heart was hurting; I kept hearing, "I told you so." The thoughts in my head got louder and louder; I didn't know what to do. Then I heard a voice telling me to end my life.

I once heard this voice talk to me; it was telling me if I took my life, I would be better off. After all, no one loved me. It even told me they would be sorry after all I'd been through. Now I could be happy to see my baby once more. I just got up, got all the cards he gave me, and wrote him a letter. I told him that he really hurt me and that I was going to make everyone happy. The best way I knew how was by killing myself. I would get to see my baby, and I would be happy for once in my life. I also wrote my mother a letter telling her how sorry I was to hurt her. I knew I was not the perfect daughter she wanted, but God knows I had tried.

I wrote to Dad as well and let him know how I felt. I knew that he would have been upset; I was a mess, and I needed to find some peace. I told him that I loved him so much, then I got up and went for the pills. I was just taking them one after another until my stomach was upset.

Then I felt my heart beating fast; I didn't know when I felt sleepy. The next thing I saw was an orange light. I knew that I wasn't in heaven. I lay there, waiting... For what? I don't know. I didn't know if I was going to hear welcome to hell. I knew I wasn't going to heaven once I took my own life. Then it dawned on me that I would never see my baby at all. I was doomed for life.

It was too late; there was no point in turning back. I still lay there on the bed, still not moving at all. I didn't know where I was and what I was doing. Then finally, I realized that I was still alive; I had seen the cable box light. I was such a failure; I couldn't even kill myself. I got up and called him and told him that I was going to kill myself, I told him what I had heard, and then I gave him a taste of what he did to me. I went to bed because I was drugged up, and soon, I heard the doorbell ring.

I went and opened the door; there stood two police officers. They told me they got a call that a gunshot was coming from this house. I told them I didn't hear anything; I went back downstairs when the officer left. Then Tom called me back to see if I was okay; I told him that I was fine. He did not believe me, so her called my sister to check on me.

I was so hurt because this man would not leave me alone; if I left him, he told me that he would find me and kill me and my family. He put a lot of fear into me, and when I wanted to end my life, he wanted me okay for himself. He just wanted to use me like a little rag doll. I was sick and tired of him. I wanted him gone, but I had to know how to do this. I knew that he wanted to be in control of my life. So I did what he said when he said it. Being with this man took away my time with Dad; I wasn't hearing from him at all.

I called Dad, but he was not feeling well, so I didn't talk to him much. I hung up the phone and went back into my little pity party.

Chapter 17

I thought about how no one loved me and how alone I was. I knew that if I wanted to see my baby again, I could not try suicide at all; that was not an option. The next day, I got a call from my cousin; she asked me when was the last time I spoke to Dad. I told her I talked to him two days ago. "Why?" I asked her. Then she told me that he was in the hospital. I didn't want to hear that at all. I knew that he didn't feel well, but I knew he would get through this like always. She was letting me know that he didn't look good, and she didn't think that he was going to make it. I was so upset with her that I told her I would call her back. I called my mother and told her what my cousin had told me. When I was finished with Mother, I went on my knees with the man Jesus; I was making all kinds of deals with him. I told him if Dad lived, I would never try to kill myself again. He was the only person in my life right now that made me want to go on. He made me laugh when we were making fun of Mr. Tucker. I needed him so much in my life right now. *Please, God, please.* That night, I made all kinds of bargains with God.

That night, I didn't want to talk to anyone at all; I just let everything and everyone pass me by. I didn't waste any time. The next day, I was at the hospital with Karen. Mother told us that she would meet us after work. When we got there, his sister was there, the one that didn't like me, and our cousins were there as well. My brother Edson was there too; he had driven his car. We were so nervous.

When I went into the room, my heart was just hurting a lot. When I saw my dad, I could not believe what I saw. He was swollen because of the fluid in him. His kidneys were gone, and a lot more things were going on with him. When I listened to the doctors as they talked, I told them to give him one of my kidneys. They told me I needed my kidneys if I decided to have a family.

I told the doctor that he was my family; they didn't understand the relationship I had with this man. He was my rock; I needed him just as much as he needed me. He opened his eyes and looked at all of us, then he asked me for my mother. I told him that she was on her way from work. Dad told me the most disturbing news; he could hardly talk. He said that his brother took him to the hospital by three trains and a bus. I could not believe it because we knew that he was sick back home in Jamaica.

Mother would take a cab with him whenever this happened. My uncle had a car; why in the world would he do this thing to his own family? If only he had called my brother to come and get him. We were all furious about what happened; I told him that we were here and that he would be all right.

When Mother had reached the hospital, the doctors told her what was really taking place with Dad. She came out crying and said that he wasn't going to make it. My dad needed a kidney; I told her that was not a problem because he could have one of mine. Then Karen said the same thing too.

I told my mother that he would have two kidneys now, but the doctors just walked away; they were hiding something from us. Mother didn't want to say anything at all. I was old enough to know what was going on with Dad. I told the doctor that he would be fine, but he just looked at me as if I was out of this world. Then he told me that my dad was not strong enough for an operation. I still didn't care what they said. I knew that he was going to be okay; after all, he had to see his grandchild from me. I refused to believe them; then, my cousin took me outside for a walk. Edson was in another world. I was just angry, that's all.

We stayed there until he was tired, and then we left. When we got home, I was just angry with those doctors. *Who do they think they are?*

The following day, I went to see Dad. I took the train, and when I got there, my aunt looked at me, and I did the same to her. This time I was all grown up, and there was no way she was going to tell me to leave him alone. He was sleeping when I got there; I called his name a couple of times before he opened his eyes. When he saw me, he just smiled; then he asked me how I got there. I told him by train. Then he asked me why I had so many jewels on. I told him just for fashion; he told me not to wear it again on the train.

The next day, I went with Karen. Mother was going to meet us after work; of course, my aunt was there. She didn't want us to wake him at all. When she went to the bathroom, I just went over to his ears and called his name a couple of times, and then he opened his eyes. I told him that it was I; he just smiled, then he looked around to see if his sister was in the room. I told him that she had gone to the ladies' room and that Mother was on her way. He just smiled; he wanted to hear those words. I just looked at my dad and was just wondering what life was; my dad was fighting for his life, and here I was, trying to take mine.

When my aunt came back, Dad closed his eyes as if he was sleeping. She came over to him and prayed. When she left, I told him that she was gone, then he opened his eyes. We sat with him until Mother came; she went to the doctor and talked as always. This went on for some time. We were back and forth from the hospital; then, one day, our dad's best friend came from California to visit him. These two guys went far. I always loved him. He gave us good things when he used to visit us in Jamaica.

I remember that day very well. Edson, Uncle Dickey, Mother, Karen, my cousin Tina, and I were there. When we got up the stairs, the doctors came over to my mother and Uncle Dickey; while they were talking, I was checking out some of the male doctors. Then Mother called out to Edson, and he just walked away. I knew that something was wrong. Then I went over to them. They told us that my dad was not going to make it.

Most of his organs shut down due to hepatitis. They told us that our father had gotten bad blood when they were doing his blood transfusion. They didn't know where he got it from. It could have been a couple of years back. At this point, everyone was crying, as if Dad was dead. I walked away to find my brother. When I saw him, he was in the chapel.

We were all there listening to this woman singing "Amazing Grace." At this time, I felt peace come over me. I didn't know how to explain it. I had never felt like this before. Uncle Dickey came over to me and told me thank you. I asked him for what. Then he told me what Dad had told him about me. "Your father said that you made him feel special after all he did to us." I just stood there with the tears rolling down my face. I told him he was my boy and hugged him like a father. I didn't like what I was feeling. Then he went over to Edson and hugged him like a son. God knew he needed that. Then Edson began to cry.

Mother and Karen both cried as I watched my cousin; she was crying too. I kept thinking that Dad was not dead. Why in the world were they acting like that? When I looked at my cousin, she was hurting too; she loved him more than her father. She would always talk about the things Dad did for her; Mother would wonder if she was talking about the same man. Dad was not an angel; he cursed like the devil. He put up walls around him that he didn't want anyone to get in, but I wasn't afraid to tear that wall down; after all, he told me not to be afraid of anyone. He knew that he was an overprotective parent, and this did a number on all of us.

I was the baby, so I didn't notice it at all, but the others did. Mother went through a lot with him with all the embarrassment. She did her best to keep us together at all times, even when we fought each other. That was our family, crazy but strong. We all went outside the hospital to say goodbye to our dad's best friend, and then Tina went home. On our way home, everyone was silent. I knew in my heart that Dad was going to be all right. I went home, and I prayed to God about Dad. I asked him to take care of my dad for me because he was my only good buddy, and if he died, I didn't know what I would do without him.

The next day was the same. Dad was a fighter. The doctors would tell us that he seemed better today, then the next day was something different. I just prayed and watched them dance; my dad was playing with them. On Saturday, Karen, Edson, and I went to visit Dad. Our aunt was there as always. She didn't like us one bit; she told me to leave him alone while he rested. When she left, I told him that she was gone. Then he opened his eyes; he looked at us, but I knew that he was looking for our mother. I told him, "She isn't coming today, but I have to tell you this one. You see your son over there? He's depressed. You know why?" Dad just looked at me. I told him what it was. He broke a girl's heart and left her for another woman. Then the woman he left her for left him for a man. Then I started to laugh. I said, "Dad, then this guy left her for another man." My dad started to laugh, and Karen was laughing too; Edson just looked at all of us.

The joke was on him, and we laughed and laughed. That was how the disease spread; it was nice to see Dad up and about laughing. When we left the hospital, I kissed him and told him to visit the next day. On the way home, I told my brother to get over that girl and let us celebrate. Dad looked fine, and he needed to get over this dumb chick. I told him that what goes around comes around. "You hurt that girl, and now you know what she is feeling. Get over it and celebrate." Karen was fine with it, so she called her baby's father to know where we should go to the party.

That night, I danced the night away; I felt so good and free. I don't know what it was after that woman sang "Amazing Grace." I was in another world; Edson, on the other hand, wasn't looking too well. He couldn't drink at all due to the fact he was the driver. When we got home, it was around 5:45 a.m.; I took off my party clothes and went to bed. Then I got up, and I was just crying so hard to God. I told him how grateful I was for him to keep my dad alive so that I could have someone to love me.

But to think about it. I was being selfish; I wasn't thinking of my dad at all. Everything was all about me; I didn't care if he was in pain or not. Even though the doctors told us that his organ was failing, all I wanted was for God to keep him alive. I told God to take him home if he was in any pain until I saw him again. I didn't want him to suffer or be in any pain. When I finished praying, it was about 6:20 a.m. I went to bed.

At about 7:15 a.m., Mother called us and told me that my dad was dying and the hospital had just called her for us to say goodbye. I didn't know if it was my fault, but I cried my heart out. I told Karen what Mother had told me and that our brother Edson was on his way for us. I went and took my shower and got dressed up for Dad. When Edson came, he was out of space; we didn't say much. When we got to my mother's house, we dropped off the baby at Mr. Tucker's sister's house. We were all sad at this point; there were no words in the car. I can't explain how it feels when you know that your loved one is about to leave you, and you know that he's never coming back to you. I was hurting so much.

I remember I told God that. He answered me really fast, but I guessed he would be okay. When I got to the hospital, this wasn't the man I left yesterday. He was not smiling and talking, now he was swelling, and he didn't look like my dad at all. I asked him if he needed to see Althea and Marlene; he should squeeze my hands, and he did. He wanted to see his other girls. I told him that he would see them soon; I told Dad it was okay to get some rest. When I was telling him these words, my throat was just burning me because I wanted to cry, but I had to be strong for him.

Then I went into the waiting room and fell asleep. I didn't know what happened. I felt a touch on my leg. I woke up at 3:00 p.m., and then I heard Mother calling me. My dad was gone... They had him on this machine, but he was even fighting this thing until the last moment. When I looked at everyone, they were all there; my uncle, who took Dad on three trains and a bus to get to the hospital, and he had a vehicle. I hated him for that. Then I looked at his sister. She acted as if she was the number one lady that took such good care of him. She nogged him to death. I looked at Mother. She was another one with that piece of crap she called a man.

I was so mad. Then I looked at Karen; she only called him when she needed anything; Edson was too busy running down girls. I was even upset with the pastor that came to pray for him. He was late and had his beeper on him as if he was a drug dealer.

My cousins were there, some of them; the others, I did not care for at all. I looked at all of them. I kissed Dad on his forehead and walked away. I blamed myself for not talking to him but thinking about that man who didn't love me. Forgot everyone; I told my mother that he wanted Althea and Marlene there; she looked at me and went to ask for information about his kids to come to the funeral.

On our way home, Edson dropped off our mother because she had to cook that man's food. On our way to get the baby, Edson was out of it and almost crashed the car with us. I looked at him and wondered if he was taking us to see Dad. I didn't say anything at all; we got the baby, and I went to bed. I cried my heart out. I called Elaine from school, Pam, and another friend of mine. We went to school together; I didn't know when I fell asleep. I knew that I had to do a lot now.

The next day, Mother went to work; she told us to go with our uncle to the funeral home to pick out a casket for Dad. We all picked out the same one, and my uncle looked at the price and said that it was too expensive. My dad had left all his money for that, so I told him it should not be a problem what he was buried in. When Mother came after work, she chose the same one. At this time, our uncle was going to all the banks that he knew my dad went to. But when he got there, they wanted Angela Davis. Mother didn't ask twice; she took me with her for everything.

I was his beneficiary on everything; Dad had my name at furniture stores, and he had taken me there once with him. He asked me what I thought about a bedroom set. "It is great, but too much money," I told him. He told me that it was good wood and it would last a long time. I still thought it was too much money. Then he told me that I was a pagan, his favorite word.

This man could walk, and then he told me where we were going was just around the corner. Really! I knew that I was going to miss him. Even on his job, my uncle went, and they told him no; they needed one of us. I knew that he was upset, but who cared about him? He was a wicked man. The week before Dad died, he called me to come and get his things, but I was so caught up with that man that I told him I didn't want to hear about death. This was far away from me now. Karen and Mother were on the ball to get the girls here with us. Mother went to the immigration office and got all the paperwork from the doctors. Everything went through so fast.

Mother was happy, and I knew that Dad, too, was happy. Mother took me to the bank, and we signed over his insurance money. It paid for his funeral and got the girls to America. When everything was all paid for, she split up the rest of the money with all of us.

When my sister came, I was so happy to see them. Althea was the one that looked just like Dad. I loved her so much. She was the one that had her head on her body; Marlene was the first and my dad's family favorite. She was out of it; I watched everyone embrace each other. I knew in my heart that he was happy to see all of us together once more. The funeral came, and everyone was on edge due to the fact Mother was taking over. I just laughed because Dad knew what he was doing.

He had his wife taking care of him on his funeral day. His family was so upset due to the fact that she had left him, but they loved each other no matter what. Mother called all of his friends, the ones he knew back home and the ones he knew in America. She went all out with him.

He was famous once more, and she made them know that. He was Winston Davis from Jamaica. I was proud of her and of him too, but God knows best. Maybe if they were still together, she would be dead too because Dad had hepatitis C. When they were about to put him in the ground, that's when I cried out.

He was gone and wasn't coming back. How I felt a deep pain in my soul. I told him to just get up and stay with me, but it was not working. I watched each person put dirt on his grave. My friend was gone, and that was final.

We went to the repass, where we greeted families and friends. Everyone kept telling me how I looked like my mother. Dad's family hated me with a passion; I didn't care at this point. Our dad's brother from England was there. We didn't know him at all. I didn't care either. Marlene was all over her family; I just walked away. Karen and Althea were talking to our cousin, and Edson, the only boy, was checking out ladies as usual. I sat down and was just watching all of them. People came over and talked to me, and I didn't hear them at all. The man I thought I loved much didn't call me at all. He sent me his condolence. That's all.

After the funeral, we went back to Mother's house. Marlene went over with Karen to the apartment while Althea came home with us. We just sat there and didn't say much. Edson had gotten a number from some girls he met at Dad's funeral. Althea was happy to see her son. Mr. Tucker, too, was happy that Dad was out of his life. Mother was happy that the girls were there.

Everyone had something to celebrate about. Our dad died on October 16 and was buried on 26 of that same month, a day before Edson's birthday. I told them we needed to go get his things, and Mother told us to wait. I told them that was the time before his brother took what he wanted; I knew him too well. He didn't like my dad at all, even though they were brothers.

We went to his house, after all. Of course, he didn't open the door. I was at the top of my voice telling him to open the door, while Marlene was quiet and calm. Edson just sat in his car and watched us. Althea and Marlene were at the door knocking. I just wanted his things; if only I had listened to him when he told me to get them. We called him on his house phone; he hung up.

I was so angry, then Mother called us and told us to get home. She didn't think that it was right for us to be at our uncle's house for our dad's things. I didn't care at all, I wanted his things, and that was final. We still didn't get anything. Our uncle didn't open the door at all. I guess he thought that we had gotten enough of his brother's things. I looked at my brother and told him, "What a birthday, bro." He just shook his head. Then we went home, and my mother told me I should calm down. She would not understand that I had failed him once more.

There were things Dad didn't want him to have. I didn't care about them, but Dad didn't want him to take them at all. After three days, he called my mother and told her to come and get Dad's things. They didn't want me to go because of my mouth. They went, and he gave them what he didn't want; I didn't care at all.

One day, I got fed up and called Tom just to hear him picking up his phone. He was there talking to his new girlfriend; as I listened to them, it seemed as if he was calling a cab for her. I just listened to them talking sweetly. It disgusted me so much that I called him all kinds of names; he did the same thing and told me that I wasn't a woman enough for him.

Then I told him my innermost part. I told him about his child that I had killed, and he was just dead as everyone else. I hung up the phone and was just crying out for my dad. This guy and I were over; I needed a break from everyone. Thanksgiving came, and so did Christmas. It was not the same without Dad. Now all of my siblings were here. I felt like the young one again; they didn't want to hear what I had to say.

Then one day, Marlene came to me and told me about my abortion. She heard it from Karen's boyfriend; I was hurt all over again. She told him everything about my life. I had trusted her, and she let me down. I felt betrayed; I kept thinking about who else he told. I guess I have to carry this sin for the rest of my life. Marlene and Karen were always fun girls; they would party together while I stayed home and watched Karen's daughter. Althea was more concerned about her other son back home in Jamaica. I was once more the babysitter while the others had fun. Mother didn't mind at all; she still saw me as a child, and that was it.

Chapter 18

I couldn't stay at the house anymore because my sister's lifestyle wasn't mine, but of course, my nieces were everywhere I went. I had to get away, so I went over to Pam's house. Now my sister Althea wasn't having that at all. She told Mother as it was. Karen needed responsibility over her children and stopped letting other people take care of them. Althea was firm with Mother; I wasn't. Mother had her favorite, and she didn't hide it one bit. I could talk to Althea, and she didn't tell at all. She could talk a lot, though. I did what I was told. I went over to Pam's house just to get away. I knew that I had to do something with my life.

This was getting to me, not working and just looking after my sister's child. I needed to go back to school. Now that my dad had passed, I needed to make something of myself. I called a school to see my financial aid status. They told me I had to pay back all that money. It was more than ten grand. I knew that I needed a job, but where to look? I called Pam once more, and she told me about one in Brooklyn; all I had to do was answer the phone and get paid. I didn't like this at all, so I called Frank's friend that lived in Brooklyn. He came and got me one day. Then he told me that I needed a real job; I did listen to him and went to apply at Sears, where Pam worked. I just wanted to do something with my life; this went on, and now this guy would come around a lot, telling me what I needed to do.

He was going back to school. When he was finished, he invited me to his graduation. I did go, and I met his brother and mother. I didn't think of anything. I enjoyed myself; his brother was so funny. I never laughed like that in a while. We were going out a lot now; I was called a floozy for just hanging out with this guy. No one knew what I was facing, and no one cared. They were quick to judge. I didn't let it bother me at all; then, he kept bringing up my pass. I told him that he needed to date his friend and leave me alone. I could not handle this at all; while I was just going through the motions, I got a call from Tom; it seemed as if he got tired of his other women. I told him that it was over and I was with someone else. He asked me if I could meet him to talk, then asked about my dad.

I told him that he was dead; he said that he knew. He just wanted to see how I was dealing with it. I was fine, I told him, and hung up. Then I got another call from Frank's friend; we went out, and he was the same way. This guy had a lot of issues; I didn't know what it was. He was in the army; it seemed as if he was dealing with it as well. I told my sister Althea about him, and she told me just to watch him and see. I had my share of crazy. I knew in my heart that I didn't love him and that I couldn't give him what he wanted. I had to get him out of my life. I told him I was moving back home with my mother. He didn't take it very well; I didn't know if I should just walk away or what to do. I gave him a part of me just to say goodbye; he needed help, and I needed help too. He didn't handle it very well, but he moved on. At this time, I was once more alone and depressed. I knew that something was missing in my life.

Meanwhile, I got a call from my aunt. She told me that she was leaving for Connecticut. Her husband wanted a change from New York. She asked me if she could stay with me while she went back and forth until she got a job in Connecticut. I was fine with it. After all, Marlene had gone back home to Jamaica. I still had my room at Karen's apartment. Mother was still paying rent for them; I was back and forth from my apartment with Karen. Working at Sears was nothing at all. You would get dressed up and weren't making anything at all.

I would be borrowing money to go to work. I didn't see the sense of this job. I didn't mind at all my aunt being there; she loved to cook meatballs and so on. She had a lot of fun when she went to Connecticut for the weekend. I would go back to my mother's house.

My life was at a standstill, working and waiting for more hours. This went on for months; they would give you hours during the holiday and take it back around February. My life was getting the best of me. I knew I needed something to do with myself.

The next step I needed to take was to get a better job and pay back my school loan; I didn't even know what I wanted to do. Not having my mother telling me what to do with my life. I never really knew what I did like. I didn't even think that I knew what I wanted to do. An architect was not what I really wanted. Now that I look back on it, I think it was more my sister Althea's dream. I always admired her, so I took up drafting in school; it sounds good when people ask you what you want to be.

I was on a soul-searching journey. I wanted to know my purpose in the world. I didn't know where to start; I thought about a lot of things. The first step was to pay back my student loan, and then I could go back to school and be somebody. I didn't want to be what people thought I should be. I wanted to do something that made me happy and could help people in return. I thought about this for some time.

One day, I got another call from Tom. He told me he was only checking up on me. He wanted to know if I was okay. He told me if I ever needed anyone to talk to, he was always there; I knew that much. You would think that I didn't have a brain; I kept taking his calls. We talked for a while, and then we hung up. I was getting a lot of calls from this man lately; I asked him about his girlfriends. He would just laugh and say there was no one like me.

I knew I didn't need this right now; I needed to stick to my plan. I didn't need any distractions, so I called my aunt, and she encouraged me. She asked me what I liked; I told her I didn't even know. She told me I needed something that was working in today's market. I guessed so. What in the world was I good at and loved? Then another phone call came again from this man; now he wanted to see me. I told him I was too busy for that. I must give it to him; he never gave up at all. He asked me where I worked; wrong move. He looked up and found out where I was. He never came to my job, but man, he called a lot. My supervisor was watching me a lot; she told me that I was getting too many personal calls. I asked him to stop calling me so much; he wanted to go on a date with me. I was afraid too, but he insisted. I told Althea about him, and she told me that I should go and come back; it was only a date. I thought about it a lot, but I was afraid to do so.

This went on for some time; he would call me most of the time. He would tell me how much he missed me; I would start to get flashbacks. One day, I decided to give him a chance and went out with him. He told me where to meet him in Manhattan.

He took me to the movies, and we had dinner; then he told me that he lived near the restaurant. He wanted to get something at his apartment; I told him I wanted to go home. "Please, come with me; it's just around the corner," he said. He wasn't lying at all. He had a key and went inside the apartment; I didn't know where I was. When he got inside the room, he told me that it would not take too long. I watched him as he relaxed; I told him that it would be too late for me to go home.

Then he told me he would take me to the train station when he was ready. He came over to me and started to kiss me; I moved my face, and he didn't like it one bit.

Then he came over to me and asked me if I was still having relations with that guy. Now I knew it was time to leave. He told me he was not taking me back to the train station until he was good and ready. He threw a T-shirt on me and went to bed. I kept thinking to myself. If only I knew where I was. I was afraid of taking the train by myself, and he knew that. I watched him fall asleep, knowing I wasn't going home anytime soon. I just sat and blamed myself. *How am I going to get out of this one?*

I waited until he was sleeping; then I put on the T-shirt. I took my time because I didn't want to wake him. While I lay on the bed, he rolled over and grabbed me by my throat. I cried for help, but no one could hear me. He told me to shut up; then he told me that I left him once, and nobody left him.

He ripped the T-shirt off me, then he started to hit me. He punched me really hard. I tried to fight him, but he was so angry. He told me that I was a dog. He mentioned that I had killed his baby, and this time, I would not kill this one. At this point, I was fighting; but he was too strong. I just gave up; I couldn't fight anymore. I just lay there as a dead person while he had his way with me. I didn't hear what he was saying.

I kept hearing voices in my head telling me that it was my fault. I should have known better; while he was raping me, he kept punching me like a boxing bag.

He looked me in the eyes and told me that if I left him ever again, he would find me and kill my ass, not to mention when he was finished with me. I could become a lesbian; he wanted to put that much fear in me that I would be afraid of men. As the tears rolled down my face, I kept wondering why he didn't just kill me and end this life that I had. When he was finished with me, I was in a lot of pain all over.

The following morning, he told me that I didn't need to go to the police station. They wouldn't believe a dog like me; he said I had no right to be at his apartment, and moreover, people saw us together having dinner. I looked at him, and I knew in my heart he was right. He told me to get dressed and take my dog self out of his house. I got dressed, and he pointed to the train station. I didn't know my way around the place; I could see now because it was morning, and I asked for directions to get back to Queens. When I came off the train, I took the bus and went to the house. When I got to my mother's house, she had gone to work already, but Althea was asleep.

Mr. Tucker was there too. I took my shower, and as the water ran down my body, the tears started to flow. I just heard those words from him, that I was a dog, how I had killed his baby. I wanted to end my life at this point, but it wasn't time yet. I had totally forgotten about the promise I'd made to God. Right now, I wasn't thinking about him. I was thinking more about how foolish I had been. I knew better not to trust him. He was sick, and I was even sicker to think that he had changed.

I had to call out from work for two days. When I went to work, they told me my boyfriend called me a lot. A co-worker asked me if I was fine, and I told her yes. Whenever I was at work, he would call to see if I was at work; sometimes, he would call just to harass me. He wanted me to get fired, but I told my co-worker to cover for me. If he called, she should tell him I was not at work; she would help out a lot. But when she wasn't there, he would have a field day with me; I needed my job. I tried to keep him calm, but he was a man on a mission, and I was it. I kept thinking that it was karma for leaving that guy.

Whenever he called me, I would get palpitation. I knew that I was stressed out a lot, I wanted to just run away, but I had nowhere to go.

This went on for a while, he wanted to see me, but I would be a fool to go and see him. He told me he could find me at work, but I still didn't let anyone know what I was going through. Whenever I left work, I would be watching my back because I was afraid of that man. I would have some wicked chest pain, and my fingers would be swollen a lot. I told my mother about it. She told me that I needed to see the doctor. I went to the emergency room due to the fact that I didn't have any insurance.

I took two buses to get to the hospital. They took my vitals and told me to urine in a cup. After asking me a lot of questions, I was told to go into the waiting room. Once more, before I saw the doctor, they told me that they wanted to do a heart mammogram; but they had to wait until my blood work came back. I stayed in the hospital for four hours; then I saw the doctor. He told me that my heartbeat was irregular; he didn't know what had caused my fingers to be swollen like that. Then he told me that I was pregnant and needed to run more tests. I asked him what he said about being pregnant. He looked at me and told me that I was pregnant and needed to go to the clinic to run some more tests.

I came out of the hospital; I didn't make any appointments. I was like a zombie. That day, I walked home. The cars were beeping me to get off the road, but I was in another place. I didn't hear them at all. I was just spaced out; I was pregnant for that monster once more.

I didn't know what in the world I was going to do; he had raped me. I was in a total stack; I didn't even know that I had walked home from the hospital. Mother was there, and she asked me what the doctor said; I just looked at her and told her that they had to run some more tests. I went outside the yard, and my brain was going crazy. As I sat on the wet grass, I didn't know what to think.

I didn't know how to tell this man that I was carrying his child; I knew he would be in my life forever. The tears rolled down without any control; I didn't know if I should just die; I sat outside for hours and then went back inside the house. Althea asked me where I was; I told her I was just thinking. She thought it was about Dad. I knew that he would have been happy, but what about Mother and to know who the dad was?

I had to really get my thoughts in order; I really didn't know what in the world to do. So I called Karen and told her what was wrong; she was upset that I had sex with him, and she didn't know he had raped me. My sister asked me if he knew, and I told her not yet. She told me that he needed to know and that I could do what I needed to do; I didn't know how this man was going to act.

I waited a week before I told him, but she insisted that I should tell him right away. I knew I needed to tell him. I was getting sicker by the day. One day, he called me just to aggravate me; I told him that I could not deal with him right now. He told me that whenever he called me, I should shut up and listen to him. I couldn't handle it anymore. I told him I was pregnant, then he got silent for a while.

Then I heard him laughing in my ears, "Do you expect me to believe that your baby is my child, you tramp?" He laughed and laughed.

I hung up the phone and started to cry; I didn't know what to think at this time. I kept hearing the voice in my head telling me to end it.

I was in a trance, then he called back. I kept picking up the phone because I didn't want anyone to know what was happening to me. He told me I should just kill myself and the baby that wasn't his, and I didn't have any purpose to live. I was ashamed of the human race, weak rat, and he went on and on. I heard a beep on the other line. I went over while he was talking. It was my friend Pam.

She wanted to know how I was feeling. I just burst out and cried. I told her that he wanted me to kill myself. She asked me what I was talking about. I told her that he wanted me to kill myself. I told her that I wanted my dad so badly. She had to remind me that my dad was dead and wasn't coming back. Then the phone was beeping again. I told her I had to go and answer him. Pam told me not to. She put me on hold and called the police while she had me on the phone. I gave them his number, and they called him. The police officer told me to come in and fill out a report on him; I took all the information and hung up the phone. Pam told me to go to bed and forget about that crazy man. I was just shaking; I had the knife in my hand. When I heard that voice telling me to end it once and for all, I put the knife down and went to bed. I didn't know when I fell asleep, but I dreamt about my dad.

He came to the house for me; it was raining so hard. He called my name and told me that he was tired of seeing me crying. I didn't know what had happened, but I told him, "You're dead and should go and get some rest. I will be fine." Then he vanished in front of my eyes. I could not believe it. The sun came out, and the birds were just singing. I could not understand that dream at all.

The next day, I had to come to my senses; that man wanted me and my baby dead. I had to get some strength right now to deal with him. I know that I could not call on my dad anymore. I didn't like that dream at all. It was too real for me not to believe that he didn't come for us. The crazy man called me and told me to get rid of the baby; I just listened to him. I learned how to block people out once more.

I called my sister and told her what he told me, then she gave me a number once more for an abortion clinic. I called the number, and they told me to come in. When I went there, it was different from the first one. This time a lot of women were in the room. I listened to some of them while they talked. I heard one telling another woman that she had just gotten a new job and this child would hold her back. The other one said that she had too much and that she didn't need another one. When I went in to see the doctor, he asked me what was wrong with me. I told him that I wanted an abortion, and he asked me about my medical history. I told him that I might have a heart problem, and that's when he told me that he could not do the procedure. I was happy in a way, I went home and told Karen, and she said to me I had to find another way. I wanted my baby; after all, the father didn't want it.

I still didn't tell Althea and Mother. I was afraid of what Mr. Tucker and Mother would say; Karen called me one day and asked me the biggest question of my life. She wanted to know what if I die; that left me thinking. Who would take care of the baby? I didn't think about that at all. I told her that no doctor wanted to, so I needed to know what I was doing. She gave me another hospital to call, which I did. I called and made the appointment.

When I got there, everything seemed different. I sat and listened to the ladies as they went on. One asked me how much I had; I told her the one. She told me why not keep it then. I smiled at her because she was right, after all. When I went into the office to see the doctor, he told me about the procedure.

He said that it was like giving birth; I would be up for the entire thing. I would have to spend the night over for that kind of procedure. I had to wait two more months for the fetus to get bigger. Due to the fact of my heart, he didn't want to take any risk at all with me.

When I was in that room with all these ladies, some were silent, while others were just talking as if it was nothing. I just listened to them. You could see the guilt on some of their faces. I didn't know what was on mine, but alone and afraid. When I went home, I just took a shower, lay down, and held my stomach. I just talked to my baby and went to bed.

Now as the week went by, I didn't hear from Tom at all. I was happy, with no stress or anxiety. I even got more good news. Mother was going to Jamaica for a while. I wished she were taking Mr. Tucker with her. I knew that I would be happy for a while.

When my mother left for Jamaica with my niece, I felt a load come off my back. Althea and I were happy; we even went to dinner with Mr. Tucker. I couldn't believe it myself. I wasn't thinking about anyone but my baby. We were together after all; Althea asked me if I was pregnant because I was eating like crazy. I just smiled and ate some more. Mr. Tucker seemed different these last days. He wasn't talking too much. I didn't know if he missed my mother or what; we were at a Christmas dinner with him at his friend's home.

When we got back to the house, I was spotting a lot; then, it got worse. I was passing a lot of blood, and I didn't know what to do or say to my sister Althea. I went and lay down and was just praying for God to help my baby. I called Karen, and she told me to lie down, which I did. I didn't want to lose my baby. I was having more chest pain than ever; I didn't want to go to the hospital either. I knew that I was on a suicide mission with my baby.

One day, I was in the bathroom washing my clothes when Mr. Tucker came in with tears in his eyes. He told me that his daughter was pregnant; as I watched this big man cry his eyes out, he turned to me and told me that I should go to school and make my mother proud. It seemed as if he had just stabbed me in the heart. All this time, I was just thinking about myself and my baby.

He got me thinking about my mother, how she would feel to know that I was pregnant, and who the father was. I didn't know how to tell her. I was in some deep mess; my heart felt it for him and for Mother as well. When he walked away, the tears rolled down my face. My heart was on fire. I was in a total mess. I had to make up my mind and really fast. I didn't care if I lived or died. My baby was on death row.

One day out of nowhere, Tom called me. He wanted to know if I was still pregnant; after two months of not hearing from him. I told him what he wanted to hear, "Yes, your baby is dead." This piece of crap cursed me out. He told me that he was going to kill me and that he was going to burn the motherloving house down with everyone in it.

This man was crazy. I didn't know what had happened, but I lost it. I told him that he only cared about his kids when they were dead. He didn't care for the fact that he raped me that night. He didn't care if I lived or died. "I watched you beat me, not once but a lot of times, and even hit me in my stomach while I was pregnant so that the child could die. The pain you put me through was unbearable. You hurt me mentally and physically, and now you are asking me about a dead child! Motherlover! As if I care; kill them all, you piece of crap, and yourself as well. You took the one thing I love the most, and that was loving you!"

I told him he only cared about his children when they were dead, and then I hung up the phone. Not before long, Karen called me and told me he called her crying too. I told her to leave me alone and hang the phone up. This went on; then Mother was back home once more. Now everyone was on edge; Mr. Tucker was back to his old self, cursing us and calling me a wench. I just wanted to die at this point, then that crazy man kept calling me. I was angry most of the time as the day approached.

One day, Mother and her children went out. Althea, her friend, Mother, and Marlene came up from Jamaica again. Edson and his girlfriend went with Karen on a boat ride; I told them that I would stay home with my niece and nephew Derrick.

Mr. Tucker was upset. He told Mother that she could not leave the house; it was a different story because this time, he wasn't dealing with Karen and me but Althea and Marlene. They were fighters back home. This man didn't know what he was getting into with them. It seemed as if his world was falling apart when he found out that his daughter was pregnant. When they all left for the boat ride, he was cursing a lot of bad words. I took the kids in the bedroom and locked the door. He told me to open it, but I didn't. Then he cursed some more. He was drunk; I wasn't afraid of him anymore. I told the kids just to go to bed. Then I paged my brother to call me when they got off the boat. I listened to him curse as he changed the locks on the doors. I just waited and waited until my brother called the house phone. I told him what was taking place and not to tell my mother. I knew that she went out with her kids, and this man wanted to soil her fun.

When they came to the house, I went and opened the door for them. Althea and Marlene came in first and then Mother, Edson, and his girlfriend too. Karen had gone home with her man. I didn't know what had happened, but Mr. Tucker and Mother started to argue. Then I heard a lot of noise; the man was out of control; he was destroying Mother's thing. How silly can you be, trying to hurt a mother in front of her kids? He left his hand toward Mother, and Edson held him back, then the fight began. Althea and Marlene jumped in and started to destroy his things as well.

They beat his ass; oh, I waited for this day. I was so bitter and angry that I went and got my mother's jewel box to hit him with. I held it up to beat him really well, then Mother held my hand and shook her head at me. She

115

went on the phone and called 911; then, she called his sister to come over. It was a mess, but a good one. Man, I had waited for this day to come; when the police came, they could smell the alcohol on Mr. Tucker. My niece saw what he was doing, so she told the police what he did.

Mr. Tucker went into the bedroom, took out Mother's money, and went with his sister to her house. Mother was just crying; I didn't know if we had broken up her love life or what. Then she went into her room and came out crying. She couldn't find the money that she got from work. It was the rent for the month. I didn't know what to think at this point. She worked hard for this man and helped him while he stayed home. When he lost his job over three years ago, and she was the only one working to help everyone, he was so bitter with all of us. He had controlled her all this time. I looked into myself and was just thinking that I was in the same mess; things we do for love. That night, everyone was uneasy; I knew that Mother was sad to know that her love was gone.

The following day Mr. Tucker came to the house with his sister and the police for his things, and my mother asked him for her money. He told her he knew nothing; then the man went into the bedroom to get Mother's envelope with her pay still in it. She caught him with it and called the police. When the cops asked him how much was in the envelope, he didn't know. Her name was also on it. How dumb could he be? The cops just told him to leave the house and then talked to our mother. I went downstairs and just listened to them. I had my problems as well; I had only one week left to make up my mind.

One day, I heard my mother as she spoke to her sister; she was telling her what had happened. She started to tell her about his daughter, about her being pregnant, and all of that. I just shook my head because I was in the same boat as this girl. The only difference was this girl was keeping her child; I couldn't handle this at all. While all of this was happening, I knew that Mother was sad. After all, he was her life. They had been together for ten years; who were we to get into that relationship? As I listened to them talk, I got a phone call from Mr. Crazy.

Chapter 19

He wanted to know how I was doing; I just told him I was still pregnant with his child. He was silent on the phone. He thought I had killed my baby, so he could play the guilt trip with me. But surprise—I was still pregnant. This was the point I was waiting to hear him say that he was happy that our baby was alive. He asked me what I was going to do; my heart just dropped. Then Tom told me whatever I decided he would respect. He didn't want any more children. Who was I kidding to think that he cared?

I told him that I was going to have the abortion the following Monday, and he told me that he would come with me. What I saw happen to Mother, after all the love and sacrifice she put into a relationship that didn't last, who was I kidding? The following day, I went over to Karen's apartment to see this guy, but he never called or showed up. I cried most of the time. I was alone and afraid again. Karen had to go to work, and only this guy and my friend knew about it. Being a Christian, she didn't want me to do it, but it was my choice.

As I held my stomach, the tears went rolling down like a river bed. I told my baby I was sorry I was born because this could not have happened to it. "I don't know if I will ever meet you again, not in this life or the life to come..." I was broken. I didn't know what I was feeling. I took out the iron and pressed my clothes for that day. I went to bed, but I could not sleep; if only my dad were here...

The following morning, I was just crying; Karen told me what to do, and I left. I didn't know where I was going or what I was doing. I took the train to Brooklyn on the number J train as I approached the hospital. I just wanted to run away, but I got numb. I went inside and got registered, and then the nurse told me that I needed an ultrasound to see how big the fetus was. This was a different story; now, I had to see how big my baby was. This was more than punishment; where was this man when I needed him? He told me he would come with me, and now no sign or call from him. My heart was hurting; my mind was running all over the place.

When I got to the room, my heart was beating fast. I almost passed out. They told me to get undressed and put on a gown. I did what they told me; then the man came into the room and told me what he was about to do, but while he was talking, my mind went blank. He did what he had to do, and then he told me if I wanted to see the baby, I turned and looked at the monitor. There was my baby, just lying there; at this time, I should have gotten up and just run away; but where could I have run to? My dad was gone, and no one could understand me at all. When he came out of the room, I got dressed and went over to the TV monitor.

I told my baby, "Mommy is really sorry for what I am about to do. I don't know if I'll ever see you again, but I love you…" I kissed my finger, put it on the face of my child, and walked away. Then the nurse told me where to go; I left that building and went to another one.

When I got there, there were five of us ladies, two in each room. I was so nervous. The young lady with me had a friend in the room with us. She was not allowed in there, but she hid her in the closet. The nurse came in and told us what was next; she told us that the doctor was only coming in to give us a needle into our stomach, and that would be all. Not before long, the doctor walked in. She was right. He did give me a needle, but it was a big one; as I watched him insert the needle into my body, the nurse came over with a bottle of liquid to put inside the needle. I asked them if that was the poison, and the doctor told me then I would be dead. He just walked away with no remorse.

As I watched the needle move from side to side, I knew my baby was dead. I didn't cry. I just watched her as she did her job. She told me to hold the gaze for a while; then she told me to take a walk. I walked and walked; then I started to get thirsty; they told us that we could have nothing to drink. I asked nicely, but still no. I went to the restroom, but they turned off the pipes. I had no water to drink.

I went into the bathroom again to get some water, but they were serious about it. I looked at the toilet bowl and was tempted to drink from it. I wanted water so bad. I didn't have any tears to drink from; then, at about 3:00 p.m., they gave us something to eat.

They didn't give us anything for the evening; I didn't know when I fell asleep, then I heard someone call me and told me that I had a phone call. I thought it was Tom, but it was my friend from school. I asked her how she got the number; she said she called information. She told me that I was in her prayers and that I should trust the Lord; then, she hung up. I knew she could not be a part of what I was doing, but she called me to let me know that.

While I walked away, it hit me so badly that my friend had to call to let me know that I was in her prayers, and my sister or that man didn't call once. When I went back to the room, the pain hit me. I didn't know what it was. Then the nurse told me that it was time. Soon, the young lady started to scream. The nurse went over to her; I just lay there.

Whenever I felt the pain, I held my mouth and cried. I wish my mother had been there with me; as I listened to the young lady while the nurse attended to her, I held my stomach and told my baby that everything would be all right. I didn't know what I was thinking, but I was talking to my baby. I couldn't hold it anymore; I just cried out, then the nurse came over to me. She told me to push, then nothing came out. She told me to push once more; still nothing. I pushed with everything in me; then, I felt something. She told me to wait. She then pulled my baby out from me. The only thing I saw was my baby's pink feet. They were no bigger than my hands; I asked her what kind of baby I had, and her response was that it was not a baby but a fetus. I told her that I wanted to see my fetus, but she just put my baby into a bin as if it was trash. I cried so much, then she told me to go into the bathroom, and she would be there. I got up and went to the toilet. Then I felt something coming out. I cried for the nurse; she told me it was only afterbirth. She told me to clean up myself.

I was in a lot of pain; blood was everywhere. I was so weak and tired. I kept crying for my mom. The nurse had no compassion; she was so cold; no wonder how she did that kind of work. She looked at me as if she didn't care if I lived or died; after all, I just killed my baby. She didn't even tell me what it was; the ultrasound didn't tell me either. That night, I could hear all the ladies' cries. I was in a lot of pain; the nurse came over, gave me painkillers, and went over to my roommate. As I lay on the bed, the tears rolled down my face. I looked at the window with my thoughts gone. I saw a tree branch as it danced through the wind. The tears I could not control anymore.

As I lay down, I heard another baby cry out for help. I felt guilt and shame; I should have died with my angel. I fell asleep. I was woken up once more. The nurse woke me up to give me pain pills. Then I took them; this pain was unbearable, and my heart couldn't take it at all.

In the morning, at 7:15 am, the nurse came back with breakfast and told us that it was time to leave. They were changing shifts; another nurse came in with paperwork and prescription to be filled. I asked for a letter for work so that I could keep my job.

I was in a lot of pain, thinking about how far I had to go for the train. The young lady that was in the room with me told me to come with her into the cab, which she paid for, they took me to the nearest train station, but it seemed as if it was the wrong train station. I had to climb up a lot of stairs and was in a lot of pain. The people were just looking at me while the tears came out. I had to keep on walking; I couldn't hold back the tears. Finally, I got to my sister's apartment; she didn't have any money to fill my prescription either, so that night, I was in so much pain.

I couldn't tell my mother what I did because it was a secret and no one needed to know. I called Tom, but no answer. I went to bed with a lot of pain; I didn't feel so much pain before in my life. I stayed with my sister for two days, and then I went back to my mother's apartment. I had to go to work in two days. I then asked my mother for some money until I got paid. I told her I needed it for bus fare.

When I got it, I filled out my prescription. I could only get a few of the pills. I didn't have insurance at the time, and my job didn't give part-time workers such things. When I got to work, I had to put on my happy face. I would have to smile in front of customers, and when I went into the bathroom, I would cry my heart out. I kept hearing how I was a murderer and I should be punished; this voice never left me at all. It was my life sentence that I had to live with for the rest of my life. The week went by, no call from that man. I was bitter and angry. I wrote him a letter, telling him what I had been through.

I told him the pain he put me through was unbearable; as I wrote the letter, the tears were just rolling out. Then I realized that I was feeling better, so I went and looked for his mother's number. I called her because I had to know if he was such a monster. I called the number and spoke to her; she told me that he was fine and doing well, and she asked who I was. Then I told her my name. I knew he told me not to call his mother ever, but I had to close this part of my life. It didn't work at all; I was even more bitter than before. At work, one of the customers held my hands while I was giving her change back to her. She told me I was hurting badly and should talk with someone. I didn't know who she was, but she was right. I didn't tell Pam at all, even though she was my best friend. I didn't call Elaine either; she was too godly for me. I was a sinner who needed to be punished for all the crimes that I did.

I couldn't trust my sister Althea at all. Karen didn't say anything, but she would tell her boyfriend everything. I didn't want to hurt my mother after all. I did what I did, and that was about it. I went on feeling guilty as always, feeling sorry for myself. One day while I was coming home from work, this guy saw me. He was just there talking to me; he would never know the mess that I was.

I listened to him as he kept talking; when I went home, Mother told me that some lady called me. It was Tom's mother; I was so nervous. I didn't know if she wanted to talk to me about her son or just curse me out. When I called her back, she told me that her son was in jail, and he told her to call me and let me know.

It was like a load came off me; I knew in my heart that he would have never left me like that. He was the kind of person that would keep bothering me. I know I was a fool who still had feelings for this man, even though he hurt me so many times. She told me he was going to call me the next day at 5:00 p.m. at my sister's house. How I wanted to hear his voice… I knew that I couldn't see him at all. That night I didn't feel guilty at all; I just wanted to know what had happened. The following day, I called out from work. I didn't want to miss his call; he kept his promise, and he did call me.

When I heard his voice, I just cried and cried; he was even crying too. I asked him what had happened, and he told me that he could not have talked but told me he was sorry and loved me. That was what I wanted to hear; that he still loved me. This went on for a month, so he would call me, and I was happy to hear from him. One day, Karen told me I got a letter from my love. I didn't waste any time. I called the man I met in my mother's neighborhood; he came and took me over to Karen's apartment.

Then she gave me the letter; I couldn't wait to read it; I told the guy to wait a while with my sister. I went into the bathroom; I wanted to hear what Tom had to say. As I opened the letter, I was so happy; this is what it said:

Dear Angela,

I am writing you this letter not to hurt you but to be honest not only with you but myself. I no longer want to be with nor will I try to have any contact with you. When I am released, I will do everything in my power to make things work between myself and *Shela*. I am madly in love with her, and I will not allow anything to come in between us. You are young and have your whole life ahead of you; go to school, go out, meet people, and believe you will find someone to make you happy. I am sorry for any pain this letter will cause you, but I must do what I have to do. Please be happy and good luck.

Tom

P.S. There is no need to write back, my mind is made up, and it won't change.

When I read the letter, I felt like this man had killed me all over again; I was hurting even more. When he mentioned his ex-girl, the one who embarrassed me at school, at this point in my life, my heart was gone. I was in the bathroom talking to myself; there were no tears at all. My throat was burning a lot; then I came out of the bathroom smiling as if I had heard good news. Meanwhile, my heart was racing out of my chest.

The pain and shame I was feeling, now how can I really trust and talk to? The following day, I left work. I knew that I didn't have any reason to live at all. I couldn't end it at all because of my promise to God. I remember crying out to him and telling God to take this pain away; I didn't know what I was thinking or ever falling in love.

I did just what he said, go out and have fun. I went out and drank and got drunk, and I still felt empty. I was looking for love in all the wrong places. This went on for some time. While I was staying at my mother's house, Karen called me and asked me if I needed a job. It was babysitting work; of course, I agreed. I needed money; then Mother told me that she was moving into a bigger house so that each of us could have our own room. I was so happy; a new beginning. Now I could give up the room I had at Karen's apartment, even though I was not there at times. My aunt had already left New York and went to live with her husband in Connecticut.

This job was the best thing for me; I gave this child all the love I had to give. I took care of him as if he was my own child. He didn't want anything in return but for me to love him. I got my life in order; I was still paying back my school loan. It was a good thing that I had left that job. I was putting too much into it and didn't get anything in return; it reminded me of Tom.

As the months went by, I saw where I could save money as well as pay my bills. Things were going well for me, and I even went to Jamaica with Karen and Edson. We had a lot of fun; I saw my brother Gary as well.

He treated me like a princess. I knew I had to change my life and be someone. I could feel in my soul that there was more to my life than this. I didn't know what it was, but I could not keep still after all I'd been through in life. Tom had come out of jail and called me once more. If only my mother would have changed her number.

He wanted to get back with me when I told him no, and he threatened me. I told him to go ahead; he loved to put fear in me whenever he didn't get his way. He would threaten to kill me or my family.

Now I didn't care at all what he wanted to do with me; enough is enough. I was over that piece of crap. I wasn't afraid of him; moreover, my mother had moved, and he didn't know where to find me. I was free indeed; I didn't know if it was God that took him out of my heart, but that day I called out to Jesus and asked him to give me peace. The same one I felt at the hospital when my dad was sick.

My life was not the same; I saw so many things happening to me. I was still searching for someone to love me and for me to love them back. I didn't know what it felt like. One day, Mother had dinner for my sister Althea, and she invited some of her co-workers. One of them wasn't bad-looking. I told him, and that was it; then he asked for my number. I told him he had it once he had Althea's number; he just smiled.

He came around more often; I was old enough, but it seemed as if my sister had a problem with me and this guy. I knew that he had his baby's mother, but I was just having fun. It started to get bad when my sister and I were not talking at all because of this guy.

She would call me a minx and all kinds of things. I was used to that by now. Mr. Tucker called me that enough. I didn't stay long with him because there was no future for us because he was a handsome guy and had a lot of women, not to mention kids. Then I was once more in a love triangle with two brothers. One had liked me a lot, while the other had his eyes on me. I knew what that could cause between family, so I walked away from them. Families should stay together without anything and anyone making a mess of things.

The next person who had their eye on me was my sister's boss. He had his own business; of course, I was tempted, but I didn't fall. He was married; I didn't have a thing for married men. I always thought that he should stay with his wife because I knew God didn't like it at all. I don't know why I felt that way, but I knew that girls my age would have died for the position to be with a man like that. He was well-known. Whenever I went to parties or clubs and saw him, I was treated like a lady, but he was married, not for me. I knew his wife wasn't feeling good to know that he was out there with someone else. It could be me; after all, I was once there.

One day, I told my mother that I was going back to school. I knew I still owned my school loan. I had to stop babysitting now, and I was doing home health aids. It was a start for me. I was the youngest among these women in the class. Whenever we did our tests, I would help some of them. I didn't call it cheating; just helping. I'd learned from them; I was always around older people. I didn't know why, but I remembered what my dad told me once. He said I should listen to young people's music, but I love country music so much. Being with these ladies was like home. I finally finished my course and got my certificate; I was on my way for a real job.

The agency sent me all over the place for work; I would leave one and go to another one. Taking the train in Manhattan wasn't any joke. The days were hot, and the subway wasn't any fun. Some of my cases were the worst thing I ever had. I didn't know that there were so many sick people in this place. I thought I had a problem, but they made me look like an angel. I had a patient that was just crazy, and if I had stayed with her, maybe I would be just like her. I saw so many things with this kind of work, family fighting over their parents' money, even nieces and nephews too. It was sickening, but I guess that was just greed.

Things people do for money, they would kill their loved ones, so sad. I worked and worked as hard as I could, but I still felt that I was missing something. I told my mother that I was planning on moving out and trying to fly on my own; she told me that I wasn't ready at all. I didn't just move out; I waited until my sister Marlene came back from Jamaica, then I gave up my room. Being in the house with them, too much was going on. Everyone had their boyfriend and girlfriend there living with them. No one was married at all.

While I was working, I was buying things I needed to move out. I was in a savings thing called partners, which you save each week with a lot of people, and then each person got that hand. I went to the place where my dad had put down some money for his bedroom set. When I got there, of course, my name was there.

I didn't buy his bedroom set at all. It was beautiful and expensive, so I took Althea with me, and she liked a table set which we both agreed on. I got a nice Italian dining table with four chairs and a sofa set. I started to buy up my pot set and so on. I wanted to start my own life; I wanted to know what it felt like to be on my own. I finally did it. I moved out and got a one-bedroom apartment; it wasn't a big place. I was in my bedroom, then, with three steps, I was in the dining room. As I said, it wasn't a big place. It had an attic that wasn't finished; a family friend had helped me get the apartment, the same guy that helped us when Mr. Tucker had put out Karen when she was pregnant. He wanted the attire for his business. He told me he would give me some of the rent, which I thought was great. This didn't go too well; he wanted sex, and when I refused, he moved out, and I was left with a thousand-dollar rent.

I could not cover all my bills, so I called my mother, and she told me that she was born again. It seemed as if she had given her life to the Lord. She would give me scriptures from the Bible to read. Then one day, I called my brother Edson and told him what was happening to me. I told him I didn't want to come back home because I didn't want to feel like a failure, so we hung up.

I remember the scriptures that my mother gave me. It was Psalm 27. I read it, and I felt better. I was more focused than ever; some of these words in the Bible were big words that I could not read. This went on for a week or two.

Edson came over and went up the stairs to the attic, then he came down the stairs and asked me if I had money. I asked him why, and he said that I could fix it and rent it out. I looked at him and smiled; he was thinking like my dad.

The same way he fixed the living room at my sister's apartment. He came over the following day from work, and we went to Home Depot. We got all that we needed, and he fixed that place the way our dad would. When he was finished, I wanted to move upstairs. He told me not to worry; he got my back. I told my sister to ask if she knew anyone to let me know. I would work seven days straight to pay my bill; I could have stayed home with my mother and siblings. I refused to; I wanted to be independent, so I worked as hard as possible. I would call my mother at night, and we would talk.

One day at work, my boss came and asked me if I knew anyone that wanted a job at night. Of course, I called my mother and told her. We did this for some time; whenever I was bored, I would visit my mother and stay a while. Whenever they got on my back, I would go back to my apartment and chill. My sister Karen called me one day and told me that she got me a roommate; it was a guy.

He was from Haiti; I then told her that he could come and look at the place, which he loved very much. He moved the following week. I told him the rule and everything; we didn't have a contract or anything, I told him that he could use the living room if he wanted to, but he didn't at all. He was a clean person, and I didn't see him much; when I got home from work, he was still at his, and sometimes I would be at my mother's house. One day, my brother asked me if I had an apartment; I knew what he was trying to tell me.

While I was at my apartment, I got a call from my friend Pam. She wanted to go to the club with me, but I refused. I didn't feel up to it at all; I was feeling more like talking to God and listening to what Mother was telling me. As the weeks went by, on my way home from work, I saw this young man. He came over and asked me my name. I told him Sophia, which I knew I had just told a lie. He was a tiny little man. I knew that he could not hurt a fly after all I'd been through with that monster. I took his number and then went home.

Chapter 20

When I got home, I called Mother before she went to work. I did my usual things. I would pick up the Bible and read a couple of Psalms. This was my everyday thing. I was fine with what I was doing, working hard to pay back my school loan and my bills. Karen called me one night and asked me how things were with my roommate. I told her great; we were just talking, then she asked me if I was ever going out and found someone. I started to laugh. I told her that I met a guy on the train, he wasn't mad-looking. He was short. Then she asked me what was wrong with that. I didn't know if it would ever work at all. He was short, and if I decided to wear my high heels, how in the world would we look? Then she asked me if I was going out on a date with him; I told her no. She told me I should call him and see if he wanted to go out; after all, it was only a date. I took her advice and called him. He totally forgot who I was; then I forgot that I told him that my name was Sophia. He was there, talking and talking; he asked a lot of questions.

This went on for some time. Now I wasn't reading the Bible as often as before. I was curious about this guy. He wanted to know if I would go out with him. He looked like a preacher's kid with a past like mine. I didn't want to hurt anyone at all or to be hurt myself. So I played it safe. Whenever he wanted to take me out, I would tell him that I was at work, which I was. By the time he got off from work, I was still at work, so we talked a lot. He told me that I was too busy for him and that if I wanted to see him, I should take some time off.

I was a little afraid to date once more, but if I was looking for that perfect person, I should just let go. I finally agreed to go out with him. On our first date, he took me to the Fun Land; this guy had me on the merry-go-round. He was just laughing, and I was just asking God, *Please, don't let me hurt him.* I thought I opened up my heart too much over this guy; I thought he could do no harm.

At this time, I had put God aside and was just enjoying myself. We went to movies, dinners, parties, clubs, the beach, and so on. We even went away for the weekend, which was great. That night, he told me that he wanted a child, but he only wanted the child because it would be a beautiful one. I told him that I would not give him a cat, I would have to be married, and that was final. This thing went on for almost seven months; we would go to party after party.

One night, I went to a party with my sister Karen and Edson with his girlfriend; I was just there, dancing and drinking a wine cooler. It seemed as if everyone was moving really slowly. Then I heard a voice asking me what I was waiting on. I just looked at my wine cooler. Then I heard the voice once more, asking me if I was not tired of this lifestyle. Then everything went back to normal; everyone was dancing at a regular pace. I didn't understand what had just happened, but I still danced the night away.

The following day, I called the guy that I was seeing but got no answer. I was getting tired of this as well; whenever I called him, he was always at work or too busy to answer my calls. Whenever he wanted to go out with me, I was at work. Things were always getting into the way. One night, I called him at around 2:00 a.m., no answer. My head was running wild; I started to think that he was with another woman. The thought I got was crazy, so I got up and called him back and broke up with him on his answering machine.

That night, I had two dreams I remember very well. The first one was not a good dream; it was more like a nightmare. I dreamt that two black dogs were running me down; I tried to get away, but they were looking for me. I was so scared that I jumped out of that dream and called that guy. I told him all the dirty bad words I could possibly think of, and then I fell apart that night. I called out to God once more; I told him that I was so sorry, that I had put sex and fun before him. I felt dirty and ashamed. I only called on him when I needed something. I cried like a baby to God; I asked him to please help me. I fell asleep and had the other dream.

The second dream was totally different; I dreamt that I was on a big bus. The ride was long, but the place I was going was beautiful. It had a lot of green trees, and it was peaceful; when I reached my destination, I went into an apartment building. It seemed as if I knew the place because I was talking with the doorman. I went upstairs and opened the door. It looked as if I lived there.

While I was in the apartment, the doorbell rang, and I opened the door. It was the same guy that I had broken up with. He came over and kissed me on my forehead; then we went into the kitchen. I was frying chicken; I jumped out of that dream. I didn't know what it meant, but I slept like a baby that night.

The following morning that guy called me back. He told me that he had fallen asleep and didn't hear the phone at all. I listened to him as he talked and talked; I asked God to show me this guy who he was really. I didn't like what I saw; now I knew he had to go. Maybe when God was ready, he would change him, but for now, I didn't like what I was seeing. I finally let him go and focus on work now. My boss told me about extra work with her brother, so I asked my sister if she wanted to do the weekend with my boss. Then I could work with her brother's friend; he wanted me to do the job, but it wasn't a lot of money at all. They paid only $7 per hour, which wasn't a lot, but I did what I could to pay my bills. I put all of my time into work and the Lord.

When you would think that things were getting better, I got a call from my landlord; he told me that the house I was living in was sold. I didn't know what to say or think; I was in a big situation at this time. I didn't know what to do at this point; my thought was running wild. I didn't want to move back home with Mother and the rest of them, and I didn't know if my roommate would want to move with me. I didn't think too hard on this one; I knew that the Lord would help me on this one. I got a call from my aunt in Connecticut; she told me how she got saved like a mother. She told me what the Lord had done for her and how happy she was. My aunt, whom I loved, told me to come and visit her one day, but due to the fact that I had to work, I didn't have any time at all. I knew that my school loan was almost paid off; thank God for that.

It is really hard when you own money. Plus, the interest doubled the amount you owe; life was more like a routine, the same thing every day. I would go to work, then come home. Paid my bills and off again once more; I knew that there was more to life than this. Something was missing, and I could feel it. I wasn't getting any younger at all; each day counted. I knew that I had to make a change in my life right now; I had to find somewhere to live, but where?

One day at home, I got a call from Pam; it was the same story. Party, sex, and drinking; I didn't know if she wasn't tired of the same thing over and over. I know I was tired of hearing the same thing over again; I just felt empty in my soul, with no joy at all.

I had finally paid off my school loan; now, I was really ready to go back to school; right now, I wasn't interested in architecture at all. I had to go into a field that was going to pay a lot with the market today. So I called my sister Karen, and we were just talking; she asked me if I would change state. I told her that it never crossed my mind at all; then, she told me to call my aunt in Connecticut.

I didn't waste any time; I called my aunt and told her how I was feeling. She was just laughing and thanking God. She told me that was the same feeling that she had. I told her I would come down and visit the place to see what it was all about. I didn't tell my mother at all what was my intention. I told her that I was going to visit my aunt. I took two weeks off from work and went to see her.

When I went to Connecticut, it was way different from New York. Everything seemed so slow, while New York was fast. My aunt's apartment was really nice and big, not to mention the rent. A place like this in New York would cause me a lot of money. She asked me if I wanted her to take me to the office, which she did. I went in and filled out the paperwork. I didn't know what had happened, but it took me less than two days to be approved. My aunt was just laughing hysterically; I told her not to tell Mother just yet.

The apartment wanted two hundred and fifty dollars more; would you believe it, my aunt got a call for a weekend job that paid exactly two hundred and fifty dollars. I was just smiling. Then my aunt said that it was Jesus doing all this. I could not believe it at all; everything was falling into place. I went and did the weekend with this woman; it was the same home health aide job. The place I went to was even more beautiful. I left the job that Sunday evening and paid the apartment complex the rest of the money. I could not believe it at all. Like my aunt had said, it had to be Jesus.

Everything went well; then I called my mother and told her what had happened. She was silent on the phone. I didn't love to tell her anything because she would let me know that it was too far or I was all alone up there. I know my mother very well, the same thing she said, then she asked me about my job in New York. I told her that I would do the same thing my aunt used to do; she would commute back and forth. As for my job, I wasn't going to leave it until I got another one. I didn't tell my boss anything at all because she took me for a ride.

The job that her brother had gotten me for the weekend really paid ten dollars for an hour, but she paid me only seven per hour. It was not like she needed the money. She was a lawyer, and her husband was a doctor. She thought that she was robbing me, but she was only robbing herself.

I went there for just peace of mind and to help him out. He would ask me a lot of questions and give me a book to read. Then the following week, he asked me about the book. He was more like a professor; I loved that about him. He challenged me to think.

When the two weeks went by, I was back in New York. I told my roommate to find somewhere, which he did. Then the person that had bought the house told me if I moved out early, he would give me a thousand dollars. I didn't waste any time.

I called my brother, and he got a friend with my nephew, and we moved my things to the apartment. Edson loved the place a lot.

I told him to move from New York. He looked at me as if I was crazy. He told me he could not leave like that. I wasn't afraid to make changes at all. I even got back my security deposit, which I put into the bank for a rainy day. Now I got help to pack out my things, and my brother and the rest of them had to go back to the place they loved. Where there is peace, you will find me. I went back to do my everyday routine. I would take the Greyhound or the Peter Pan bus to Hartford.

One day, I came to work late, but good thing Mother was there; she stayed a while before I came. Then my boss wanted to know why I was late. I told her that I had missed the early bus to New York. She was silent on the phone like Mother; at this time, I couldn't lie at all. This church thing let me feel a different way; I felt more at peace.

When I was in Connecticut, I would go to church with my aunt. It was a different thing when I was in New York. I would go to church on Easter Sunday and Christmas Sunday, but on New Year's Eve, I would dress for a party; I would still go to church after that leave and go to a party. I would wear my long coat and keep it on, but under all that, my party clothes were waiting to be seen. I always thought that it was fine because on New Year's Eve, everyone would be kissing their loved one, and I would be just looking around. I could do like some of my friends, just get a man for that night and then drop him; if you didn't get dumped yourself. That was more like my life; it was not that I was having sex with them.

I would watch these people worship the Lord; some of them were all over the floor, and some were running back and forth. I just looked at them. I didn't know that church people did this too. Some were dancing as if they were in the club; I guess you worship the way you want to. This was a new thing for me, but one day, I would get there.

Every Sunday morning, I would go to Sunday school with my aunt; man, I knew nothing. This made me feel so stupid. This went on for a while. I wouldn't go to Bible class because I was at work in New York. I would have to give up the job, but my boss told me that if I did, she would have fired my mother and sister, so she had a strong hold on me. When I thought about my life, I knew that God had called me for something; I didn't know what it was. To think about how I got that apartment was unbelievable.

One day while I was at work, my mother told me that she wanted me to stay in Connecticut because she knew that I was traveling too much, but I told her not yet. I did my daily thing each weekend. One Friday evening, on my way home, a vision flashed in front of me.

I saw myself on this big bus going to the country; when I got off the bus, I went upstairs and saw my boyfriend. I could hardly control myself. I cursed a big bad word. People were looking at me; I don't know if they thought that I was crazy. The dream I had with that young man was coming true; I was freaking out. Then it came to me, that young man was coming back too. I didn't know what was happening, but I could not wait to see the outcome of this. The outcome came too early. My boss came to her mother's house and told me that she didn't want to let me go, but she was afraid that I would not come back. She went and got two ladies for the job. She let go with my mom and sister as well. She told me that she had our two weeks' pay and was sorry. I was more worried about my mother, but she wanted me to go anyway.

That was so fast, I was let go from work, and now I had to get something in Connecticut. I thank the good Lord that I had two thousand dollars to keep me over until I got something to do. In all of this, my aunt told me that it was time for us to be baptized. They had some kind of rules to follow; they wanted you to attend church for a while and to make sure that you were ready. I didn't know all of this. In two weeks, we were getting ready for our baptism. They told us what to wear and what to do, even what to expect.

I went with the flow; my aunt was a people pleaser. I was not; I did things my way. As the week went by, I went out and filled out applications all over the place. Still no call; then I would go to work with my aunt. She took care of two lovely kids; the little girl had me for a while, and we played in the dirt. She loved worms and butterflies, while her brother was just as handsome as can be. This had my mind off things. I was on another journey. Didn't know where I was heading, but I had to trust the man Christ Jesus.

The big day finally came; we went to church that Sunday morning. All of us who were going to be baptized were there. They had us wear name tags; it was new for me. I watched everyone smile and laugh. Then they told us to come an hour early. My family in New York couldn't make it at all; only my aunt and I were there. They had all of the new converts sitting in the front seat while another church was there too, waiting to be baptized. We all had to get up and give our testimony. Two men were before me; then I went up. I was so nervous that I sang. My aunt told me I was to testify, but I did my own thing.

When everyone was finished telling how good God was and what he had done for them, I sang. I didn't know if I sounded good or not, but that was just me. Now it was time to say goodbye to the world I once knew. As the pastor held my hands while I entered the water, he asked me if I was ready to give my life to the Lord. I told him yes. He asked me something else, and I just said yes. Then they both put me under the water. Then I came up; at this time, the whole church was singing. The ushers took me to a room to get dressed; then, I got dried off and put on my blouse.

I could not find my skirt; my aunt came into the room. I asked her if she had seen my skirt, but she didn't. She helped me look for it, but she had to go back to the baptism. I was left alone in the room while everyone got baptized and left. The usher came back to see if I had found my skirt, but nothing. She told me to wrap myself in a sheet; I told her no way; then she told me that she would call her daughter for one of her skirts.

I just sat down and waited while everyone dressed and went out for the service. I just sat down and talked to Jesus; I was just having a conversation with him. I asked him how he was doing. As you can tell, for me not too good. I lost my skirt; I didn't know if any of the sisters had taken it, but I couldn't go outside to see or hear what they were saying. I told him this thing was new to me, and I thanked him for calling me. I really didn't know what to say to Jesus; I just told him that I loved him. Then I told him that no one turned up for me today from New York, but I knew he was with me. I did most of the talking, and Jesus did most of the listening.

He didn't talk much, but I didn't give him any time at all. Not before long, the usher came into the room and gave me her daughter's skirt. I put it on and went outside to hear them singing another song. They were all finished, then my aunt came over and asked me where I was. I didn't dare answer her because I just had a talk with the Lord. I didn't want to mess that up. When I got to my aunt's house, the skirt was right there on the floor. I just smiled and went home. While I went home, I was still talking to the Lord.

I dared not let people see me doing this; I called my sister Althea and told her my experience, and she asked me how I felt. I told her, "Pretty much the same." Then I called Mother. She told me how sorry she was because she couldn't get a ride to see us, but the following week she would.

As you know, things were the same as always. I was waiting for a call from any one of the applications that I had filled out; I was really being tested now. My aunt was calling me, with fear, about a lot of things. I still had a thousand dollars left to pay my rent and bills.

She cooked, so I would go by her place for dinner; sometimes, she wanted me to come with her to her job. I was working on my book that I wanted to write for the longest but didn't have the time until now. I started it, but something always came up. I didn't want to be a bad person in the book, so I would leave out most of everything. I wanted to put the abortion aside and not bring it up ever, but it was always there to haunt me; the guilt and shame I was feeling were not good.

Chapter 21

I still didn't know what this Christian thing meant; this was the reason I went to church so often. The following Sunday, I sat down beside the same brother that got baptism with us. I introduced myself to him again. I didn't know anyone much in the church, but he just stared at me. I asked him if he was okay because his leg was in bandages. I told him to put it on the chair, but he was just looking at me. I kept wondering if I had something in my nose. I was going to ask him what was up, but I had to behave myself and act the part of a Christian. When church was over, he asked for my number. I didn't think twice; I gave it to him.

I went to work with my aunt as if it was my job; when I came home, I noticed he called me three times; I kept wondering why he called so much. I didn't call him at all until later that night. When I called him, he was at his mother's place. He had surgery on his knee. I didn't talk for too long. I told him good night. I took my shower and had something to eat. I then went and got my Bible, read a few scriptures, and prayed.

The following day, my aunt wanted to know if I was coming to work with her; but I stayed home and did what needed to be done. I did what I knew best. I woke up, said my prayer, and read a Psalm or two, then I had breakfast and went on my book. I was just into this book. I remember writing about all my brother did to me; I was so angry. I cried so hard; then I remembered my aunt in Jamaica. She hated me; she would cook and not give me anything to eat.

They would send me to the shop and buy what she needed, then cook, and wanted me to wash the dishes that they ate out of. I was so bitter and angry with everyone and that man who beat me to nothing. Then he made me kill my babies.

My heart gave way. I asked Jesus if he was real to help me get over these feelings. I didn't know what had happened, but my life was like an open book. I saw the pages of my life flashing in front of me. I could not believe it; the tears were flowing out of my eyes like a river. I was just calling on the name of Jesus. I told him to help me. I didn't know what had happened, but I felt lighter. That night, I felt at ease; my aunt called me, but I was in another world. My life was on a different roll; this man, Christ Jesus, was real, and I wanted to know all I could about him.

He took me to this place for a reason, and he wanted me for himself. I was really hungry for his Word. I knew in my heart that he could change me. That night, I was in love with the man Christ Jesus; I didn't want to talk to anyone but him.

Edward kept calling me and asking me what I was doing. I could not talk too much with him. I was busy writing my book; then he asked me if I had read my Bible. I told him yes, and also prayed. One thing I was still doing was watching soap operas.

I had put Jesus on a schedule and did my everyday thing. When Edward told me that it was not right for me to be watching things of the world, I didn't understand him at all, so he explained it more clearly to me. He told me that God was a person that should be respected at all times, not when I felt like calling upon him, but to be ready when he called upon me. I listened to him as he talked, and he asked me if I knew the scriptures. I was dumb about what he was asking. I told him to go on. As I listened to him, he knew a little about the Bible.

At night I would read the words; what I didn't understand, I would call him; his mother knew the Word more than he did. She knew where to find the scriptures, while I had to look into the contents. There was a lot I needed to learn about God.

Night after night, we would be on the phone searching the words; I was getting so hungry. I didn't know that there was actually a real story in the Bible. I thought that this book was a holy book, but man, I was wrong. It had a lot of killing and love stories too, even betrayal. It was even better than the soap opera. I didn't know that all of this was in the Bible.

I didn't read it at all; I always thought that it was a holy book and I was not worthy to read it. I knew that it had a lot of big words in it, but with the help of the Lord... He did help me a lot.

One day, I asked Edward what kind of work he did. He told me security. I asked him if they were hiring, and he said always. The following day, he asked a friend to take me to fill out applications, then he took me to the police station to get a police record check out. He told me I needed to get one for an interview if they called me. My aunt called me and asked if I wanted to come with her to Bible study. I went, but the pastor didn't want to answer most of the questions I was asking him.

I still asked because he was the man of God, but I think I was embarrassing him. I kept my mouth closed most of the time. I couldn't wait to get home for real stuff; at church, they want to keep you on the same level, but I wanted to know more about this man Christ Jesus. I fell in love with Jesus; I was so in love with him. I didn't know I could have felt like this at all. I remember just talking and singing to Jesus; he really made me feel special. I remember one night, I was talking with Edward, and he asked me if he could wait on me. I asked him for what. He told me that he really liked me and he was looking for a wife. I told him no; I had a boyfriend back in New York who was going to come home at any time. I didn't dare tell him about that dream; he wouldn't understand at all. I didn't want him to think that I was a nut. I kept it real; not my type at all; he looked really old, not like the crazy Tom. *No, no, no. Heck, no*, I thought to myself.

I tried to stay away from him at times because I didn't want him to bring up that question once more. He called almost every hour; he wanted to know what I was doing. I told him the same thing I was doing an hour ago. We talked, and then my aunt called me too; she told me about a course. It was a CNA class where I would study and get a license to work as an aide. The difference with this work was that I could work in a nursing home or hospital. She told me that I could finish my education by being a nurse.

It sounded good, but I needed a job right now. I didn't want to depend on anyone to pay my bills. I went to Jesus that night; I was just pouring out my problems to him. I told him all that was bothering me, and I wanted his help.

I didn't get an answer at all, but that night, at 12:00 a.m., while I was talking to Edward, I heard a bird tweeting. I didn't understand it at all. I went over to the window, pushed my head to the window, and told the bird that Jesus loved it and God too. I went back to lie down.

I could not believe what had happened; the bird came to my window and was just tweeting. I got so scared that I closed the window and put the pillow over my head. I said the 23 Psalm. Then I waited to see what the bird was going to do; it seemed as if it had flown away. This thing was too strange; a bird at that time of the morning.

I didn't call my aunt or Edward at all. I just called on Jesus once more. I knew he was good with these things; that was what the Bible says. The next morning was not even good at all; it seemed as if I had caught the flu. I had a temperature; I didn't feel good at all.

My aunt came over and told me that she didn't want to catch the flu, but I didn't let that bother me one bit. I didn't need to call Edward at all; he talked too much and kept asking me the same thing. I thought to myself, *He can't go to his apartment because of the stairs, so how in the world he wanted to come to mine?* I lived on the third floor, which could not help him at all.

I stayed home and let the fever take over my body. That night, I was feeling a lot of pain; I was so weak; how I missed my mother. I knew she would have been here with the flu or no flu.

I understand that my aunt didn't want to get sick. That night, I just lay in bed. I got up to use the bathroom. I remember very well when I went back to bed, I was coughing up mucus; then I called on Jesus to help me. I could not believe my eyes: a small man came around my bed at this time. I could not move or talk; I tried to call on Jesus, but my mouth was closed. I felt like I was paralyzed. As I watched this little demon come beside me, I was so afraid. What happened next was unbelievable. I saw two angels standing at my bedroom door; they asked the little man what he was doing. He could not answer them, so they were rebuking him in the name of Jesus. I tell you the truth, I was more afraid of the angels than the devil.

They were the most beautiful things I'd ever seen. I didn't know what had happened to that demon, but I closed my eyes and was just calling on Jesus to help me. I felt as if I was being turned all over by the angels. I called out to Jesus for him to help me. I told him that I was afraid of all of this. I could not understand what they were saying and tell you what they were doing. I closed my eyes. I didn't want to see them at all. I wanted my mother; I was afraid to call anyone. When the room got quiet, I called my aunt.

She asked me what I had eaten that night; she was laughing at me; she let me feel as if I was mad. Then she said that the flu had gone to my head. I didn't say anything else because she was just making fun of me. I was so afraid; I prayed and went to bed. The next day, Edward called to see how I was feeling. I told him that I was fine. The flu was gone, and I felt really great; he then told me it was not the flu I had. I just told him that could be true. I didn't dare tell him what had happened because I didn't want anyone else to laugh at me.

He wanted to know if he could come over to the house for Bible study; I told him that I would tell my aunt as well. He didn't have a problem with that. I didn't know him that well. It was almost two months now, and I have been seeing all these demons and angel things. This was too much for me if I told anyone about what I'd experienced. They might put me in the loony bin. I kept my mouth shut. Edward was coming the following evening, so I told him what time my aunt came from work, but he came early. I don't know why.

I was still cooking when he came; I was frying chicken. When I opened the door, he came in and kissed me on the forehead. Just then, the dream I had nine months ago flashed in front of me; I remembered having that dream about my ex-boyfriend kissing me while I was frying chicken. I felt as if I had an out-of-body experience. I told him I would be back; I went into the bathroom and looked up. I told God that he must be kidding me, not this man. I told him that he was too old and he was not my type; I was making all kinds of compromises with God about him. I told him I would do anything that he wanted but to please not let him be the one. Then the bell rang; it was my aunt. I said, "Thank you, God." I told Edward it was my aunt. He asked me if I was okay. I shook my head.

When she came in, I hugged her, then he came over to her and did the same thing. They were both talking while I was getting dinner finished. We ate, and then he asked to wash the dishes. My aunt looked at me; I still didn't want to go there; my heart was set on that man back in New York. The Bible study went well; then, my aunt went home. I thought she would have waited for him to leave, but she told me she had work in the morning, unlike me. That night, he didn't go home; we were all in the Word.

I was just thinking of all the drama that took place in this apartment that night. I didn't want to ask him what time he was going home; I knew he should have known better. He was at the apartment at 2:00 a.m. when I asked him to leave; he got so mad. I shook my head; I knew something was up with this man. I was a little bit afraid of him. I didn't know what else to do. I just took it easy with him; I felt like I was with Tom all over again.

On the second day, he was still at the apartment; I told him that he needed to leave because it didn't look good at all. He just looked at me as if I was crazy. Then I got a call from the agency. They wanted me to come in for an interview. I called my aunt and told her what had happened; I didn't let her know that Edward was still at the apartment; I didn't know how to tell him to leave. He stayed in the living room; I went and did the interview. I thanked God I got the job; it was a lived-in job. I knew I had to tell him to leave, which I did again, but it seemed as if he didn't have anywhere to go. I went to the job, then he called me and told me that he didn't want to leave me in Hartford like that. It wasn't safe at all. I didn't believe him; I just wanted him to leave.

I had to take care of a patient with Alzheimer's; this was the most difficult case ever. One minute the patient thought he could not walk, and sometimes he would just get up and run. I had to run him down; one night, I put him to bed. It seemed as if God had woken me up; the patient was in the hallway running all over the place. I caught him and told him it was time for bed; then he realized that he could not walk, and he almost fell to the ground. I wasn't trained for all of this. I had to put my whole strength into it. I got him back to bed.

I stayed with him all night, and the following day, I gave him a shower. I cried; it was too much for me. I called the agency and told them about the situation that took place. Then they sent a nurse to come and check his medication. I then called his daughter, and she stopped by. Then she told me that he never had these problems before. I don't know if she wanted to believe me or not. When the nurse came by, she noticed that his medication was not right. She told me the patient was being overmedicated, and when the medication wore off, he got up and started to walk. I told her that they told me that he could not walk, then he started to run. She laughed and said, "That is Alzheimer's for you. One minute they remember, and the next, they forget." I knew that this job was not easy. I had to watch him every second.

I was getting drained out most of the time, I would call Edward, but he was having fun at my house. He claimed that he was cleaning the place. I didn't let that bother me at all because I was at work. I would get home on Friday evening and leave Monday morning.

I didn't get to go to church; I had to wash my clothes on Saturday and Sunday, getting things ready for the rest of the week. My aunt would call me and ask if I was coming to church, but I would tell her that I had to do a lot of things.

Edward would clean the apartment when I came home. That night, he asked if I would marry him. I told him that I was still waiting for my boyfriend, and he then told me okay. This man would not leave for anything; when I asked him to do so, he got mad. I didn't want another Tom situation on me. I knew that God would move him. I went to church that Sunday morning, and all went well. Then my aunt asked me if I was coming that evening. I told her that I had to get things ready for work the next day. Then he told me I should go. I didn't know what he had up his sleeves.

That Sunday evening, the pastor told his congregation that he had a member who wanted to make an announcement. I just sat down, watching them. Then I saw Edward stand up. They told us to come to the altar. I didn't know what to say. I saw Edward go on his knees in front of the church. He was asking my hands in marriage. I almost fell out; I had told him that I was waiting on my boyfriend in New York!

As I stood in the church in front of all these people looking at me, the pastor asked me what my answer was. I was so nervous; I said yes, and my heart dropped. Then my aunt stood up and praised the Lord. He got up and kissed me on the lips; if only the ground could have opened up and taken me in, but I didn't want to go to hell. The whole church was happy; they all came over and congratulated me.

I just smiled, but deep down, I was just losing my mind. I didn't know how to tell my mother this news at all; I still didn't know what had just happened. How in the world could I say yes to a man I didn't know to even say yes to?

I told my aunt that I was afraid to tell my mom, but I had the courage and did it. She was there laughing and telling me that she was happy; I finally found someone. My aunt told me she had told my mother long before I knew because he had asked her first. I didn't know if I was waiting on someone who didn't love me, but I knew that I didn't love Edward at all. I didn't feel that love.

It might seem crazy, but I wasn't in love with him or loved him at all. I didn't tell anyone but God; I told him that I know that I always pick crazy guys; now, this man can't take no for an answer. He put me into a spot; I told him yes in front of the church people. I know that the dreams that I had were coming true. I started to think, *What in the world is going on with me?* First, I had a dream about dogs running me down. Then another one where I saw myself moving to the country, which came true.

In the same dream, I saw my ex-boyfriend at my apartment while I was frying chicken; he kissed me on my forehead. Then the same thing Edward did while I was frying chicken. This was too much for me. Then I saw angels and a demon. I didn't know if I was making the right choice at all.

I knew that he was baptized, and he knew the Lord more than I did. I remember telling Jesus I loved God but had to keep my word. I said yes in God's house.

The best part of our friendship; I wasn't home most of the time due to the fact of work. I told him no sex until marriage, and he agreed. Then he told me why he wanted to marry me, he told me that my place was so clean and I didn't have any kids. I wanted to know what he meant by that. He said he didn't want to deal with any baby's father drama. I asked him about his family and if he had any children. He told me he had one daughter, and she was in Jamaica with her mother; he told me that he was looking for a decent woman for her; he knew that I would take care of her.

I then asked him how old she was; this child was almost a lady; then I asked him his age. The man was thirteen years older than I was. I knew that I didn't look that old; why in the world all these old men were after me? He told me all about his life story, how he was married twice to the same lady. I asked him why, but he said it was not meant to be. He told me how his father treated him. He had a lot of issues, and I knew that I could not help him at all; I looked up and asked God to please help me.

One thing I can say; he didn't pressure me at all for sex. That weekend I did what I knew best. Pray and ask God to help me.

Chapter 22

The following week, I went to work, and they told me that the case was ended. The family had put the man in a nursing home where he could get proper treatment. I was happy about that; the next case I got was way different; this man was a dirty little man, and he wanted sex. I didn't waste any time; I called my agency and reported him, and went home that weekend.

I was home for a while, and they had to wait for another case. Now I was home with this man; it seemed as if I was getting to know him even more. One day, his mother called me and told me that she had heard the good news; this time, I was on trial. She asked me if I knew that he had been married twice; I told her yes, then she asked me if he had told me that he had a daughter. I told her that she was in Jamaica with her mother, and she wanted to know all that he told me; then she told me that her son was very sick and he didn't need anyone to hurt him. I guess he told her my age; I didn't care at all. He was the one who wanted a wife; I didn't know what I was getting into.

I was afraid of telling him about my past, so I kept it that way. I hung up the phone and called my friend Elaine. I told her that I was getting married; she asked me if I was crazy. Then she asked me what I knew about this guy; I really didn't know anything at all, only what he told me. She left me thinking; when I hung up on her, I called my sisters and told them; they were even more excited than I was. I called my cousin in the Bronx; she knew everything about baby shower parties, etc. I didn't want to think about what Elaine had said, but I was now suspicious of him.

One day, I went into my closet to clean it out; I took out my leather jacket, only to find a woman's number in it. It was the area code for Hartford. I took it to him and asked him who it was; he looked at me and told me it was his ex-girlfriend. He told me that he saw her in the store the other day; I just walked away. I knew that I could not handle this right now. Then he told me that he was sorry, he had to say goodbye. I didn't care at all because I wasn't in love with him.

The following day, I got a call once more for an interview; I asked my coordinator why I should do another interview. She didn't say anything at all; when I went there, I was the youngest one in the room; they asked me a lot of questions. They told me I would have to do many things, like hook the lady up to her feeding tube and go to her appointments. Then I would do housework and a lot more things; the pay was still the same. This lady looked like she had money because her home was very big. She told me that she had three sons, and her husband was her fourth one. She told me all about her neighbors and the mailman; they told me they would call me and let me know if I got the job.

When I got home, Edward told me that his sister wanted to meet me. I told him whatever. I just wanted to know if I got this job; I needed to pay my bill. One day, his mother called him and told him his landlord wanted to know if he was coming back or not. She wanted her money for his rent; I told him to bring his things to the apartment. He wanted me to follow him; man, it was a lot of stairs, and he was staying on the third floor. I was living on the third floor myself, but this seemed far up, more like the attic.

When I went to help him, the lady was cursing for her money. Then I saw what he brought out; I thought he had more things. He had only some clothes, which I think he could do better. I asked him where the rest of his things were, and he told me at his mother's. I told him to let it stay there until we got a bigger apartment. He wanted his daughter to come right away; I told him to wait until we had gotten a two-bedroom place. I remember sleeping on the couch when I got here; that was no fun. The next thing I did was take him to the store; he had a little bit of clothes. I didn't want to be all dressed up, and he didn't. I was getting into this married thing too much. I would call my cousin and talk about the wedding. She asked me if I knew what kind of wedding. I told her of course. I was just going on and on, but Edward only wanted a few people there. I told him that this was my first wedding, and if I didn't get what I wanted, I was not going to get married after all; I was not going to do it again. He was upset. I still didn't care at all.

This was the first wedding for our family, and now this guy wanted to ruin it for me. I remember telling Jesus how I felt, that this man was robbing me of my special day; I didn't say much. I felt like a spoiled kid. I didn't talk much to Edward; I went to Jesus.

It seemed as if anything I wanted was done. One day, he came to me and told me how sorry he was; because he was married already, he didn't want to spend all that money when he could do something else. I listened to him; then he told me whatever I wanted. I ran and kissed him; then I was on the phone with my cousin again. She got the okay, and now, the wedding was on. I could not believe my ears; all of my family wanted to take part. I didn't mind at all; my brother had a son; he was too small to be the ring bearer. So I ask Edward about his niece's son. I knew my niece and the little girl that my aunt took care of could be the flower girls.

I was so happy. *If only my dad were here...* I knew that he would be so proud. I was so happy, for once in my life. I was finally getting married. I think that it was every girl's dream. As the week went by, I was called for the work, the one I did the interview with. It seemed as if the lady liked me; her husband and I could not see eye to eye. There was something about him; that seemed off. I went to work and did what I was told; I prayed most of the time.

The house was big and spooky; the lady had her own room, while her husband had his. My room was next to her; there were two beds in the room. The other lady who did the weekend job had the next bed. I did my part for her.

Whenever she wanted anything, I would hear a voice telling me to check on her. She opened her eyes and told me that I was like an angel. She said that she wanted to call me, but she was too weak to do so. "I open my eyes, and there you are," she said.

I didn't dare tell her that. I heard a voice telling me to check on her. I did what I was told; this went on for a while. I would listen to the voice of God, and he would tell me what to say or sometimes not to talk at all. I would just smile and walk away. One day, the nurse came over to show me how to give her the feeding tube. She told me that I had to clean the area where she was going to get the food really well, then she showed me how to get the machine ready to pump the liquid into the machine and then into her stomach. I had to make sure that all of the air was out of the tube, or it would not work. I didn't know too much, but I asked God to help me, and he did. She only got it at night so that she could move around during the day. I didn't drive at all, so her husband took us to the store and to the doctor's office.

One day while getting her dressed after her bath, the feeding tube came out; she told me to call her husband. When he came into the room, he panicked because the tube had fallen out. While I was in the office with her, she called me over to her and fixed the neck of my blouse. She told me that it was crooked; I just smiled and told her thanks. Meanwhile, her husband and everyone else were looking at me, they both went in, and I waited for them. When they came out, she told me to come. I did what I was told; I didn't ask her what the doctor said at all.

It wasn't my place too; that night, while I was fixing her feeding tube in, she wanted to know about my wedding. She asked me if he was a good man. I told her I think so; she laughed. Then she told me all about her sons. She said that each of them was so different.

She said the oldest son had married an old woman, who he thought she didn't like at all, so he stayed away. She said she loved him so much and she knew that he would be a wonderful father, but she couldn't have children. The other one married a Chinese lady who had a son. Now her baby called her and told her his wife was a Philippine. I just looked at her and smiled. She was a rich white woman, and she could not control her boys. She told me it was sad; all these years in school, and now she was a housewife. I asked her if she had any siblings, and she told me only a brother.

He didn't come around much, she said, but they were not on talking terms. I just listened to her; she told me she was sick and tired of being sick. She just wanted to die; I asked her if she had given her life to Jesus. She told me she went to a Catholic church, if that counted. I told her I didn't know much about that religion, but I am a Christian. I told her what I believed in and how he made me feel. While I was talking with LoLo, her husband came into the room.

I got up and walked away when he came out of the room. I went back into the room and put her back on her feeding tube; she told me to open the window a little bit. I gave her the medication and told her to call me if she needed anything else. I was so tired that I went to bed at about 2:00 a.m. I heard God telling me to wake up and check on her. I told him I was too tired right now. I needed some sleep; if only I had listened to him. The next morning at 6:00 a.m., I checked on her, and she was up. She told me to close the window. She was cold all night, she said that she tried to call me, but I didn't hear her at all. I felt so bad because I was told she needed help, and I ignored the Lord.

I knew that it was he who told me to wake up. I never questioned him anymore. When he told me to jump, I did just that. I stayed with this lady for a while. When I got home, Edward had cleaned up the place and was just waiting for me. He had made me a nice bath with flowers in the tube. He told me just to enjoy myself; he saw me naked for the first time. I was tempted to have sex with him. Then, I remembered that we weren't married yet. We did make out, but I told him that I loved the Lord and we were going to get married after all. So we waited.

I really wanted to have sex, but this Christian thing, God was always watching you. I soaked for a while, and then I washed off. I went into the room just to catch him with a needle in his stomach. I almost passed out; I said, "No, how dare you take drugs in my house? Who the heck are you? I almost had sex with you; get out!" I was at the top of my voice; then he told me just to listen to him. I told him that I didn't want to hear anything that he had to say. He told me that he had sugar; I asked what in the world sugar had to do with this. He then explained that he was diabetic. I still looked at him. I didn't know what he was talking about. I was in that field, so you would think that I knew something about sugar. I called his mother and asked her about him; she told me yes, that was his sickness. Then she asked me once more about him being married twice. I told her I knew about that.

She told me that he was her baby, and she didn't want anything happening to him again; his daughter didn't need anyone to hurt her. I just gave him the phone and went into the living room. Edward then came to where I was; we started to talk. I told him to come clean with me; if there was anything else I needed to know about him before I said, "I do." He told me no; then I thought he needed to know about my past; after all, I was not a saint.

I told him about what I'd been through with Tom and the abortions. I thought that I had gotten over it, but I was still hurting inside. I was still in a lot of pain; he told me that I should ask God to forgive me and let it go. I tried, but I kept picking it back up again. My past wasn't good at all; I had a lot of healing to do, and so did he. That night, we both promised each other to come straight and clean.

The weekend went well; we overcame a lot of our issues. Now we could move to the next step. There was a lot I needed to know about him, and there was a lot he needed to know about me. I wasn't perfect, but I didn't need another Tom.

The following week at work was the hardest one; I finally met LoLo's second son; he came with his wife and the baby. At this time, my lady was getting worse each day. She would vomit a lot; I watched her as she disappeared in front of my eyes.

I asked God what was my purpose for being there. I felt so sorry for the family; I didn't know what to tell her, but one day she asked me if I thought that God would heal her. I told her yes; then I asked her if she wanted to be healed. She told me no; this puzzled me a lot. I wanted to know, so I asked her why. She told me if she was healed, then she would have gone back to being evil once more. I listen as she pours her heart out. She told me why she was not talking with her brother. She said that she was the eldest child of their parents; when they passed away, she sold their house and got a million dollars for it.

She didn't give her brother any, and that was the reason why they were not talking to each other. She told me that she tried to reach out to him, but she was full of too much pride. I told her I thought that she should call him and make it right with him. She asked me if I thought that he would forgive her. I told her as it was, you would only know if you tried. She smiled; then I asked her if she wanted to give her heart to the Lord. She said yes. As I told her the Sinner's Prayer, and she repeated it, then she accepted Jesus Christ into her life; her husband was upset with me, and he told me that his wife was not a sinner.

She was a good woman, and he was so upset. I asked him if he wanted to give his heart to the Lord too, and he told me that he was going to hell, and that was final. I didn't dare bother him. Whatever he believed, I could not change his mind.

The next day, the delivery man came with her food, and he asked me who I was. I told him the help and why. He told me that he came one day and saw a Philippine lady and thought she was the helper, but she was the daughter-in-law, so he wanted to make sure he didn't have it wrong this time. I just smiled and told him she did well with her boys.

Not before long, her brother came by with his wife. She told me she took my advice and called her brother. She was so happy, the look on her face was so beautiful, she didn't look like death anymore. She was just smiling as I introduced myself to him and his wife. I took him upstate to see his sister. They hugged each other and cried. I walked away and left them. Her husband was so mad at me, but I didn't care at all. He said that he wanted to go to hell. I knew LoLo was not going with him. That cancer thought that it got a life, but it lost.

While I was in the kitchen, her sister-in-law approached me, hugged me, and thanked me. I told her that I was doing God's work. She told me that she and her husband were also Christians. I just said, "Praise the Lord!" I knew that my work here was done.

The house felt lighter than anything; I was going home the following day, so I had gotten the place ready for the next worker.

LoLo called me into her room to talk with me. She told me she was ready to go; she didn't want to stay here on Earth anymore. I told her that it was not my job to decide, but I would pray and ask the Father to help her. She was smiling and was just happy.

When the young lady came to release me, I told her what was taking place. While I went to call my cab, the young lady told me not to. Her son was going to take me home; I went upstairs and kissed her for the last time and told her I'd see what I could do. She smiled, and we parted; I went into LoLo's car while her son took me home. He told me he didn't know what kind of friendship I had with his mother, but it had to be a good one. She didn't let anyone drive her car at all. She is a perfectionist; she was hard to deal with. "I don't know how you did it, but you did. She likes you a lot." I told him that I did not do anything, but it was the Lord who got through to his mom. He told me that he was not a good son to her at all; he didn't listen to her at all. He did what he had to do, and it hurt her so much.

Chapter 23

I told him that she told me about his wife. I told him that she loved her, the only reason why LoLo didn't want him to marry her was that she could not give him children, and she knew in her heart that he would have been a loving father. That young man stopped the car and cried; everyone needed healing in that house. When he took me home, he told me thanks and drove off. I was happy for them; they didn't talk much, but they needed to tell each other how they felt.

When I went into my apartment, Edward was not home, so I took a shower and unwound. I tried to relax, but I just could not. I remembered what LoLo asked me to do, so I knelt and prayed for her soul. I asked God to watch over her for me, and I told him that she was ready to see him. I prayed for her family as well and mine too. I prayed for everyone, actually, even my enemies.

I called my aunt to see if she was okay, and that was when she told me she was filled. I asked her, "With what?" Then she explained that she was filled with the Holy Ghost. I felt numb; I always wanted to be filled with the spirit of God. I was a little bit jealous about that. I thought that I was not good enough for God to use me. This was one of the teachings I got from church. I knew I didn't attend church regularly. I had to work, and I knew that God understood; the only things that came out of my mouth were groaning and tears. I cried a lot. One of the things that hurt me most was to forgive people who hurt me and walk away. It killed everything that was in me.

Revenge was sweet, but it came with a price. When Edward came home, he greeted me with a kiss. I told him the good news about my aunt. He told me that she must have felt good; I guessed so. He told me to invite her over, for her to tell me how it felt like to be filled.

I knew I didn't need to call her for that, but I did anyway. She told me she could not come because she was going too fast that day. I told her that we could fast together. Then she told me that she was going to fast breakfast, lunch, and break it at dinner time. She didn't want to fast at home because of her husband; he was not saved at all. The music that he listened to would break her spirit. I agreed to that.

When my aunt came over, she looked so proud. She came into the apartment and was singing; I just stood there. I asked her how she felt; she was awesome. Then she started to pray; she read a Bible scripture. I was eager to know what took place because, at church, I always saw people falling all over the place. Some ran, and some skipped; some danced while others spoke with words. I didn't understand.

I told her that when I read 1 Corinthians chapter 14, it told me something else. She told me that when you love the Lord, he gives you what your heart desires. She let me think I didn't love Jesus, so I did the next stupid thing. I started to pray, and in my mind, I was putting back the Lord on the cross. I told him I would take his place so that he would not feel so much pain. I did the wrong thing.

I was there chanting and putting Jesus back on the cross. I did this in the bathroom. I didn't know what had happened; I only felt my body like a rag doll tossing back and forth. I fell inside the tube; I almost hit my head on the wall. Then I heard a voice ask me what I was doing. Then it said, "How dare you put my son back on the cross? You are full already; you don't need to prove anything to anyone at all. God is who you need to love, not man." I got up from the tube and shook myself up. When I went into the living room, Edward and my aunt were on their faces praying; then I sat on the couch. I was in a lot of pain because I really hit my body hard.

Whoever threw me into the tube, it was no joke. Then I started to hear more voices telling me that I was hungry. I smelled things that were not there. I was very hungry, and my stomach was growing; I walked away. The voice got louder and louder; my aunt asked me if I was hungry.

It was quite obvious; she started to laugh, then she told me, "I have five more hours to go; I can not handle this hungry feeling." I was hearing all kinds of voices in my head. Some of them were hostile; they cursed and told me what to do, but I had to keep praying and ask God to help me go through this fasting. I fell asleep; then I was awoken by my aunt's food. That thing woke me up; I wanted food very badly; she and Edward kept looking at me, then she started to laugh. This Christian thing was hard. First, I was thrown all over the bathroom; then, I put Jesus back on the cross.

The hungry thing I knew little about. I didn't understand what had happened to me with that. My sister Marlene and my aunt back home taught me a lot about that. Man, the devil was on my back; I guessed I needed to read the Bible some more and prove myself. There was a lot I needed to know, and what I thought I knew, I knew not. When I ate the food, it felt like heaven.

I didn't tell them how I felt about the whole fasting thing, but you have to be really strong to do that. If you are not strong, you could end up hurting yourself and others. To think that Jesus did it for forty days, I bow down to him. I heard all kinds of temptations.

That night, I went to bed. I dreamt about LoLo. She came to me and asked me if I could follow her to heaven's gate. When we went there, it was really a big gray gate; the place was gray all around. She stood there and told me goodbye. I told her to tell Jesus I loved him and would see him soon. As I watched her walk in, no one was there to see her in. I could not enter at all. She just disappeared out of my sight. I then walked away. I jumped up out of my sleep, and then I told Edward what had happened.

I got up, took a drink of water, and went back to sleep. The next day at church, we did the usual thing. Edward got filled too; he was on cloud nine. I only groaned and cried. Then three of our church members came over to our apartment, and one of them stayed outside for a while before he came in. They were all speaking with tongues and praying and rebuking spirits. I didn't understand what was going on in this place. I just sat down and watched them. Then one of the brothers asked me for some olive oil, which I gave him. He anointed my head and feet; then he told the sister to anoint my stomach. I didn't want the oil to catch on my couch, but I kept quiet.

These people knew everything about this God thing; I was young and still didn't understand much, so they started to explain some things to me. I was taking this thing too lightly about God; I didn't know I was fighting spiritual warfare. All this time, I thought I was getting mad; it was only the enemy trying to let me think that way. They told me the apartment was full of evil spirits and that the devil wanted to hurt me. I told them about the experience I had with the demon and angels. One of the brothers got up and was smiling; then I heard praise from the Lord.

"She is covered." I still didn't understand them at all; it all seemed crazy like I was in one of those horror movies. When they prayed out of the house, it felt lighter for real. Then I asked Edward if he knew anything about this; he said yes. This was the reason why he came to Christianity and not other religions. He told me that Jesus was powerful. I asked him why it took him so long to find the Lord. He said that his brothers were Muslims. I asked him why he didn't stay with his god. He told me the love he found in Christ was different from the others. I acted as if I understood him; then I asked him if the demons saw me naked, and he just smiled. He always took me to scripture that told me how a woman should act towards her husband. Most of them I didn't like, but it was the Word of God, and I should be obedient to God's Word.

It was about 5:30 a.m. when I got a call from the young lady at work; she told me that LoLo had passed. She didn't want me to come to work, and then I had to get back home. Not before long, the office called me with the news. I didn't cry at all, but I felt sad. I knew she wanted this. I only hoped that her family was taking it well. I told Edward that I was not going to work once more because my patent had died; I then told him that I should go back to school and become an aide, then a nurse, wherever the good Lord led me.

He didn't say anything at all; I called my aunt later that day and told her that my lady had passed away. She asked me what was next. I told her that I was tired of people dying. She asked me if I thought that I was ready for school. I told her yes. I had too much on my plate; I was planning a wedding, and now I wanted to go back to school.

I got a call from my co-worker about LoLo's funeral; she told me what time and where it was kept. I told Edward about the funeral, and he told me I was not going. I really thought that he was joking.

He created a scene. I could not believe this man of God was acting this way. He told me if I went, what he would do; that night, I cried because I was seeing Tom once more. I was a little bit afraid. Then I just stayed home. One thing I gave thanks for was that her husband sent me a check for one hundred and fifty dollars. I called him and thanked him; he sounded sad. I wished him all the best. Then we said goodbye. I called the agency and asked them if I could change my schedule for work; I wanted a weekend only. That was not a problem. I went to Capital Community College and got registered for class; the courses didn't take long.

I had to go through a lot with Edward's mom; she told him that he went and picked up a young girl to help while his daughter back home needed money. I felt really bad to hear this. He told me that his family didn't like me at all. I was too young for him, and they wanted him to marry his daughter's mother. I told him that he should let his mother know that I was working on the weekend too. I was not living after her son's paycheck, and moreover, it was not a lot of money he was making. She wanted him to send for his daughter, but there was no room for her at this time.

This was always a burden for me because he thought I didn't want his child to be here with him. He would always bring up my past about the abortion, which made me sad. I kept thinking to myself, *This is too much right now.* I had to study really hard to pass these classes, and then I had to go to work. This was no fun at all; the work that I was getting was the worst. I went into homes that were dirty, some were clean, but the people were nice, and some were not.

One of the homes I went to had a dog; that dog was beautiful but a devil himself. The first day I saw him, he came over and smelled my foot, and then he vomited in front of me. She smiled and told me it was the first time she saw him doing that. I had to clean it up.

Then she told me to take him for a walk; when I took him outside, the dog got loose. He was running all over the place; I couldn't catch him. Then the lady came out and saw him on the street. She almost had a heart attack. She told me to please get him; I was on the street. I was running him down, but I still couldn't catch him. I stopped in the middle of the street, looked up, and asked God to help me.

I don't know where this man came from, but he came and got the dog. I told him many thanks; then I told God, "Thank you for sending this man out of nowhere!" I looked around once more, and the man was gone. I went inside and locked that gate; then she told me to make supper for her.

I didn't like this place at all. She wanted me to go into her attic to get her dolls. I told her I was not allowed to do so, but she insisted that I should. She told me if I didn't go and get her doll, she would get it herself. I should have let her get it, but I went and got her doll. I couldn't wait to leave this place; it was getting to me. I felt heavy most of the time; I had my Bible open in the room all the time; she went into the room and saw it; she wanted me to get rid of it. I read it more; I didn't have time to study at all; she had me busy, but with that place, I didn't leave my Bible.

I was rebuking everything in that house, even the toaster. This wasn't good at all; that Sunday evening, when the lady came to relieve me, I told her what had happened; she looked at me differently. She could not understand; I kept thinking about what the church people had told me; this was not the time to play church. There was good and evil in this world.

Edward was at the house. He told me that his sister was coming over to meet me. I was too tired, but they came anyway. He introduced me to his sister and niece; they heard so much about me. His sister was a nurse, and his niece was studying to become a social worker. They told me I had a clean place and asked what I had seen in her brother. I told her that I had a dream about him. She looked at her niece and then at Edward. I knew they might think I was crazy; at this point, who cared?

The following day, she called me when Edward was at work. She told me not to tell him that she had called. She told me that she didn't think that it was a good idea for him to send for his daughter. The child was in a good school and knew her brother passed. It was best that we let her stay with her mother. Basically, what she was saying was if Edward and I didn't make it, she didn't want that responsibility. I told her that it was not my choice to make;

it was his. She didn't say anything else. When she hung up, I kept thinking about what kind of person would want to keep their child away from their parents. I didn't tell him at all.

As the holiday approached, I went to Hamden with Edward. I took my aunt with me; his brother had kept Thanksgiving dinner. I met most of his family; I met one of his brothers from Florida. He seemed very nice, and the other one was bougie. His wife acted as if she was rich, they showed us around the place, and she told us that the school system was great.

When he sent for his daughter back home, she loved this place. Edward liked the idea; I didn't say a word. The place was really nice, and it was close to my family in New York. I had no problem with that. The only thing that was a problem was transportation. My aunt didn't say anything at all.

We ate, talked, laughed, and had fun. His other sister didn't talk much. I just stayed away and kept my distance. When we got back to Hartford, we dropped my aunt off. Then we got dropped off too. He told me that his brother liked me a lot; he wanted to know when he was going to meet my family. I told him soon; Edward was excited about the place and told me that he was going to move to Hamden; I didn't care at all. I had gotten my certificate for a CNA, which means certified nursing assistant. We helped the nurses, so I could work in the nursing home or hospital. I asked him if he wanted to get his certificate in plumbing because he was good at it; he told me no.

I tried everything I knew how with this man; I saw all of the signs to run, but I stayed because he loved the Lord. As we approached the Christmas holiday, we went to New York with his family. Then, we stopped by my mother's place. I was so happy to see my family. When they saw Edward, they didn't say much. I know them so well. Mother just looked at him and then looked at me.

I went with his family, not that I wanted to, but I wanted to know what they were like. I called my mother when I was going back home. She told me I needed to come to New York and look for my dress. Now this was fun.

This was the worst experience I've ever had; it was more my mother's dress, not mine. When I tried on anything I liked, she would tell me no. My sisters were the bridesmaids. They were the ones that picked out their dresses. They wanted to look good; I was really getting tired of this; everything that I liked or loved, Mother would tell me no. I guess I didn't have any taste; then I finally put on the one Mother picked; all eyes were on me. Then she said that was the one.

I looked at the price, but it was too much for me, it was only a few hours I had to wear the dress. *Why in the world do I need to spend so much on it?* I had to keep quiet and just smile. *I guess Mother knows best.* After all, it was her day as well as mine.

I was back and forth to New York with this wedding dress, the girls had theirs, and they were okay. This thing was causing me too much. Edward had gotten a new job, so he was happy too; it paid a little more than the other one. It was so funny; when he used to get his small check from the security job, he would give me the check to pay all the bills. Then he would talk about how he was a good man.

He loved praise from people; I just listened to him. He would tell them that I got all his paycheck, and he loved to give it to me because he got it back in the house. I had to do the finance and see to it that all the bills got paid. Sometimes, his mother would call him and ask him for money for his daughter. She told him he was taking care of his young girlfriend; this would really hurt me a lot.

I was working too; I tried to keep my distance from them. Edward was only working two hundred dollars, if so much sometimes. I was just going on with the flow; I did what needed to be done. It was funny when he got his new paycheck; things changed. He gave me the same amount that he got off the old check; now it was half and half. We both had to put the same amount to pay the bills. The time was getting close to the wedding, and my family put a lot into it. They were happy for me; my sister Althea and my mother paid for my wedding cake. Karen paid for my limo, while Edson told me he had the photographer.

My cousin Tina did all of the flower arrangements and favors; everything was on the right track; the only thing Edward and I had to do was pay for the catering service. We went to the place and paid down some of the money; he told me about a photographer as well. The price was not bad at all, so I called my brother and told him.

The only thing I had to do was get our house in order because he wanted to move so badly to get his daughter. The lease for the apartment was almost up. Edward insisted that we move to Hamden before the wedding; for some reason, he didn't like Hartford; I didn't care at all. I didn't know Connecticut that well, so this was the best time to move to Hamden.

His sister gave him one of the cars that she had, so he didn't have a problem getting back and forth to work. I, on the other hand, had to make all the plans on how to budget what was coming in. When I did all of the financial budgets, we were way over. I called my brother and told him if I could have my wedding present early; he didn't have a problem with it at all. He even came down and helped us move to Hamden with the boys. They loved the place a lot, it was too much money, but Edward wanted to move to a decent place for his daughter. It was a gated community; the only thing I liked about it was that the place was close to New York.

We were moved and were getting settled in, but he still insisted that we send for his daughter. I told him that he had to wait until she was out of school, but who was I kidding? He wanted her now, and that was final. I just wanted to know the place so that I could do what I had to do. His brother took us to the supermarket with his wife. She was showing me the place. She went inside with me to the supermarket while I was picking up my things. She would tell me what to buy and what not to. I told her I only buy what I like, and she smiled and walked away.

When we got home, I told him to take me around the place so that I could fill out an application for work. I went to a nursing home and agency. Now it was time for me to wait and see. He would go to work in the morning while I waited for my calls. Still nothing.

One day, I got a call from one of the agencies; I took a cab to the workplace; I didn't know anything or anyone. I had to pray and ask God to help me. They gave me all the dirty work and the heavy patients to take care of. When I left the job, my body felt like a truck had just run over me. I was in a lot of pain, but I had to do what I had to. This went on for a month or two; they would call me in the middle of the night, saying that they had a callout. They gave me the address, and that was it; working with the agency was no fun; I would go from place to place. Some of the nursing homes were far, but I had to do what I had to do.

We were back and forth when Edward was off from work; we would go to the place to talk with our consultant for the wedding. Where we were getting married was in a garden setting, it had a gazebo there. We chose to get married there because it would be too much driving for our guests. The one thing this place didn't have in the garden was a walkway to walk on. This really bothered me a lot, but I had to work with what budget I had. We made our final arrangement, and the only thing left to pay for was the photograph, which I had used the money for our new apartment. Edward had to come up with a thousand changes for the rest of the guests who hadn't replied as yet.

Edward called me one day from his job and told me that they had just let him go; they were cutting staff, and since he had the least seniority, they had to let him go. This was getting to be too much for me. With the money he had to pay for the rest of the places, he went and got his daughter's ticket with the help of his mother. I knew that I was in a lot of problems now. He was only thinking of what he wanted, and he didn't care at all. I was only getting calls here and there; it wasn't enough. We didn't even have a bed for his daughter as yet. I asked him if he could please get some help. He told me that there was nothing he could do at this point. I was going crazy, everyone was calling for their money, and I was panicking all the way.

I overheard Edward inviting more people to the wedding, and he knew that we didn't have any money to pay for them. I could not ask my family at all because they were doing a lot at this time. I knew that it was the bride's family who was responsible for the wedding, but my dad was dead. He still didn't care at all. He was Mr. Big Shot, and I was having a panic attack. The place where we were getting married, they, too, were calling us for the final payment. I didn't have it to give them.

I finally called my mother and told her; she told me to come to New York and get it borrowed from a friend. I felt so embarrassed to know that I was getting married and could not pay for it. If only he didn't lose his job. He didn't want to ask for help at all; what a way to start our life together.

I had only gotten a thousand dollars; I still needed a thousand more. When I came back to Hamden, I paid what I had; at this time, I wanted to just walk away, but I had to stand my ground. I would get one and two calls for work; it wasn't enough. I was so stressed out; I had lost a lot of weight; when I went to try on my dress, it, too, had to be adjusted.

This man was killing me; one evening, I heard him talking to his friend; he was just showing off; and was inviting more people. I told him that he could not do that, but he just fanned me off as if I was not important. I lost it; I went into his face and told him to stop acting as if he had money. He looked at me and told me that I wanted a big wedding. I should pay for it. I told him that he was a piece of crap, and that was when he hit me so hard. I was too upset to cry. I fought that man like a man; he didn't think I would hit him back. After all, I was the good Christian girl he wanted me to be. I had to put all my fears aside and let him know I was not afraid of him.

Chapter 24

I knew he was a big man, and I was this little woman, but I told him the next time he put his hands on me, he would live in a light bulb. When we were finished fighting, my sister Marlene called; I wanted to tell her so badly, but Mother was so happy about the wedding, and I didn't want to hurt her. That night he came into the room and was just crying and telling me how sorry he was; I just sat there as cold as ice. I kept thinking that I was marrying my ex-boyfriend. I was so ashamed and embarrassed.

I got up and went into my bathroom in my room. I let the shower take most of my thought away, then I spoke to the Lord. I told him how sorry I was because I had totally forgotten about him. I was doing this thing all by myself, and right now, I needed his help. I just let go and let God take control. It was four more days before the wedding, and Edward could have asked his family for help, but he didn't.

We got a ride from our church brother to Hartford; he went over to his mother's house while I went to my aunt. When she saw me, she told me how I looked horrible. That's one thing with my family; they tell you like it is. I was there, and I was just lost; my aunt asked me if I was sure I wanted to marry this guy. I told her yes with a smile. Knowing that I was not happy, I trusted the Lord with this situation.

The day before the wedding, my sister and cousin came down with my brother and mom. She didn't bring my dress at all, so I was just looking at all of them, excited as if it was their day. My mother and brother had to get back to New York for the cake and my dress.

The same evening, half of my wedding party was in New York; I took the rest and went to the church. When I got there, Edward's brother from Florida was there and the rest of his family. I finally got to meet his daughter; she came over and introduced herself. Everyone was happy; I was still thinking about the rest of the money to be paid. Then the ring bearer told his mother that he didn't want to take part in the wedding anymore. She told him that it was okay; that's when I just walked out of the church and went on a bus to my aunt's house.

A lot of things were going through my mind at this time; this child went and got his clothes fitted for the wedding, and now, of all time, he didn't want to take part. This was a child, who had gotten fit for his suit, and now he didn't want to take part.

Forget all of them. I went on that bus while Edward was calling me. I did not look back; I sat on the bus, and the tears were just coming out. If my family didn't put so much into this wedding, I would have just walked away.

When the bus reached my aunt's house, I saw all of them. I walked in and went to my aunt's room. She came in and held me; the tears could not stop; then she told me not to let them see me this way. I went back downstairs with my cousin and niece and Edward's family. Everyone was talking; I was just looking and thinking really hard.

His brother asked me why I walked away. Then my aunt told him that we didn't have the rest of the money. She told him as it was; he just shook his head and told us that he had a thousand dollars and it was for our gift. My aunt told him that it would be good if we got it early. He came over and gave it to me; and told me that he knew his brother. I told my cousin to go with him to the place in the morning and pay the balance. That night was a big turnaround; they ate and talked and went back to Edward's mother's house.

He left his daughter with me; my cousin and sister were there with us. Edward's daughter's skirt suit fit her well, with everything. I was the only one that didn't have my nails done. I had an appointment in the morning for my hair; I finally got some rest, but it was a big day for me.

I told my cousin what to do with the money that Edward's brother had given us. I told her not to give it to him. Then I left and went to do my hair; my aunt gave me some extra cash to get my nails done; she told me that she would pray and I should do the same thing. When I left my aunt's house to get my hair done, I felt a peace come over me. I was just thanking God.

I did my hair and nails; the lady even did my eyebrows for me; I was so grateful. When I came back to my aunt's house, I heard that Edward and all that went with him were in an accident. I asked God if this was a sign for me to turn back now, but they told me they were all fine.

I didn't know what to think; I went into my aunt's room and went to pray even more. This wedding kept me on my knees most of the time. Then we were all waiting for my mother and the rest of the wedding party with my dress and cake.

When Mother finally came, it seemed as if she took most of my guests to my aunt's house to get ready; at this time, the house was full of people and hot. It was only one bathroom and a lot of noise. I really wanted to run at this time. Then I heard someone calling me. It was the limo driving. He came for me and the wedding party to take us to the guest room. I had totally forgotten that I had booked it with the package. Mother was so upset, she wanted me to get dressed at my aunt's house, but there was no room, and the place was hot.

It was chaos in that house. Mother was at the top of her voice. She wanted me to dress at my aunt's house, but my aunt told her it was a good idea for me to leave because the house was hot and full of people. So I went into the limo with my cousin and some of my wedding party; we had to stop by Edward's sister's house to pick her up with his niece. Now this was another drama; Althea and Edward's sister almost had it out in the limo. At this point, nothing surprised me.

When we got to the place, they all went into the room. I sat down and watched everyone get dressed, who had makeup to put on and hair to fix; when they were all done, then they left the room. I went and took a quick shower; so did Mother. She was calmer now; I knew that she had invited a lot of her friends, and she wanted to look good; I could not wait for Sunday to come. When all of the bridesmaids left, Karen was putting on her dress, and then my aunt came into the room to help Mother get me dressed again.

They both dressed me for my high school prom and now my wedding day. My sister Marlene came and put on just a little bit of makeup on my face. Now Karen and I were walking to where the wedding would take place. They put us behind a brick wall because they didn't want the guests to see me until I was ready to walk in. I looked up and said to God, "Take over this now, please, and thank you."

Just before I was about to walk down the garden part, the limo driver saw me and told me to hold on. He told my sister to go ahead; what he did was not rehearse at all; he put me back into the limo and told me to put my head through the limo roof. Then he told me that when I reached my guests, I should wave at them. I almost died; I did what I was told to do. When I reached my guests, I just waved and smiled; the only thing I heard was, "Wow!" Everyone was amazed by my entrance. I was so happy. I kept on thanking God. My brother came to the limo to get me. He was so happy for me that he said, "Sis, you did it!" I told him that it was God.

As he took me down the pathway, I could not believe my eyes; it was paved with concrete. I was just thanking Jesus for all that he made happen; as I walked down the pavement, everyone was taking pictures. I saw my friend Elaine and her husband, church family, aunt, and cousin. Pam didn't come at all; even another high school friend came. Everyone was just looking at me; at this time, I knew that my heavenly Father had his hands on me.

I wanted to cry for all he did for me, even when I wanted to run away. I know that God loves me, and I am grateful to him. As we said our vows, we kissed and went over to the garden to take more pictures. After that, we went in and did the usual wedding dance and speeches. It went well. We thanked all who came and took part. I was so grateful to my family and Edward's brother David, who helped out just in time. We didn't owe anything after the wedding, thank God. Everyone had a long drive back to New York; they didn't sleep over because some had to go back to work the next day while others had to just go home. This thing was a real headache, but in the end, God took over and put his hand in it.

Edward's brother took us back to our apartment the next day; my aunt wanted us in church the following day, but I didn't have a ride to take us back to Hamden. I knew that we had to get things in order. The following day, we opened our gifts and cards, and we got enough money to pay our next month's rent. I just kept on thanking God.

Edward was eager for his daughter to come to the apartment, even though we had no bed for her. I told him to let her sleep in the bed until we got her a bed. We did this for a while; it was no fun at all; the floor was hard.

Edward needed a job, and so did I, and we needed a bed for his daughter to sleep on. His mother told us that she had a wedding gift for us. I told him to buy her a mattress and box spring. My brother called me and told me that he was getting a bigger size bed, so I got his dresser and headboard for Edward's daughter. Her room was looking great when we were done with it.

I even got my niece and nephew to come and stay for the summer. My brother took the kids down; they loved the place very much because it was near the mall, and we had a swimming pool in the complex. So it was like a mini vacation place.

One day, I got a call from one of the nursing homes, and the good news, it was close to our apartment. I went and did the interview. I got the job and started on July the fourth; God didn't waste any time. We got his daughter into school, which was within walking distance from the apartment. Even Edward had gotten a job too at Petco;

everything was close by, even the supermarket. The car Edward's sister had given him kept shouting off in the middle of the road. So we got rid of it.

The only problem we had was going to church. It was too far for our church family to come and get us, so we were back in the Word again. Summer came and went, and the kids went back to New York, and Edward's daughter was in school. She didn't talk with us too much; she was with her uncle and his wife, helping them with their kids. She would just dress and leave the house; she came home at night. Then she took her shower and went to bed.

I didn't mind at all; she didn't talk too much to me, and she was always over at her uncle's house. One day, her father told her that she should stay home and clean up; I told him no. I would clean up my own place; one thing she should do was clean her room and the bathroom they both use because I had one in my room.

Whatever they ate out of, wash it up; she was responsible for washing her own clothes because the machine was in the apartment. She had everything for her comfort; this went on and on, and she kept to herself. I tried to talk to her, but she didn't have much to say, so I left her alone.

When I went to work, her mother would call her, and they would talk. I didn't let that bother me at all. Until the bills started to come in, it would be two or sometimes three hundred dollars. I asked her about it, but she denied it and told me it was not her, even though it had her mother's number on it. I did everything possible for this girl, but she was set in her ways. Now I knew why Edward's sister told me to let her stay in Jamaica.

One day, she came into my room and was just talking to me; I thought that it was a good thing. She told me that everyone loved her in his family, and they told her if anyone hurt her; she should let them know, and then they would come and take care of business. It sounded like a threat to me, but little did she know I was not afraid of people. I may be a tiny lady, but I would fight any giant. This kind of treatment was constant; she would do things in the house, and if I asked, it wasn't her, or she didn't know.

Her dad thought that I was picking on her a lot. I told him like it was: keep my place clean, and you won't have a problem with me. This girl was my test; she didn't know I was helping her ass. If I didn't marry him, he would still be living in that same one-bedroom apartment. I don't know why I thought that I could save the world; that was Jesus's job.

As I went to work and paid the bills, so did Edward; he gave me what he had. I still had to make up with him so that we had a roof over our heads. I made a lot of sacrifices so that we ate every day and our bills were paid on time.

One day on my day off from work, she came home from school and came into the bedroom. I don't know if the devil had sent her to me, she was just there talking, then she told me that her father was married twice, so that was the reason her aunt didn't want to come to our wedding. She even told me that they didn't like me at all; that didn't hurt me one bit because no one ever did. As I listened to this child belittle me, telling me about her dad's second wife, I left blood rushing into my head.

I couldn't take it anymore; I called Edward's mother and asked her about Edward being married twice; she told me that she had asked me about it. I told her that her son told me that he was married to the same lady twice. All this time, Edward was lying to me about his last marriages; he did have a second wife, and I was number three.

This man took me for a ride; as the tears rolled down my face, I kept hearing her voice telling me that it was too late now. I gave God my word, and I was a Christian.

I could not have gotten a divorce; my heart fell. I was just crying at the fact that he kept on lying to me. I was so ashamed to call my family and let them know what this man had done. She asked to speak to her granddaughter. I just went into the bedroom and closed the door; after all, she was right about that. I had given my word to the Lord, and that was final.

This was something that I had to live with... When he came home from work, he was yelling at his daughter and mother. I kept thinking about how long he thought that it would have lasted. I went outside of the apartment and took a walk. I was just crying to God and asking him why, even though he had nothing to do with it. All the signs were there; I was not paying any attention.

All the mess I'd been through with him, the lying and cheating, I was too smart to not have known this. I had learned from the best. I felt really hurt because his daughter had pleasure telling me this; the look on her face was priceless. She had fun just to hurt me; she didn't even know who I was. I always try to help people, and I always get hurt in return. I helped my sister's kids when my brother took them out of the house; then, I was responsible for them. Then she ran away; this was too much, but I had to clear my head. I went back into the apartment and went right into the shower. I just let the water run and run. I knew that his daughter did not know the Lord.

When I got back into the apartment, he was just talking to me; but I blocked him out; more lies I didn't want to hear. We kept our distance, and now I knew why he was married so many times. He loved her so much, and she knew it; I guess she wanted her dad for herself. I just played the game she liked; she didn't know me at all, that I had gone to university with people in my life.

One day on my day off from work, she came into my room; it had a balcony where her dad loved to sit. She was just sitting next to him; I asked her when she was going to give her heart to the Lord, and her father jumped up and told me to leave her alone and mind my own business. I just shook my head; now I knew what I was dealing with. The devil in disguise, they both came into my life to test me.

Now I had to put on my whole armor and pray up because this was a warfare that only God could fight. I had to pray all the time; you would think it was coming from outside, but I was sleeping with the enemy. At this point, we had stopped going to church; I didn't know the place that well, and the only close church we went to was crazy. The pastor was just singing; he didn't preach at all but was singing while he preached. While I was in the service that day, I was just laughing. I would not believe that these people thought he was giving them the Word. When we got home, Edward said that it was a good service. I just looked at him and walked away; he was gone.

He had made a 360-degree turn from the Lord; I had to fight him and his daughter. They would play all kinds of music in the apartment, but I would stand up for the Lord. I told them, as the good Bible says, as for me and my house, we would serve the Lord. I was the crazy one in the house; I needed to get into the program. I had to fight them both to keep afloat. Living for Jesus is no joke because you have to give up yourself all the time. I had to fight them at home, and when I went to work, I had to fight them too. I was a tiny lady, so most of the time, people would try to intimidate me. I realized the best way to overcome this fight was to sing. I started to sing a lot to keep my mind focused on the Lord.

When I came home, the place was in a mess; I had to clean it up. I knew that I was not going to church as I wanted to do, but I would listen to Joyce Meyer and Creflo Dollar ministries; they kept me in the word. I was not paying my tithes, so I was partnered with Joyce's ministries. This was my daily food; I was just talking and singing to God at all times. I even knew when his family was coming to visit him. They came when they knew that I would be at work. I know they didn't like me; I was okay with that.

As the months went by, I was not feeling too great; I was just watching my cycle. I went and bought a pregnancy test. I was pregnant; I was so happy. I looked at this as if it was a turning point in my life. I knew after all we had been through, he would be happy. I called my mother and told her the good news. She was so happy that she called everyone and gave them the news.

She asked me what Edward had said. I told her I did not tell him as yet; she made a funny noise and said that he should be the first one to know. I wanted to give him a surprise after all we'd been through. I made dinner for him, and then we went to bed early. The same night, I told him, and he told me that it was too early to know that. I looked at him and said I had taken the test and was pregnant.

He looked at me and told me that he had a child already. He told me he didn't want another child right now, and moreover, we could not afford it. When he was finished talking, I heard Tom's voice talking to me. I had told my mother and family, and they were happy, and now he wanted to routine this day for me. I looked at him and told him if he wanted to leave, the door was wide open.

This time, my baby was going to be born with or without a father. He just looked at me; I was going to fight for this one; no more abortion, no more killing innocent life. The devil thought I was the same Angela that he once had. I was a child of a King, and no weapon could harm me. I told God that I was so happy for the gift he gave me, and I promised to raise his gift the way he wanted me to.

I didn't care what it was; I was only happy that God had blessed me once more. He finally came around when he spoke to my mother, and then my sisters called him and congratulated him. He was playing the husband role really well. I didn't even let them know what took place.

Now being pregnant and working as a CNA was the hardest thing anyone could have done. I was on my feet most of the time and handled these heavy patients; it was no fun. This went on for a while; then, I finally told my co-worker that I was pregnant.

I almost cried; they were so happy for me; they treated me like their little sister. They didn't want me to do any work at all. My job there was to get the patients watered and pull the beds down for all of them. Then I would do the bookwork for them as well; they took me to doctor's appointments; whenever I needed to go, the only time I had a problem was when our weekend came up. We worked the opposite one, but I still had the male CNA who took me home at night.

Edward had it easy; I always thank the Lord for helping me with these people. The nurse on our floor was the mother hen; she saw to it that we were okay, and she took care of us. It wasn't like that before with her. I always thought that she hated me because she would find faults a lot. One day, she told me I could never become a nurse because I cared too much, and with this job, you had to be tough. When we were wrong, she would put us in our place, and she would give us advice.

Sometimes, we thought we were old for some of them, but she was our mother hen. This pregnancy wasn't good at all; I could not keep anything down most of the time, then a dizzy spell came with it.

Miss Smith would check my vitals and tell me to sit down; she kept asking me if I was okay. She was worried. I did this for a while. When I went home, I didn't let anyone get to me at all. I would talk to my baby, read the Bible, and then sing to my stomach. It was the happiest time of my life.

One day, my family came to visit us. Edward and my brother went over to the mall to get something; he had his son Steven with him, and they took Edward's daughter as well. I was home with my mother and sister; when I got the call from Edward's sister. She asked for her brother, and I told her that he was not home. She then told me that his brother David had died. The same brother that helped us on our wedding day, I broke down, and my mother took the phone. I was just crying because, out of all of his siblings, he was the only one who showed me compassion. I didn't know how to tell him, but Mother was there to help. The day started out happy and ended up sad.

When he came back, I didn't know how to tell him; but I had the courage to. He was on the floor crying, and his daughter too. He went and called his mother. I didn't know what to say to her, then my mother took the phone from me and told me to stop stressing myself out, then she spoke to Edward's mother. I looked at my brother and thanked God for him, but Edward had lost the only person in his family that really loved him. He took care of him when his dad didn't, and now he was gone.

When my family left, I tried to console him, but he wanted to be by himself. Now they were making funeral arrangements. Edward wanted me to go with him, but Mother told me to consider the baby. He didn't care at all. He told me that he needed me to be there. I was his wife, and I should be there. Edward had gotten some money from the accident he had with his leg; you would have thought that he spent the money wisely, but he didn't. I had no control over it at all.

I was told that he got some money from his accident; I didn't dare ask him how much because he would not speak the truth in any way. When we finally got there, it was too much drama. Everyone was at each other's throats; I just watched and listened. His brother was a Muslim, which means he had many women. I just watched as the drama continued. His wife was sad, and also all of his children's mothers.

Chapter 25

While we were in Florida, Edward's daughter had a field day with me due to the fact that she knew I was not their friend. She enjoyed making me feel sad. If only I had listened to my mother. I just kept my cool when we went back home to Connecticut. I knew that this girl was up to something.

When I went back to work, I could hardly hold up my head. The dizzy spell was getting worse; then Miss Smith told me I needed to stay home and take care of myself. I told her that we needed the money, and she told me that the God I serve would take care of me.

I didn't listen at all, but I had to go to the hospital a lot at work. One of the nurses had to take me twice to the emergency room. Edward didn't come because he didn't drive at all. I just wanted to make sure that my baby was all right.

Miss Smith came to me once more and told me that I was not being fair to myself and the baby; she went on by letting me know that the job would always be there and that they could easily get someone else to replace me. When she was finished talking, she walked away; I took her advice.

Edward was so mad; he told me that the women worked up until the time to give birth. I didn't care what he had to say. I did what Miss Smith told me to do; I had to drop my insurance because I could not pay the co-payment, and I was not working. Now I had to go to the state for help. They would deny me a lot; they would give Edward's daughter, not me. I cried and told God that I needed his help right now.

After a month and a half of stress, they finally called me and gave it to me. Things you had to go through, and because I had to be honest, this made it even worse if I had lied. I might have gotten it sooner, but I had to be faithful to the Lord. While I was home, I did those wifely things and saw to it that the house was clean. I washed and cooked his meal; I would get tired really fast, but I still managed to finish.

One day, I had a dream about giving birth; it was really strange. I had just given birth, and when I was finished, I sat down and put on my shoes. When I asked the nurse what kind of baby I had, she told me that it was a girl. I just smiled and told her thanks.

I thought that this was strange, so I called my cousin, and she told me that I was going to have a boy. I don't know how she knew this; not even the doctors knew. Edward didn't talk too much; sometimes, he had me feeling as if I was worthless. I had to depend on him for things, which was killing me. *I am a woman who depends on myself; now I have to wait on him.* It was hard, but God brought me through it. My mother had called me and told me they were keeping a baby shower for me, and it was around our wedding anniversary. Of course, I wanted to go, but Edward told me we were not going.

I knew he was not talking to me because he knew very well that he was not going to help me with anything. Whenever he went shopping, he would buy the best things for himself and would try to buy cheap things for me. After all that I did for this man. When I met him, he didn't have much. I had to do without so that he had even clothes to wear. I was not used to this at all, but I knew that God would take care of me.

I did what I had to; we went, and he was upset. I didn't care one bit. It was my day once more; my cousin came and helped with the shower as well. Not one of his family came; I didn't miss them at all. His daughter was with us; she was enjoying herself too. The following day was our anniversary; we were in my mother's room. Edward was still sleeping; I felt a little pain. I told him I was not feeling well, but he ignored me as always. I then felt the bed wet; I told him to get my mother for me; he hissed his teeth and turned to the other side. Then I told him to please call my mother for me. Then he got up. She was in the room in no time; she asked me if I thought it was the baby. I told her that it was not time as yet, and she went on the phone and called my brother.

Then she told me to get dressed and called my doctor. While I was in the bathroom, I kept praying and asking God to help me and the baby. I knew that it was too early for my baby to be born. We still didn't get my brother, so our church brother, who came to the shower, took us. We didn't waste any time. I told my mother that the doctor told me to come back to Connecticut, then my mother said she must be crazy. This child was unpredictable; whenever we went to do the ultrasound to find out what kind of baby I was going to have, we could not find out; the baby would show everything that needed to be seen, except the sex. Edward wanted a boy to carry on his name, but if it was a girl, he wanted her name to be Genesis. I wanted Abigail; she was smart and beautiful, and she was full of wisdom.

We both agreed on the boy's name; he would name after Edward; when we got to the hospital, they told me that I had time, and because they didn't have any information about me, it was a lot of paperwork that needed to be filled out; but it seemed as if this child wanted to be born.

When the nurse took me to see how far I was dilated, I was told by the nurse not to breathe or move. I could not push; she saw the baby's head. At this time, everyone was running; this child was on the way. I remember giving birth while the nurse was asking me a question.

I pushed about three times, and out came my baby. I asked them what kind of baby, then they told me that it was a girl. As I watched those little tiny feet moving, one of the nurses was laughing and saying she was moving her feet as if she knew how to walk. I only saw her at a distance because they knew nothing about me, if I had gotten any shots at all.

They had to keep the baby away from me; then everything was over, and they took her into ICU because she was tiny. She came early, and they knew they had to watch her. I cried and asked God to take care of his angel. Edward and Mother went in to see the baby. When they got me all cleaned up and ran more tests, I was in a lot of pain. When my mother came and told me how the baby was doing, Edward was still in the nursery with the baby.

I felt really bad not being able to see her. I knew she wanted to hear my voice, but I had to wait until all the tests were done.

They took me into another room. I still couldn't see my daughter at all; they had protocol to follow. I had to wait until they did all kinds of tests on me before I could even breastfeed my baby. She was really tiny; my baby weighed only five pounds. I was just praying for my baby girl. When everyone had seen my baby, Mother told me she was pink the same way I was. Then Edson came and told me congrats, then Edward came in and kissed me. He told me she was fine and that he wanted me to see her, but I still had to wait until the tests were done. How it killed me to not have seen her. I knew that she missed her mother.

They didn't stay too long because they had to go back home as Edward's daughter had to go back to Connecticut for school. Our church brother was going back for work as well, so he took her home; she stayed at Edward's brother's house until he got back. When they left, another mother came in with her baby. She asked me where my angel was. I told her where she was; she said that she was sorry, but she knew that my daughter would be fine.

That night I remember having a dream about the whole event. I dreamt that I had given birth to my baby, and when I was finished, I got up, tied my shoelace, and asked the nurse what kind of baby it was. She told me it was a girl. Now I knew that her name was to be called Abigail.

The next day, Edward came and asked me what I named her. I told him, "Abigail." He told me that her name should be called Genesis, the first book of the Bible. I was debating at this time. My mother told me that it was a pretty name. He was the man, and that was his child, so he wanted Genesis. I just prayed on it; they left me and went to see the baby.

It was the same thing every night; they came and went back home. I was just praying and asking God whatever name he wanted that she was going to be called. The following morning, I got up and cleaned up myself, then the nurse told me it was time for me to name the baby. I didn't want to upset her dad; then, another nurse came in and asked me if I was ready to meet my angel. I could not believe it; they took me to the nursery. I had to put on a gown to see my baby. When I went in, one of the nurses had the baby, and she was reading the Bible over her. I could not believe it.

I asked her what she was reading; she thought I was upset. She told me about King David. Then, I asked her if it was the part when he married Abigail. She smiled. I didn't need her earthly father to tell me what to name her because her heavenly Father had spoken. That was how she got her name. She asked me if I wanted to hold her. I sat down and held my angel for the first time.

She was just there looking at me, and I was just looking at her. I introduced myself to her. I told her I was her mommy and that it was nice to meet her. They gave me a bottle to feed her; she didn't drink too much, then the nurse took her from me and burped her. They were ruff with her. As I watched them hold her, they put her back into the incubator and put back all these tubes on her. I started to cry, then the nurse told me that she was fine, but they had to make sure that she was okay when she was sleeping; better yet, keeping an eye on her.

She told me that Abi was in good hands. I thanked her and went back to my room. When I went back in, they told me that they were releasing me, but my baby had to stay until she put on more weight. That was the worst thing they could have told me. When my mother came with Edward, they told them I was being discharged. I was just crying, all this time waiting for her, and now I had to go home without her.

This wasn't what I had planned. When Edward heard what I had called her, he was upset. It wasn't what he wanted her to be named. "Genesis is her name," he told them. "I still give her that name; it is her middle name," I told him. When I got to my mother's house, I was still crying. They didn't understand why.

I didn't want them to hurt her like the other ones. I was feeling depressed and tired. I remember my sister Marlene telling me to stop crying, for God knew best. She told me I needed all the strength I could get for her. When she got home, I listened to her. They had my baby there for almost a week. I was getting tired most of the time. I told Edward that I didn't feel well enough one night to visit Abi, and he went off on me. He told me that it was my fault that his daughter was born early and now I didn't want to visit her. I was just crying even more; he let me feel as if I was the wickedest mother who did this to her baby girl. My mother told me to rest, and she went with him. I asked him how she was. He told me if I wanted to know, I should have come and seen the baby.

The next day, I went and looked for my angel; she was in the incubator still. She didn't have all these tubes like before. I went and put on my gown, and then I put my finger through the hole and put it into her tiny hands; she was just looking at me. I knew she was wondering where I had been the previous day. I told her that Mommy was not feeling too well. At this time, Edward had to go back home to work, and his daughter had to finish school. Edward came down that weekend to see us; then they called us to give me the good news.

She was coming home; my brother, his son, Mother, and Edward went to the hospital. When we went to the nursery, she was off the tubes and was ready to be dressed. The nurse with Mother put on her tiny clothes. I was afraid to get her dressed; we took some pictures of her with the praying nurse. God bless her. When we went into the waiting room, my brother and his son were there, then his son said out loud, "Look at Grandpa." We both looked at him and smiled; it seemed as if my dad was there too. After all, it was Father's Day. I could not stop thanking God once more for his gift to me. When we got into the house, everyone was waiting to see this baby girl. I could see the look on some of their faces; she was tiny; I just said, "That's my five-pound baby."

I was told by the doctors that I had to stay here in New York for Abi's five-week checkup; that made Edward mad to leave us once more. This gave me some rest; after all, I needed it. I was lucky that I was home with my mother; for the two months I was in New York with Abi, my mother cooked and washed both of our clothes. She cleaned this child while I got some rest; she told me I needed to see the doctor when I got home. Abi would sleep all day but wake up in the night. Sometimes, when I wanted to sleep, she would be up with my sister Marlene.

I didn't know if she was watching TV or what. She would not go to bed at night. I remember my sister telling her that when she went back to the country, she had to go to bed really early. This was okay with me. Abi was still a little baby, and whenever anyone came to visit, that was their word—she was tiny. I kept thinking to myself, *If only they could stop.* When I held her, I would put her on a pillow.

One day, Edward's brother and wife came to visit us; they, too, said the same thing. I didn't care at all. My mother had sent my brother to Hamden. He went and shampooed the carpet before we went home. It was the saddest time for my mother because we were going home.

She was sad, but we had to go. I took my nephews with me because it was summer once more. When I got home, it was a mess. Edward knew we were coming home, but it was a payback for staying away so long. I started to clean up and get the house back in order. When I got back home, things were not the same; Edward was acting differently. His daughter had her friends coming over, and they would go to the pool. Even my husband went with them; I stayed home with the baby while my nephews went.

This went on for a while, her friend would come over often, and Edward would be on the carpet listening to reggae music with this girl. Everything in me was just boiling up; my spirit was so upset. I could not take it anymore; I just went into the living room where they were and told him, "Don't you dare disrespect me like that?" She looked at me, and he was staring at me too. I told the young girl that she came to see her friend, not her friend's father. I told her to leave the house; they thought that I was getting crazy. I knew I was not getting mad, but this man was very disrespectful.

They called their family. Of course, it was my fault. The crazy wife was back. I didn't care at all. I had to do what I had to do; I was not going to let anyone come into my house and treat me like a child. I had to deal with his daughter and now her friends. I was on their hated list. I didn't care at all. The summer came and gone; now I had to send my nephews back home.

Edward came to me one day and told me that he could not handle this too long; he wanted me to go back to work. The baby was only three months old; in September, the first I had my baby's christening. My co-worker came to the dedication, and so did his sisters. I kept it in New York; we went back home the same day; Edward decided that his daughter would watch Abi for two hours until he got home from work. He worked 9 to 5, and I would have to work 3:00 to 11:00 p.m. He worked it out so well because he could not handle all the weight, he said. He told his daughter that she had to get home at 2:30, which gave me thirty minutes for work. I just listened to him. I didn't know what to do; I could send her back to her mother. Then I would not see her at all.

The day came, which was the 10th of September. I got my baby ready for the day until her sister came home; all her bottles were ready, and I was waiting for my ride. I was so nervous about the whole idea; I had to do what I had to. When I went back to work, I was even more tired than before; I called the house until I knew Edward was there. The next day, I got a call from my aunt. She told me to turn on the TV, and I asked her what was happening. She told me that New York was under attack.

I was on my face crying and just praying as I watched the news. I could not reach my family at all; I prayed and cried because I didn't know what was happening. All the towers were down, so it was impossible to reach anyone by phone. Then my sister Althea called me and told me that they were fine and she would call me later. My heart felt relieved.

As I watched the news, I was just crying for all the pain that these people were feeling. I was crying even more than anything. How in the world were people so wicked to hurt innocent people like that? My heart was hurting. I looked at my daughter and said she was born into a world like this. I was on my knees, just praying and asking God to have mercy on us all.

Chapter 26

When I got to work, every TV was on the news; this was the saddest time in America. All these lives were gone, and all the family members were just waiting for their loved ones to come home. My heart was hurting for America; how in the world could we hurt people in the name of their god? The God I know doesn't hurt; the God I know is love and peace. This was a wake-up call for this country. As the world comes to see how wicked our hearts can be, we need Jesus. No other gods but the only true one, Jesus Christ. These guys had put fear in me; every time I heard a plane, I would call out for Jesus and run to where Abi was.

Every day, we hoped and prayed that they found more survivors. As I watched the world embrace each other, it has to come to this for each one of us to know what love is; as I watched blacks and whites, young and old, come together in prayer for all the souls that were lost, my heart went out to them. Love is what conquers us all. "For God so loved the world, that he gave his only begotten Son..." (John 3:16a)

As the month went by, they were still looking for survivors. We were still hoping and praying, but no one at all. I was still facing my everyday life as well; I would get a call from Edward's sister telling me that it was too much for his daughter to be watching my child, and it was not too much for me to go back to work so soon so that they could have a roof over their head.

This went on until one day, I took some time off from work, I took Abi, and we went to visit my mother in New York. I told Edward to stay with his daughter because she was still going to school. I wanted some downtime with my daughter. We were only there for three days when I got a call from Edward crying. I asked him what the matter was, and he told me that his family just called DCF on him, and now they were coming for my baby. I told him to get a hold of himself. Then he told me his daughter and he got into a fight, and she ran over to his brother's house. The next thing he knew, DCF was calling him, and the police came too.

I asked to speak to his daughter, but she was at his brother's house. I called her, but his brother's wife told me that I could not talk to her. I then called his mother, and she told me everything. She kept saying, "Poor Edward," and I should come home and help him. I thought to myself that they could take my child away from me. Then fear was crawling its ugly self once more in my life. I didn't want to go back to Hamden; they didn't know where I was. My mother told me that he could not tell them that he had hit her because they would take Abi away from us.

I told her if they took her, they would take her, but there was no way he was going to lie, and I served a God that was bigger than I. Then I called him back and told him I was not coming home until the weekend, but I had to leave the next day.

My brother had to take me home once more; when we got into the parking lot, the Lord told me that the lady was sitting inside the car. I knew she was watching me. I just took my daughter out of the car in her car seat; then, my brother came in with me and Abi's bags. When I came inside the house, this big-grown man was still crying. Then he told me the lady was there. I told him I knew.

The doorbell rang, and Edward opened the door; she came in and was just looking at me. She came over and shook her head. I asked her what was wrong because I was not home. Then she told me now she saw the big picture. It was the young wife and the young daughter's issue.

I didn't know what she was talking about; she told me she handled these cases all the time. The fathers would marry young wives, and then the other kids would get jealous, but she didn't understand why they told her that Abi was being starved.

She looked okay to me. I asked her what she meant by. She was real with me; she told me his brother wanted my child for money. They had foster kids, and they wanted more. The more kids, the more money. I looked at him and shook my head; I asked him when his family would ever give up. Then his daughter came home from school; the lady went inside the room with her, and they were there for a while.

When they were finished, they told me that she had to stay in the house and that she should not go back to his brother's house. I guess she didn't like what she heard at all.

I was angry with his family; I hated them for what they tried to do to me, but their own brother. I was devastated. I just could not understand them at all. I know they hated me, but why would they want to take my child away from me? I could not put this thing down; I was getting bitter every day; it had a strong hold on me. I could not forgive them; I was bitter and angry.

His daughter didn't say anything to us at all. I didn't even know if I could trust her with my daughter at all. As the weeks turned into months, I still could not understand this man and his family; why were they so bitter with each other? I knew that I was not getting any better with things. I remember one day, the Lord told me to call all of Edward's family and apologize to them.

I told the Lord that he must be mad or something. They were the ones who needed to apologize to me; this went on for almost two months. The day I finally went and did it, I cried so hard. I remember telling God that I didn't need this at all, I did them no harm, and why was I the one to deserve this? The Lord wanted me to apologize so that I could heal myself because of unforgiveness. It was eating away my soul, and he could not work in me the way he wanted to.

I could never forget what some of them told me; they told me that they really appreciated my apology thanks; some of them even laughed at me; I would laugh too because I must be an idiot to be calling people that hurt me and apologizing to them. I did as I was told. During the past months, I was feeling better; I didn't hate them as much. I had to accept the price of being this man's wife.

I didn't know what else to do. I had to leave Abi with her. Now she was getting home late; she knew I had to be at work at 3:00 p.m., and she would come home ten minutes to three, or sometimes even at 3:00 p.m.

I was always late; I had to tell my friends to go ahead because I didn't want them to be late too. When she got home, she didn't talk at all; I would call her dad, screaming and asking him where she was. Unlike me, he didn't know either.

She didn't see the sacrifice I was putting into this family. I went as far as to ask one of the supervisors in the maintenance department if they had any opening. He told me that all I needed was to fill out an application so that he could get something better to help with the bills. Edward told me no! He didn't want to clean up anyone's mess; that was my field. I could not believe what he told me; I just looked at him. I knew how to budget the money, but now I had to buy diapers and toiletry for both myself and his daughter.

I told her if she wanted to work on the weekend to get some extra money to buy things she needed, she told me that it would interfere with her school work. I just lost it one day and started to curse; I even cursed a bad word. That was the end of my life, a Christian cursing. He got home early and called his mother, and now his family was making all kinds of remarks that I should get a babysitter, but his daughter wasn't there for that.

I did the next thing I knew how; I called my mother and told her to get Abigail for me; she didn't waste any time. Now I had to pack up my daughter and send her to New York while they lived easily. I couldn't believe these people; they didn't care at all; my child was away from me, and I had to get up each day and work so hard for them. I let it happen for a month too long; then, I lost it.

I started to pack up my things, and I told him to do the same as well. I was sick and tired of the bull; I had to work while the both of them enjoyed themselves. My daughter was gone, and I had nothing; no joy at night when I came home. I told him to find a way and put his daughter because I was leaving. They always made it seem as if it was my fault; I just couldn't get it. This was her own sister that she was helping with. She didn't have any Cinderella kind of job.

I knew how it felt like being a stepchild. I tried my best, and now everything was falling on me. If this meant that she had to go, I had to do what I had to. The day before she left the house, I told her to pray to God that this would never happen to her, when you needed help and couldn't get it. She told me as it was: that would never happen to her because she would be going to school and would have a better education than I. She would have a good job and career. I shook my head and walked away. She was right; I didn't have one. I only took care of people and their problems. She left the following day; I was all packed up and ready to move.

One of my co-workers told me about an apartment close to her house. It was in the New Haven area. I didn't like it at all. I still needed a vehicle to get to work and drop off Abigail. I looked around but still could not find anywhere to live. I wanted to see my daughter so badly; it hurt. I would count the days as they turned into a month; then, one day, Edward told me I should go and get Abi. I asked him what he was talking about, and he told me he could do some overtime and pay a sitter to help out.

We got a sitter in the neighborhood. It was a young girl we knew; her mother used to perm his daughter's hair. I went out and got things for Abigail's room. We painted it and put her crib in it; when she came home, it was like my heart was mended. She was just looking at us. I think that she missed my mother as well. I took her to the lady's home, and she was okay with it. I dropped her off at 2:30, and I was off to work.

I walked this time; sometimes, the days go by so fast. I did my everyday work at home. I would cook and clean and get Abigail ready for the day. When I got to work, I was so tired; but I had to do what needed to be done. At work, we had to put up with a lot of abuse from patients and their family members. I didn't know what racism was until I came to America. In Jamaica, we had prejudice, which we could deal with. This thing called racism is pure evil. How can we hate another human being like that? They hate people because of their color; I think it is ridiculous. If everyone were blind in this world, how could we know what color they are and judge them for it? God has created us all, and he is no respecter of persons. He only goes by our hearts, and if it is wicked, then he judges us from it.

The patient would tell us that we were black and ugly and looked like monkeys. Nothing came out of it; we are Jamaican. We didn't let it get the best of us due to the fact we weren't born into racism. My co-worker told one of the patients that called us monkeys to take a good look at us, we are beautiful ladies, and more than ever, she was the one in the cage. She got so mad that she shook the bed rails; it was fun watching her get mad. She tried to let us down, but we did not have it at all.

People will treat you the way you let them; we are all God's children, whether we like it or not. I believe we should stand up for what is right; don't compromise with the devil at all. Unity is strength; if only we can see what we are doing to each other, just like 911. All of this is just the enemy's plan; he knows that God loves each of us, and he played with our emotions. That we kill, steal, and destroy each other for what? Pure evil. Even Edward's family showed me the evil things people could do for money.

They wanted to take my daughter away from me; they didn't consider the fact that I went through to bring her into this world. Even parents have to say goodbye to their children when they send them to school. The world in which we live is pure evil. It's up to us to choose who we will serve. God is love; that is what I know. Being an aide, I saw a lot of this. People would get upset about everything.

In life, we can make a difference. That was what we did. At work, we would do our job and work together as a team; the work got done easily and quietly. Whenever someone's bell was ringing, we would get it for the next person, if we were not busy. It was not like that before I went on the floor, everyone for themselves.

Most of those workers had left; now we were new ones. We worked together most of the time; we were like a family there. On the holidays, we would keep our Christmas party. We would cook each dish and take it to work. Then, we have our names picked for each other's gifts.

It was not so, we all got each other a gift, and we enjoyed ourselves. Our patients got to know us, and we were like that happy home. We would have Bible studies when we were finished, but Miss Smith told us that we were not at our home; we had to stop it. I still read the Word of God when I was on my break or in my patient's room with them.

One night at work, I was with my patient reading the Bible; when I came upon a verse. It seemed as if God was talking to me; as I read the Word, the Bible actually opened up to me. I was seeing things I'd never seen before, even though I had read it before. It seemed as if God was giving me a new name. I didn't know what it was, but I really felt like it was my right name, Hephzibah. It was Isaiah 62:4. I looked up and asked Dad if he really wanted me to change my name, but I never did. Our happiness at work didn't last long; we made the enemy come in.

Now there was an argument and fussing on the floor. I tried to keep the peace, but it was too much. I know that I don't take stupidity too long. I told them my mind and went to the office and asked to be removed from the floor. They didn't like it one bit, but they let the enemy in and took everyone for a ride.

I thought it was getting better at my house, but now Edward was looking at someone else; it seemed as if he met her at Petco. Whenever I came home from work, the place was in a mess; Abi would have things all over the floor; she was up while her dad was sleeping. She would mess up the place, but that was okay. I got home to see my baby girl. Whenever I was home with him, he would find all kinds of things to say about me; it didn't bother him before. Whenever he got a phone call, he would go into the hallway to take the call. I just watched him as he played the fool.

One day, I called Edward from work and asked him what took him so long to answer the phone, if he had a woman in the house. He went off on me. I was only kidding, but I was no fool to know that all the signs were there. I was not quick to judge, but the good Lord had me on guard. Whenever I came home, I would hear the voice telling me to press redial on the phone. Then I heard a woman's voice answered. I did this for a while; things were not right in the apartment. One day on my day off, while he was still at work, I called the number out of curiosity.

I opened up the Pandora's box; the young lady told me that she didn't know that Edward was married. He told her that I was his niece and we both lived with him. He had invited her to our apartment for Bible study, the same line he used on me. He even wanted a relationship with her, but thank God I called her in time. This man would take Abigail to the sitter just to have time alone with the girl.

I wanted to kill him; I didn't know what else to say; he must have done something to me. I know that I was no fool to be putting up with all of this; I was so angry that I didn't even cry. When he came home, I reached the point that I beat the crap out of him with the same phone that he used to call her with. "Whatever you did to me, why I am the way I am, is going to end," I told him. When I was finished with him, we had to go to the emergency room.

They asked him who did this to him; I just sat there and watched him. I didn't know if he was going to get me arrested, but I didn't care at all. How much more can one take? When we got home, I let him call this girl and ended it. He called her a floozie and how she only wanted to break up his marriage. Then she called him a liar and sheep in wolf's clothing. Then I told her that I did not blame her because I knew my husband. She wanted to know why I was still with him. I told her that I had made a vow to the Lord.

I told her goodbye. I knew that there was nothing I had to say to him, but it hurt to think that all I had done for this man… and he was treating me like this. When I knew him, he didn't have anything; this took a toll on me; every minute he was late for home, I would have thought he was with her or someone else.

The devil got me in a trap; I would cry and ask God why. I even went and called my sister's pastor and asked her what I should do, but she told me that he was my husband and God could fix it. I had to just pray and believe. I was hurting inside out; the devil had me once more.

He was playing with my mind and heart. I called my mother and told her; of course, she called everyone else and told them; now they all were telling me to leave him. I didn't listen to my family at all; I listened to the pastor; I did what she said, but I routed my friendship with my family. They all thought that I was a fool to stay with him; they did not understand the relationship I had with the Lord. I just wanted to know if this woman was pretty or what; no matter what I did, this man was not happy at all.

I was at work one evening when I kept thinking about what this man did. I was too ashamed to let my co-worker know, but I just wanted to know if this girl was more pretty than me. I kept thinking to myself if she was fat because I knew he loved fat women, and I was skin and bones. I ate a lot of food to put on weight, but I was not built for that.

It seemed as if I was being tested once more by the devil. He told me that Edward was having sex with this girl as we spoke. I had to come to my senses and rebuke him. I told him to get behind me; I was a child of a king.

I didn't care at all what he was doing because I was not the one who was going to hell but he and that girl. The feeling left me; I felt lighter than before; the next day, when I went to work, I was standing at the nurse's station waiting to get my assignment; while I was waiting, this girl came there talking and telling everyone her business. I heard a voice telling me that it was the girl that Edward was talking to. I recognized her voice as well.

When I turned around and looked at her, she was even more skinny than I was. She had a lot of false hair on her head and was not pretty at all; she was a made-up girl. Nothing about her was real; he had nothing about him, and to think that I was comparing myself with someone I didn't know. This girl must have thought that I was crazy by looking at her. I just laughed to myself and asked if he was cheating on me, at least with someone better than I was. I got my assignment and went on the floor. I went upstairs to the Alzheimer's unit.

Chapter 27

I passed a group of women talking to themselves. I didn't pay them any attention. I was focusing on Edward. When I heard one of the ladies call to me, I ignored her; then I heard her shout out, "Hey, you, hallelujah, kid!" She said it twice. I had to stop and look at her. I then pointed to myself, and she shook her head. I had to go over to her.

She didn't know me like that; this was a different unit I was on. I only went to feed one patient on my assignment. She asked me if I was okay; I told her yes, then I asked her if she was fine. She said yes, then she kept on saying yes. I told her bye. I looked up and thanked the Lord. He was watching over me; even the Alzheimer's patient knew who I was in Christ, and I was letting the devil use me like that.

From that day on, the devil didn't tempt me anymore with this girl. During the course of the month, I got a call from Edward's daughter; she wanted to know if she could come home once more.

I told her I was afraid of what she might do next, but she told me that she was not happy where she was. It seemed she was doing even more work than what she was doing with us. I told her dad she called me; he answered it was up to me. I did what the Lord had me to do. We took her back in. I was called a fool once more; she was in Abi's room even though Abigail didn't sleep there.

I still let Abi go over to the babysitter's house. She was more used to them by now; his daughter told me that she would watch Abi for us, but I told her it was okay; I knew that she was going to college pretty soon, so she would be leaving us once more. She asked me if I could sign up for her to get financial aid for school. This one I know pretty well; I told her no. I had to sign up for Abi when she was ready. I told her to ask her dad or his family. She did, and they told her the same thing.

I was sorry, but I was not going to put my name on any more school loans except Abi's; I didn't tell her that. I told her I did it for myself; she didn't want to hear that. She was not pleased, but I knew best; I then asked her about her high school prom. She told me that she was not going because she had no money. I know that those things can be expensive. I went and asked her dad. Edward told me she was old enough to get a job.

I went and got her ready for the prom; I paid for her ticket and called my sisters to see if they had any dresses that could fit her. She got everything she needed for the prom. She didn't even have a date, so I asked a young man she knew if he would go with her. She was shy to ask him. She went and enjoyed herself; that was a young girl's wish to go to the high school prom. This all went well. Abi's birthday was coming up, so Edward bought a cake, and we did a simple thing because her sister was about to graduate from high school. We took her shopping to buy a dress for graduation. It came, and her family came as well. She enjoyed her day very well.

Now the summer was here, I went and got my nephews; this was our thing. They loved to visit me in the summer because they could go to the pool and mall. They just had fun; I let Abi stay home with the kids. As the summer came and went, I was buying things for her to go to school. Her dad thought that she should have gotten a job in the summer for school. She asked her aunts as well; I don't know if they even helped her. I did the best I could; she was off to college. I would call her now and again but couldn't get her.

We went on with our daily lives. I was still working, and Abigail was talking about. I took pictures of her, and she would pose. When she had enough, she told me no more. She was my little company. We would read books together, and even her own Bible. I tried to keep up to my end of the bargain. I told her about Jesus's stories and what he did for all of mankind. I knew she understood.

She was a smart child, and she loved her dad. Whenever she wanted anything, and I told her no, she went to him, and he gave it to her. I told him not to spoil her but to teach her the right things. He did not, of course. He wanted to be number one. So he let her do whatever she wanted. This was a big deal for us, but I let her know when she was with me.

I tried to discipline her when she was being bad, but he was always there to undo what I fixed. He even taught her to cook at the age of two. I told him that it was just crazy; she was too young to be in the kitchen. This would lead to an argument; there was never a dull moment with us. If only we could work together and not against each other.

One day at home, I noticed blood on the floor, in the bathroom, and on the kitchen floor. I didn't know where it was coming from. I asked Edward, but he told me he didn't know what I was talking about. I looked at Abi, but she was fine. This went on for some time; then I saw Edward. He was dressing his foot. I asked him what was wrong; he told me that it was nothing. I noticed him each day dressing his foot; I asked him to show me his foot, but he told me that it was just a little cut. I told him about a diabetic patient that I have at work. "I see what it can do to you." Some of them lost their foot. He told me that it would not lead to that; one afternoon, he came out of the shower, and he was there dressing his foot. When I noticed it, I started to scream and tell him that he needed help. He told me to shut up and leave him alone.

I knew at the end of the day, I was the one who was going to get blamed. I called his brother and told him; Edward's brother didn't call him that same day, but when he did, I heard all kinds of bad words; he told me words that should not be repeated. I just went into the room and cried.

I didn't need this at all. I was only trying to help him; I did what he told me to do, leave him alone. The following week while I was home, I got a call from Edward's workplace. They told me that he had passed out; I didn't know what to do. I told them to take him to the hospital; he didn't want to go. So he came home. He had just gotten a new job at Sears Hardware; he was the supervisor. He didn't want to miss any day from work, so he went to work all day. I didn't know how to reach this guy. All weekend, I saw this man in pain, still refusing to get help.

It was Monday midday. When I was getting things ready for the day, I got a call from Edward again. This time, they took him to the hospital. It seemed as if he passed out once more, and they could not get him up. I called his brother and then the babysitter. I took Abi over there and went with his brother to the emergency room. He was on one of the beds. He was crying and telling the doctor that I was his wife. They told us that he was about to lose his leg, and I almost passed out.

I just sat down; while his brother asked them what had happened. Edwards' foot had gangrene on it. He was there crying and telling the doctor that they were wrong.

I just looked at him; he was talking, but I could not hear one thing coming out of his mouth. I was in another world. I don't know if I should just walk away; God knows I was sick and tired of this.

They admitted him to the hospital; he was still in denial. I was wondering what in the world I was going to do with all this... If only he would have listened to me. He knew everything now; I was left with a decision I didn't know what to do. When I got home, I called his mother once more; she just prayed for her son. I said amen.

I didn't have words right now; this was too big for me. I was on the phone once more, calling my mother to get Abigail. I knew I would have to be up and down with this man. I had to live by my wedding vows, in sickness or in health. Now I knew that it was too much for my co-worker to take me back and forth to the hospital. I had to take two buses just to get to the hospital where he was. I brought him lunch and clean clothes; he didn't like the hospital food.

It was too much on me. I could not call out from work, and I didn't have any vacation time left. They didn't do the surgery as yet. They wanted to see if there was any more option. This went on for weeks, I was going back and forth to the hospital, and then I had to go to work as well.

When I saw him, he had more of an attitude as if it was my fault; if only he had listened to me. I was so alone; I called his daughter, but no answer at all.

I went to the hospital every day, and this man only complained that he needed clean clothes or he wanted Jamaican food; it was too much for me. I still had to go to work. I was the only one with all of the bills.

The day came for the surgery; his family came down from Hartford; I was praying my heart out. I even told God to save his foot, and I would never get angry with him again; with this man, it was impossible to live without God.

When he came out of surgery, they took him to the recovery room. We all sat there waiting for him. Then the doctor came into the waiting room; he told us great news that they had saved his leg and gotten only his big toe.

I was there thanking God for all his wonderful work. I couldn't wait to see him; when he woke up and saw his family, he was all fine. Then he looked at me and told me that it was my fault; if only I had taken better care of him. I was so embarrassed that I just walked away. His sister came and got me, she told me that he was her brother and she knew him very well. He really hurt me with what he said.

I did my daily duty as a wife; I washed his dirty clothes and cooked his meal. He stayed in the hospital for three weeks. One day, he got fresh with me, and his roommate told him how selfish he was. The man let him look small, but he told him to mind his business. I really didn't know what was wrong with me, for Edward to be treating me this way, and I did not react to it.

Now he came home, and there was more work for me; I had to cook as always, get him cleaned up, and wait for the nurse to come; she would show me how to change his dressing. It was too much; then I had to go to work. He had a wound vacuum, which I had to clean.

One day, he told me to get Abigail because he missed her. I didn't mind at all, so I called my mother once more, and Abby was home again. Now my work was twice the load; I was feeling a lot of pain, but I had to keep on moving.

Now I was on my own with the bills, no help at all. I told him to go on social disability, but Edward told me no. I had to do it all by myself. He didn't call for help at all. I worked and worked; I was wondering if it would get any better.

I ate chicken cooked in all kinds of ways. I was sick and tired of it, but that was the only thing I could afford right now. I had to buy diapers and wipes, pay the rent, and all the bills. Food was always the same, chicken. I would buy one and get one free; that was my life.

One day at work, I met a young lady; she was a Muslim from Morocco. She would wear her wraps, and most of the workers didn't talk too much to her. I took it upon myself and became friends with her; she lived in the same complex where I lived. I didn't talk to Elaine and Pam that much since I got married. I lived in a different state, and I didn't see them as much. The lady seemed nice. We worked the same shift, and she had a daughter the same age as Abi. She also had a son. He was a baby. Beautiful children she had. I didn't know anything about her culture, but I was willing to learn. I didn't like judging people until I got to know them.

We would go to work together by walking to work and back home. She would tell me more about her religion, and I would tell her about mine. I wanted to know about this culture; why people hated them in general. She told me that it was almost the same as Christianity.

I looked at her; she told me they had more than one Muslim group. There were the violent ones and religious ones as well; they would die for what they believed in. She gave me a book to read about their culture, which I read. It was the same as the little Gideon Bible that we took around; it told about the Ten Commandments and how you should serve God. It also mentioned Jesus; Muslims did not believe he was the son of God, but they noted that he was coming back to judge the world. I did not understand that part, so I waited until I saw her.

I asked her why she became a Muslim; she had a dream, and she told me that there was a lady who was wrapping up her face and so forth. I didn't judge her one bit because my story was not better. I asked her why she didn't believe in Jesus Christ. She told me that there was no way God could have sex with a woman. I told her he didn't need to; he just said the word, and it happened, not to mention he did not physically make the earth or light. He said, "Let there be light: and there was light" (Genesis 1:3). The part that got me puzzled was the part that Jesus was coming back to judge the earth.

If you guys know that he was coming back to judge the world, to begin with, why not believe in him? If I was in a courtroom and the judge would sentence me, do you think I could tell him that he couldn't? I would do what he told me and thank him for his help to set me free. She didn't say anything else, and then she told me to leave it alone. I did. This was how our friendship began; we would walk to work and then walk back home.

When I had a day off, I sometimes watched the kids, and she would watch Abi too. We helped out each other a lot; she was a Muslim girl, and I was a Christian.

One day at work, I was with a patient; he was very difficult to handle. She came into the room looking for me. I asked her to help me. When the patient saw her, he was just smiling. She told me that he probably thought that she was a nun; that helped a lot.

While I was working on the second floor, it was different for me. The girl didn't help like my family on the third floor. They were more for themselves, but with the grace of God, he sent me my new friend. One day, I saw her going to work; I was going to the mall. She told me that she might lose her job; she had some kind of altercation with some of the workers; she walked off the job and went home. I asked her if she had told the supervisor; she told me no. I knew what this meant; she told me to pray for her with my Christian faith. I told her that I would pray for her in Jesus's name; she said Muhammad; I told her Jesus. She smiled and said whatever.

I prayed for her because she was a good worker; the following day, I saw her, and she told me what had happened. She told me just as they were about to go into the human resource office, a family member walked up to them. She told them what wonderful work she and Angela were doing with her mother. She told them that they needed to hire more people like us. She said that the supervisor and the lady from human resources looked at each other and told her to clock in for work. I was just laughing. I told her if she saw what Jesus could do. She looked at me and said she didn't know about me and walked away. I replied it wasn't me but Jesus.

Our friendship escalated, but we were both experiencing the same thing with our husbands. I didn't tell her all of what Edward was doing; I was too embarrassed to do so. We just did our own thing and went home to our family. I came home and started my other shift; I cleaned up the mess that Abi and her dad made. It was a lot, but with the grace of God, I did it.

While I got to know my friend well, I noticed that our belief was totally different when it came to Jesus. I would tell her what I read in the Bible about the Holy Ghost; she almost freaked out, and she started to make jokes about the Holy Spirit. I told her to stop because I felt really offended by what she was saying. This was when I thought twice about the choice I made when it came to the Lord.

I didn't even think that Abigail would come between me and God like that; I'd seen what they did for me. When I thought that all was well with Edward, he went to the doctor and didn't tell me that he was going to do a skin graft on his foot. He only told me the following day that he would be at the hospital for a week because he had to get this thing done. I was furious about his action. What was I going to do with my daughter? I could not leave her alone. I just went to work with tears in my eyes.

I told the human resource lady all that I was going through; she told me not to worry, just to put in the time I needed off, and she would see to it that I got paid with my sick time. I was ever so grateful; I did what she told me and didn't have to call my mother. I didn't visit him once; after what he did to me, he was selfish. He knew that things like this we should discuss, but he did things his way. When he came home from the hospital, he was mad. I was the number one dangerous wife on God's earth.

I saw some crazy days with this man; he let me go through a lot. I told him that I was moving back to Hartford because I could not handle all of this with him. I knew that being around family was the best thing for me, and at least I had my aunt. He had all of his family members there. He told me he was not leaving, but I had made up my mind.

I didn't see our life going anywhere. I went to Miss Smith. She told me that it was a good idea and I should do what I needed to do; then she told me not to listen to what other people had to say.

I told my Muslim friend; she was sad about it, but I had to do what was best for Abi and me. I would not let friendship come before the Lord I served. She was so right. I got all kinds of negative vibes from friends and Edward. He told me that if I went, the marriage would be over. I didn't care one bit; he wanted me dead; I called my aunt and told her my plans; she was so happy that I decided to move back to Hartford; I was happy myself.

I had two months to decide what I was doing, and my aunt told me about a couple of apartments. I went to Hartford and filled out the application; then, I went back to Hamden. I finally got a call from one of them; she told me to come with the deposit, and so I did. When they checked our application once more, she told me that she was sorry, but we did not qualify for the apartment due to the fact of Edwards' record. I could not understand that because they checked out his information at the place we were living. He was even working at a security place.

What could be wrong with his record? He had so many things on his name. I almost passed out; I didn't know what to do. I called his sister, and she came and got me. I was there, crying, and kept thinking to myself how we got into that apartment that we were living in. His sister asked me if I noticed him and the baby. I looked at her and said, "Oh no!" She asked me if I noticed any sign at all. I didn't want to believe that at this point. I just wanted to get away from this man and not look back at all. I had to know what I was going to do. I had to get my mind in order because what I was facing was not a joke thing. Edward's other sister told me not to worry about what the police record had said, she knew her brother, and she knew that he was not a child molester.

When I got to the house, I just went inside my room. I got Abi and gave her a bath; I didn't dare trust him with her at this point. This man had a lot of history, and he lied most of all. I called my aunt and told her what had happened with me and the apartment; she told me that God knows best. She told me that maybe I should look for a home instead of an apartment.

I listened to her most of the time. I had to find somewhere to live really fast. I looked around and still couldn't get a thing. The next thing Edward did was he went and got a realtor. He thought that we should get a home in Hamden. The same thing my aunt had said. I didn't tell him that.

Chapter 28

We could not agree on anything at all. I was focused on moving back to Hartford. The least was running out, and my aunt told me that I could come and stay with her until I got somewhere to live. I had to leave the apartment, and we didn't get a home at all.

So I packed up my things and put them in storage; I had to send Abigail to my mother's house once more. My brother came down to help me, as always, with the boys. I was with my aunt while Edward stayed in Hamden, still working. I went around with Edward's sister filling out applications for jobs. I asked my supervisor if I could have gotten a transfer to one of their facilities. She told me that there was no space at all; I still had to look around.

One day, the realtor called me and asked what I was doing with the loan that I was approving of. I told him that I was in Hartford. He told me that I could still have gotten the loan, so I could still look for a home in Hartford as well. I was happy to hear about that, so I called my aunt and told her; she didn't waste any time. She called me back and gave me a realtor in Hartford. He asked me how much I was approved for, and I told him; then he knew what price range to look for.

I was just looking back and forth, and still nothing. I remember going on my knees to my heavenly Father; I told him that I needed a job. I wanted one back in the same company that I was working for before because the banker had all of my information, and I needed to use them; I didn't have to wait too long. The next day my old supervisor called me with the information that I wanted, she told me where to find the same facility, and she told me that they wanted per diem. I was on the ball with that information; I went and filled out all they needed. About one week later, I was called for an interview.

I got the job. I didn't know if I should have danced, jumped, or cried. I just love the man Christ Jesus. I had been working at this place for two weeks then. One day, my mother called me; it was about Abigail; it seemed as if she was sick. My mother took her to me in Hartford, where I took her back to Hamden to see her own doctor. While we were on the train, she was just crying and telling me not to let her go back to my mother's house. She wanted to stay with me and her dad.

I just cried and told her that I promised her that I would not let her go back, only for visits. When we left the doctor's office, Abi had pink eyes. I called my aunt and told her if Abigail could stay with us until I got somewhere to live; she didn't have a problem with that.

I took my baby to my aunt's apartment; I told her it was the last time I would leave her for so long. My aunt told me to stay with her in the room because she didn't want to catch the pink eye. I got the disease myself. I was out of work for now due to the fact I was a per diem. I had needed the hours so badly, but nothing. I then got another job to help out because I needed the money to do a lot of things.

Edward was still in Hamden; I told him to come down and fill out an application for jobs, but he still didn't do it at all. I had to pay my aunt's landlord's daughter to babysit. Thank God my aunt told me that I didn't need to give her any money at all.

I helped out in working; I cleaned the place for her; after all, Abi was there too. My aunt cursed a lot at Abi; I didn't like it at all, but I had to keep it to myself because we were not at our own places. We stayed at my aunt's house for a few months, well before I got a call from the realtor. I hoped that this house was the one.

I was really tired of looking at places that didn't look good. When I went and looked at the place, I knew that this was the one; it needed a lot of work. I knew that we could do it. I called the banker, and they went forth with the paperwork. I then called Edward to come and see the place; it took him a while to come. This was the time when the tire met the road. Edward had only saved eight hundred dollars, and we needed five thousand dollars. I had saved up to two thousand dollars. I asked him what he was doing with his money. "Paying bills," he said.

I knew I had to get two thousand dollars fast. I put pride behind me and called my sister Althea and told her to loan me the cash, which she did. I knew that I would be wasting my time with Edward. She told me fine; I went once more and did what I needed to be done. I got all of the money and paperwork in.

Meanwhile, I was still working; my aunt asked me what was taking them so long. I guess she was getting tired of us. She wanted her home back. It was not easy living with people at all because you had to go by their rules; I never one day disrespected my aunt; in fact, I love her for all that she had done for me and my daughter. She gave me a lot of good advice and some not-so-good, but I thank God for her, even though my mouth was straightforward. I love her; she knew me, and that was it with our relationship.

Two weeks went by, and they called us for the closing of the house; Edward and I went. As I sat down, everyone was getting paid except us. We had to pay out everything we had, but it was worth it. Now the place needed a lot of work to be done. Edward was still in Hamden, working and paying his bills. I didn't see sense in what he was doing; he always thought that I was the bad woman. I told him I needed him to help me to fix up the place if we wanted to move in. He still stayed in Hamden, working to pay his rent where he was living.

I called his sister and asked her if she knew anyone to help me move the furniture to the house. She told me that she had an open-back truck and she would find someone to help me. I didn't want to bother my brother once more; God knows he helped me a lot.

She called back and told me everyone was busy, but she would get Edward's daughter to come and help us. I didn't know that she was back in Hartford. The last time I spoke to her, she told me that she didn't need to be in contact with us; she was old enough to do as she pleased. So I left her alone. Now she was staying with her aunt. She came and helped us move the things into the house's basement.

I still needed Edward's help to fix the place, so my aunt got a handyman who I had to pay. I don't know if this man was blind or what. When the man had painted and fixed what needed to be fixed, I was still working both jobs. Sometimes, I didn't even have bus fare to go to work. My aunt did much more than my husband did. I had to struggle a lot, but he finally got home. After I learned that he had gotten fired, he was home fixing the cabinets and so on. I had opened all kinds of credit cards so that I could buy things. I needed to fix the place. I had one for Lowe's, Home Depot, and Bernie's.

I had to pay off all these bills, and Edward was not working. I was so stressed out, but I still had to go to work. We lived near the bus stop; I was glad that we had gotten that house, it had all the stores nearby, and the pharmacy was nearby as well. We didn't have a car, so that was good for now; public transportation was our means to get around.

I would have to wake up at 4:30 a.m. to get ready and catch the 5:30 bus to go downtown Hartford, then catch another bus to West Hartford to be at work at 7:00 a.m. There were a lot of sacrifices that I had to make. I called my brother and told him what I was facing; he told me that I needed to pay off one bill at a time. I did what he told me, but owning a house was not easy. There was always something that needed to be fixed.

We had a two-family, which helped me with the mortgage a lot, but with other bills alone was a struggle. Edward needed a job to help me with the bills, but he thought that being a stay-home dad was helping me; to top it off, his family had a meeting, and they decided that his daughter should be living with us; after all, it was her father's house too. I told him no. After all, they put me through. I needed some break from them.

He was not working, and for me to take up another mouth, that was too much. His eldest sister came to the house and told me that this house was not for me, to begin with; it was for Edward and his daughter's mother. I just stood there with my mouth open. She was right. Two months later, his daughter moved in. Then his mother came to visit. I was so stressed out, but I still could not give up.

His other sister got him a job, while another one gave him her car. He was lucky like that; this job only lasted three months.

Our little life was the same; he didn't want to change at all. His daughter was still there, and I was getting sicker each day. There were times when I had to be sent home from work; it was too much. I could not handle all of this. Then I got a new tenant; she didn't want to pay her rent, and Edward didn't want to help. I couldn't take it at all. I called my church family that I once knew. When they came to the house, they were so upset. They told me I should be dead already; they prayed and prayed for me and then prayed the house out.

His daughter left once more; then they told me to be careful. I guess I was naïve. I always give people the benefit of a doubt. Abigail was going to school now, and Edward was still not doing anything with himself, not even going to get help for himself.

One day at work, I almost passed out, so my job had to call the ambulance, which took me to the hospital; they called my husband and told him. I was alone there. He didn't come at all. I was in a lot of pain, but still, they didn't know what was wrong with me. When I came home, his sister was there with him. We started to argue; I asked him why didn't he come and see if I was fine, and he told me that he didn't have any bus fare.

I knew that my aunt was at work and she could not come, but he was home, not doing anything. I just cried and asked God to help me. The next day, I went to my doctor to see what was the matter with me, and he sent me to a specialist. When I got there and told the doctor all that I was feeling, he told me that it was lupus. I didn't know what that was; then he looked at my fingers, and they were all crooked.

He took some X-rays of my hands and showed them to me. On the X-ray, my fingers were okay, but looking at them, it seemed as if I was an old lady. He told me to go into his office; when I went in, he asked me if I had a family. I told him yes; I was married and had a four-year-old daughter. The doctor looked me in the eyes and told me I should go home and prepare a will. I was dying, he told me.

He didn't explain to me what lupus was; now he was telling me to go get a will. His assistants looked at him and told me to get a second opinion, which I did. Then, I got another one. After running test after test, it was proven that I had lupus. I remember feeling sorry for myself that I went and looked at myself in the mirror. I looked depressed and was losing a lot of weight. I was just feeling sorry for myself and was thinking about Abigail; at this point, a lot of things were going through my head.

I went to the mirror in my bedroom and said I was dying to myself. I broke down and started to cry. Then I heard a voice in my head, as loud as can be. He asked me what I was doing to myself. He told me that his Son didn't die for me in vain; he told me to get up and fight, and that was all I heard. I don't know what it was, but I got some inner strength at this time. I called my workplace and told them that I was coming back to work; the scheduler couldn't understand at all, but I was at work the following week.

I went to one of the social workers and asked her if she could look up all the information that I needed for this thing called lupus. She didn't wait too long. She came back with the treatment center, what I needed to eat, and a lot more information. I went home and was there, reading up on these things. That voice I heard was upset that I had given up on life; now, I had to fight back. Abigail was only four years old. She needed her mother, after all; his other daughter would be in my house taking care of her over my dead body, I thought.

The strength I got was unbelievable. I had to fight the worker at work, plus the demons at home. I was in a battlefield, and the enemies were not backing down on me. I would fast and pray for Edward really badly; the more I prayed for him, the worse he got.

One day, his mother came to the house to visit us; she was there for a while. He was there limping. I asked him if he was fine, but, as always, he told me to leave him alone. Then his mother asked him what was wrong; he showed her his foot; it was the thing I saw in Hamden.

I didn't know what had happened, but I was on the floor. I could not move, but I could hear them. The same voice told me not to move at all. I told him that Abigail was crying because she saw me on the floor. I begged him, but he told me to be still.

Chapter 29

I could not believe what came out of Edward's mouth; he told his mother that I should die. He wanted me dead and gone with. When I heard those words, I could feel my spirit inside my body moving all over. I was paralyzed outside but moving inside. I could not describe the feeling, but what he said took my soul away. I was just crying and asking God to help Abi because she, too, was crying and telling me to get up. He told her to move away; I heard his mother telling him to call 911, but he refused.

I don't know who did, but the police came to the house and asked if everything was okay, and he told them yes. When his mother told him to get me up, or she was going to call my aunt and let her know, he got me up off the floor and threw me on the bed like a sack of potatoes. When my body hit the bed, I asked God to please let me move so that my baby knew that I was alive. He wanted me to know what was in this man's heart. He wanted me dead, and that was all. I was blind all the time, but I had to wake up now. I remember talking to the Lord. I told him that I knew that he would not be happy with what I was going to do, but I was going to get a divorce. I told him I was sorry I didn't keep my vows to him, but this man wanted me dead.

I told him that I promised that I would not get married again as long as he was alive. I called my aunt and told her what had happened; she was with me all the way. I didn't know how to explain to a four-year-old little girl, but I had to. This was not a road I wanted to take. God knew I'd tried.

I told him I wanted a divorce; everything went left; he went and called his family members. They took him and left. I called my mother and told her what was taking place; she didn't waste any time. She came down with my sister and brother. My brother took his new girlfriend with him; they came, and when they saw how skinny I was, my brother asked me if I was going to die.

My mother was at the top of her voice. She told my brother we needed to move out all of my things from the house. They moved them to my aunt's garage; then she told me to get away for a few days. I told her when I got some days off from work. My brother had put a lock on my bedroom door and left only a bed for Edward to sleep on. They took out everything I had bought and moved the place around. When I looked at the place, I felt sorry for him; if only he didn't want me dead. I kept asking the Lord why all these men wanted me dead. When I looked inside the house, it was empty; it reminded me of my parents' home. I didn't want this to affect Abigail at all, but being together was killing her even more; the arguments and the fighting were unbearable.

181

I was at home one day; when I got a call from a man; he asked me who he was talking to. I asked him who he was looking for. He told me that he was Edward's lawyer. I just laughed; he asked me what was so funny. I told him he didn't have money to help me with the bill, but he got a lawyer. He asked me why I was divorcing him; I couldn't hold it back. I just told him as it was; his lawyer told me, "Whatever you do, please do not leave the house." I told him what he had done, and he wanted me dead. He told me that I could lose my daughter as well as the house. He told me all that Edward was after; he wanted the house, my daughter, and for me to work and pay him alimony as well, which means as long as he was alive. I would have to take care of him.

The lawyer told me not to tell him that he gave me this information, but he was not going to take his case at all. I could not believe it at all; I didn't care if he wanted the house but my daughter. Heck, no; I did leave the house and went to New York for some time with Abi. When I came home, he was frightened when he saw me.

He thought that I had given up; he knew the law pretty well. I knew this was going to be a ruff war, but with the grace of God, he would see me through. Edward got himself another lawyer. I didn't have the money for that; after the first rounds with him, I got hit so hard. His lawyer came with Edward's sickness and how I wanted him out of the house after all he put into the marriage.

I was in the courthouse with my mouth open; they wanted me out, but the court clerk told him no. We had to live together in the same house until the divorce came through. I could not believe all of this, and his lawyer had no heart; they were after blood. No mercy or anything; I knew I had to trust God for this one. His eldest sister came to the house with his other sister and told me that they were going to see to it that their brother got everything that belonged to him.

The other one told me she would know if I was serving God. I didn't know what I was dealing with, but I had to stay prayed up. I went to church every other Sunday due to my work schedule; I called one of my aunt's friends and asked her if I could come to her church. She didn't mind at all. I didn't feel this pastor at all, but I still went faithfully. Even though I was going through this drama, to top it off, Edward's lawyer came to where I worked. His wife was sick as well.

I looked up and told God I knew it was not him; it was just a test from the enemy. I had to go into the room and introduce myself to them and ask if they needed anything. This hurt me. Then one of the nurses told me that they weren't cheap lawyers at all; you would have to have money to deal with him. I knew if I wanted to see my Abi, I had to get a lawyer myself. I got one I could afford; now, I had to pay him as well. I was tired most of the time; I had forgotten that I had lupus until it flared ups. I would be sick at work, but I had to pay the bill. It was always something with this man. He told me to leave his freaking house, but I would tell him to pay me back; things were ugly. I could not see myself at all; I had turned into this monster.

I could not believe that I was going to church Sunday after Sunday. The devil told me to stay home and fight, but I went to church anyway. When I went to church, one of my church sisters asked me if I heard the gunshots last night. I told her no; she said that a young lady got killed. I told her I didn't hear anything; when I went home, I got a call from one of my co-workers. She told me the news; it was one of my co-workers who got killed. I sat down on the floor, with the tears just rolling out of my eyes. I asked her where her mother was. She told me she was the one that found her. My heart was bleeding for the loss of my friend, and my heart ached for her mother. This young lady was so kind to everyone. She always called me when she was going to work and asked me if I needed a ride, then she would take me home.

I would offer her gas money, and she told me no; how could I face her mother? What could I say to her to ease her pain? When I got to her house, it was full of people. When I went inside her bedroom, she was on her bed; words could not come out. I just cried; she was there comforting me. I know what it feels to lose a child; it's like a part of your soul is missing. The what-ifs or the whys; a lot of things were running through my head.

I could not contain myself; I just cried out to God to comfort her. When I was finished, a lot more people came in asking her what happened; I don't think she knew that at all. She was just lost in space; I managed to move out of the way while others consoled her. This was a sad day for all of us; she was a happy and loving soul. Always having fun and loving children.

I went downstairs and saw some of my co-workers; they didn't talk much. I did the same; I stayed for a while, and then I went home. I was just thinking of her mother if she had heard that her baby was dead, but to find her dead was heart-aching.

The following day at work, no one spoke at all. I went into one of her patient rooms; she just wept. I did the same thing her mother did to me, just hug her. I knew in my heart she would miss; another soul died from gun violence. It was about a week before her funeral; Edward told me that he was sorry to hear about my co-worker; he didn't know her, but he saw her whenever she came for me to go to work. It was a dark day for her mother, but I had prayed for her so that God could give her the strength she needed. I came home afterwards.

What is life? You're here today and gone tomorrow. I was in a battlefield with my husband, who promised to love and support me in everything possible, but he was always trying to pull me down and lie. I didn't know what to think right now; my heart was telling me something while my mind was showing me all the facts. I followed my mind; I had to put a hardness on my heart right now because my heart was getting hurt all the time. I had to be strong for my daughter; this was no time for pity right now.

As I watched the weeks go by, Edward and I were at each other's throats. We would be cursing and yelling at each other. I would always tell Abi to go into another room. It got so bad that I would call the police in Hartford; that didn't do me any justice at all. They came and made me look like a mess; they were shaking their hands and telling me that I needed to go into a shelter; one of the police was going through a divorce himself. He told my husband that he knew how he felt. I didn't know what else to do; even the law enforcement was on his side. I felt alone, so whenever we had an argument, I just looked up to Jesus; he heard my cries.

Night after night, I sat in this abuse with this man; there were days when I felt like I would just run away with my child, and no one knew where I was; a lot of thoughts came to my mind. I just had to ride it out, take all the shame, and just swallow it.

Whenever I was at work, no one knew the pain I was going through. I didn't know if it was lupus or what; I had pain I never felt before. He would do all kinds of dirty things, like make a mess on the toilet seat. He knew that Abi used it too; if I asked him why not clean up after himself, I was told that it was my job to clean up after people, that it was my life to clean up people's mess. I wanted to jump on him so badly, but God kept me. If it was not one thing, it was another.

One day, I came home from work and went into the room where Abi was playing; I found a bottle of Tylenol lying on the floor. I took it up and saw that it was his daughter's chewable one, and it was empty.

I took it to Abi and asked her where she got this from; she just looked at me. I began to scream at her and asked her if she had eaten them; she told me no. I went to Edward and asked him about the Tylenol. He looked at me as if I was crazy and told me to leave him alone. I went on the phone and called my aunt; she told me to get dressed and take her to the emergency room. I was in the room looking for the empty Tylenol bottle but could not find it. I went to Edward, and he told me to leave him alone.

Now I was crying because he hid the bottle from me, and I was looking through the garbage can to see if he had thrown it out. My aunt looked at me and told me that it did not make any sense and that we should just go and check her out. When we got to the hospital, I told them I thought my daughter might have taken some Tylenol. They looked at me really strangely. They wanted to know where the Tylenol bottle was, how much she took, and how she got it. I told them I didn't know anything at all. I was at work, and her dad was watching her. I was getting upset; too many questions and no time to waste.

Chapter 30

They finally got a doctor, and he told me that they were going to give her some dye to drink and see if she had taken it at all. It took four of us to hold her down; this child was wild, but we managed to give her the dye and put a needle in her arm for the IV.

When the doctor came back, he told me that he knew that she was not in any pain; he was trying to make a joke, but I was too upset to laugh with him. Then he told me that they were going to give her something to pass it out; we were at the hospital for five hours. We went home with Abi and then my aunt as well; the next day, I had to call out from work just to watch her because her dad was not doing a good job.

Abi came and told me that she was sorry that she took the Tylenol; she thought that they were candy. I told her not to do that again; I asked her how she reached them. She had climbed up on the chair, she said; I asked the good Lord to help me, and he told me to just sing. I did it, and it actually worked; I felt like a peace of anointing came over me. Whenever he makes his mess or tries to get to me, I sing him out. He would look at me as if I was crazy. Sometimes, I had to lose some of the fights, but with Edward, I lost a lot for a peace of mind.

I was coming home from work when I saw a lady in the grass. She asked me if I knew who she was; I told her yes. She was his daughter's boyfriend's mother; she told me that his daughter had her grandchild, and she wanted him. I looked at her and told her I did not care at all because I was going through a divorce. She just looked at me while I walked away; things were up and down, mostly down. I would pick my battle with this man because he knew the system well; he was married twice.

I would fret during the winter because of the winter bills; he would turn the heat up to where he would use the fan. Whenever I told my aunt, she would tell me what to do, but I didn't follow her at all. We were going back and forth to court; he had his rights, and so did I. Edward knew how to push my button; when I came home from work, really tired, he started an argument with me. He came into my face with his loud noise; Abi came into the kitchen where we were. I told her to go back into the room; then he came over towards me.

I had the phone in my hand, then he tried to punch me, but I missed his hit, then I used the phone in my hands and hit him in the mouth. His tooth came out. He started to yell that I was an evil person. Then he went to Abi and told her I had hit him for no reason. His tooth was shaking already, and he knew this. I only helped it.

I wanted to hurt him so badly, but I got control of myself and told him not to mess with me when I had a phone in my hands. One day I called my mother and told her that I was just going to give him what he wanted because this was too much for me, and my body was calling out for help. I went to the point of giving him the house, but he wanted more. I could not take it at all; he told me that he wanted all that I had; it looked like he even wanted my soul, but he was out of luck. I had given it to the Lord already. With the laws in Connecticut, you could not leave the state with the child. I just had to fight out my battle.

One day, we were at each other's throats; while I was talking to my mother, she heard him so loud that she told me to call the police. I told her no, due to the fact of my last encounter with them. When I hung up the phone, I heard the doorbell ring; it was the police once more; it seemed as if my mother had called the cops. This time, God had sent these guys. It was a black man. When he came in, he told Edward to get dressed and leave, but he refused, and then he told him not to let him speak again. I knew that this man knew the law.

The police looked at me and told me straight; he said that he didn't understand us, Christian women. We just sit in a lot of mess with these abusers because of the Lord. He asked me if I thought that God wanted me to be in this mess. He was just sick and tired of seeing it all the time.

He looked at Edward, told him to leave, and told me to have a good night. I had to think twice about what he told me. He was right to think that I was alone. I don't know how many women in this world were going through what I was facing. I called my pastor friend in New York because the pastor I had in Connecticut did not see eye to eye at all. This pastor got mad with me because he wanted me to cosign for a loan for the church for him. This man was a teacher, and his wife was a nurse. I was just an aide. I didn't have that kind of money; he never once asked me if I needed help; he always wanted money from me.

He told me to give him a full paycheck, and that was when I knew he was not hearing from God due to the fact that God knew that I didn't have it at all, and I was looking for him at the church to help me. In the Bible, they help each other, but today, they only want to take from you to help someone else and then get the credit; first, take care of your house hole before you can help others.

There are a lot of members who are facing hardship, but due to pride and first fruit, it's a lot. I was always at his ceremony; he was always happy to see me, then he would know what to preach on that day. One Sunday, when I went to church, he was just preaching to the congregation; then, he looked at me. He came over with a smile on his face; he came in front of me and put his foot on the chair next to me.

He was preaching about people getting married... "And now they are divorced, right, sister Angela? This shouldn't have happened. God didn't want these kinds of things in his church." The tears came out of my eyes; I couldn't hold them back. I was crying inside out; I never called him at all for any advice. I was so embarrassed when he did this to me. He didn't care at all for all the pain and hurt that I was going through. Even the same church people would tell me what to do to Edward and how they would help me. I would call my sister's pastor in New York. I told him what I was going through at this point.

I told him I just wanted to give up, even my faith, because I should not be going through all of this. I was a Christian, and they should not suffer the way I was. He just laughed; he could clearly see that I was not reading the

Bible at all. He even noticed that I was angry and bitter. He listened to me as I unloaded on him, then he asked me if I was finished. The first thing I noticed about him was that he listened to my cry, and then he spoke.

He told me that the Lord heard me loud and clear; he even told me to stop listening to what people had to say. He told me that all advice is not good advice, even if it is coming from your mother. I should also remember that I was still married to this man, even though he had done all these things to me. I was to continue cooking and washing his clothes like I had promised to do. Then he showed me all I needed to hear.

He was just letting me know the truth about myself; then, he told me that God was carrying me through this test; you can pass it or fail it. It was up to me to choose if I wanted to take the test all over again. Then he told me that Jesus did the same thing as well. The shame and condemnation with people, and moreover, you are living for God because you would not have been going through all of this if you were serving the devil. He told me to continue to read the Bible and pray and sing songs unto the Lord, and he will be with me until the end. Then he prayed with me; when he hung up the phone, my flesh was very upset with him; but he was right.

I had to get back with the Lord and stop listening to everyone else but the Lord. I knew that I was angry and bitter, but I needed to pray and ask the Lord just to clean me up once more. I went on my knees, thanked God, and started listening to the Holy Spirit.

Things he told me to do were just right. I had to fight my mind a lot because he told me to wash his clothes. I was hurting all over. I was there asking God if this was him or the devil. Sometimes, I knew it was God and acted as if it was Satan, but he would watch me. I knew that I had to repent and do it all over again, as the pastor told me, since I had started cooking once more so that he could get something to eat. Since then, I had stopped going by my aunt's house for dinner. She was wondering what had happened, but I told her I had started to cook now.

I know that I could not let her know because I would have been called crazy. I did what the Holy Spirit told me to do. I was happy that I had called the pastor in New York; he really helped me a lot. I felt better with myself. I was feeling good, but sometimes at work, my body would break down. My fingers were swollen a lot, and I could not even work with the patient fast enough. My job performance was slow but sure. Edward even cooked sometimes and asked me if I wanted some; I would tell him, "I'm good," which meant, "No, thanks." I didn't trust him at all; he used to cook for me a lot; no wonder I was so messed up.

As time went by, I got a letter from my lawyer telling me I had to give him two thousand dollars more to give Edward's lawyer. I asked him, "Why? So that you can get the money for an apartment to move out?" I didn't waste any time; I did over time, a lot of them.

The more I worked, the more taxes were taken out of my check, but I still had to find his two thousand dollars as well. I finally got a date for the divorce; I had to take Abigail to school because her father wanted to make sure he was there on time. His sister took him there, the one who wanted the house so badly. I had to take the bus. When I got there, I didn't see my lawyer. Then, I saw him go over to Edward's attorney. It seemed as if they knew each other.

Here we were, fighting, and these guys were friends. Edward knew the part well. When he came into the courtroom, he had a cane with him; when he was home, everything was fine. As he was walking, he fell to the floor. I said to myself I was done for. The judge asked him if he was okay; he said yes with a pitiful voice; then I heard the judge say something to the lawyers, and they told us to go to another courtroom. This one didn't waste any time; he read everything over.

Edward was called to do his thing; then, I was next. I remember answering "yes" to most of the questions. The judge asked me if I was okay; I told him I sounded like a broken record with all these yes. They all laughed; then he asked me if I wanted my name back. I told him I didn't give it up, to begin with. I loved the name my dad gave me, but I didn't tell the judge that. He signed the decree and hit his hammer.

We got up, and my lawyer wished me congrats; it was nothing to be happy over. I had failed this test as I watched Edward's sister take him out of the courtroom. I kept hearing a voice saying how the mighty had fallen. There were a lot of demons in that courthouse. You could hear them loud and clear. They were bitter, wicked, evil, and angry. They wanted blood, and they wanted mankind to suffer.

They wanted pain and hatred to continue going on. I think we should pray for the court system a lot. When I went to the house, Edward asked me for his two thousand dollars. I told him I gave my lawyer the money to give his lawyer. Then he got angry and told me he wouldn't see that money at all. I told him that it was out of my hands now; he got so upset. It seemed as if he wanted to give it to his sister, the one who wanted the house, but Edward's lawyer won in the end. They gave him two weeks to move out; he asked me if he could stay and pay me rent. I told him that I was following the court's order. All this time, he didn't have money to help me out, and now he wanted to stay to pay rent.

His family, who was once with him, was now against him. When I came home, I called my mother and aunt and told them what had happened. They both told me to be careful; while he was there, nothing had changed at all. I still cooked and gave him and washed his clothes. He was in the house, not looking well at all; then, he told me that his mother wished to speak to me. When I took the phone, she asked me for two favors; she wanted to know if I could take care of Edward when she passed away; she even wanted me to promise her that. I asked her if she knew what she just asked me to do; she said yes. I asked her what about his family. She told me they didn't want anything to do with him.

I just told her no. It would not be fair if I got married again. I didn't think that my husband would like that, and I didn't think it would be fair for him. She told me that she understood. The next thing was that he was out of insulin, and his sugar was acting up. I asked her again about his sister, who took him to the courthouse. She was a nurse. His mother didn't have the money, and no one wanted to help him.

I told her I had just given the last money I had to his lawyer, and now I had to find two more thousand dollars for my own lawyer, plus twenty thousand dollars in the next five years to give to him. I didn't have it at all. She thanked me, and I gave him the phone. When I walked away, I heard the Lord telling me to go and get the insulin for him. I was upset; I asked him for what money. He told me that I had a credit card. I then told the Lord I had only a hundred and fifteen dollars on it. He told me to use it all; I was mad at God for that. I told him he knew what this man had done to me, and now he wanted me to max out the money I had saved for a rainy day.

While I was walking away, he told me to do it for him. God really knows how to get to me. The tears came out of my eyes as I was putting on my clothes to go to CVS. I didn't tell him where I was going. When I got there, I asked them how much money was for the insulin. She told me a hundred and five dollars. I just shook my head and swiped my card. I looked up to heaven, and I heard him telling me thank you.

I came home and gave him the insulin; then he was there crying; he called his mother and told her. She told me, "Ann, may god bless you and keep you safe and Abigail." I told her everything would be fine. I was crying even more over my credit card being maxed out.

The two weeks didn't waste any time running off. His eldest sister came for him, the one who told me that she would know if I was serving God or not. I don't know if she was a witch doctor or what. She told me as she was leaving the house, "I see that you are serving him, after all." I still didn't understand what she meant until this day.

Edward was gone, and there was a lot that I needed to get over. I needed to stop buying dry food; I could actually buy food that I could cook; it was so bad that I came home from the grocery store and went into my bedroom with the food.

I was used to this; whenever I bought food, he would eat all of it and forget that his daughter had to eat as well. So I had the custom of going to the store and storing things in my bedroom. My room was a prison room for me, and I did everything there. That day, I came home from the supermarket. I went into the bedroom. I remember the Holy Spirit telling me that it was over and it was okay to put my food back into the kitchen where it belonged. I remember I went on the floor with a loud cry. I was just thanking Jesus for what he had done. I cried so loud that Abi told me, "It will be okay, Mommy."

I was glad that Edward was gone, but I did feel sorry for him. He had listened to his family most of the time. Now, they turned their back on him. I tried to make this marriage work, but it took two people to do so. Now, the real test began. It was time for Abigail to go to school. I didn't have a car to take her. I always had my co-worker take me to the store and work sometimes; she was very helpful. There was no way I could ask Marie to take me to work every day; that was way too much.

It was a total mess. Now I had to wake her up at 5:00 a.m. and get her ready to take the 5:30 a.m. bus and drop her off at my church sister's house. She lived near the bus stop. So she could take Abigail to school with her kids. It was really hard for me because she had her dad who got her ready in the morning, which was one less stress. I had to do this for a while, which was getting the best of us. I felt really sorry for her to be on the bus so early.

One morning, a passenger came on the bus and got upset with a couple of us parents. He said that the children should be in their beds, sleeping for school. If only this man could understand the sacrifice that we had to make for our child, but I didn't have to explain this to him. I was having a lot of problems with my church sister; whenever I got to her house, she would take a long time to open the door. Sometimes, I would miss the early bus. Then she told me I should let Abi stay the night over. I could not do that; I was on the bus praying for a way out of this; it's so funny you would listen to the same church people who would give you advice and then turn around and hit you really hard. I needed help, and I knew that the good Lord was going to help me.

This went on for a good time. My aunt could not have watched her because she had work as well. We had it really bad, but I had to do what I had to. I would have to get her ready in the morning and wait for this lady to wake up. Sometimes, I would leave her at the door so that I could catch the bus. I never get on the bus until she opens the door for her. The church sister would let Abi and her kids come home together; then, I would take the bus and get my daughter after work.

One day, my cousin called me and told me that she was going to give me her husband's van just to help out. I was so thankful, but I needed my driver's license. I was doing a lot of things at this time. I knew how to drive a little because I used to take driving lessons but failed the driving test twice. I knew little about that; it took Edward and me to be separated for me to get my license really fast. When I was with him, I didn't have to get it due to the fact of me thinking about money, but God was working in my favor really well.

When I got it, I felt so good; but I was scared to drive. Everyone was in a hurry on the road; sometimes, my heart would be at my throat. My brother had taken the van, and I got a car. I even had to refinance the house so that I could get Edward's name out of it. My aunt would ask me for a ride; I would tell her no; she felt as if I was being selfish. Little did she know, I was only scared to drive. I didn't do highways at all, and if I went over a bridge, my heart was in my mouth. I couldn't wait to get home.

I would take Abigail to my church sister's house at 6:30 a.m., but it still was a problem for her; she told me that she was not a morning person. She would call me at 2:30 p.m. and tell me that I had to leave work early to pick up the kids because I had a vehicle, and she did not. I could not handle this at all, so I called her dad and told him if he could get Abi to school while I picked her up. I would drop her off at his mother's place. Then his sister would take her to school.

Now I knew I had to find another way out; I went to work and asked my boss if I would come in early and leave early; she told me no. The next thing I did was, I went to Abigail's school and asked one of the teachers if she could keep her for me until I got off work. She didn't mind at all; I gave her fifty dollars, which she didn't want to take. I did this until Edward told me that Abigail was getting to school late in the morning because it was too much for his sister to do. When you think that things can get better, it gets worse. I got the car so that I could take care of her. I was just asking the Lord what I could do; he showed me a way out.

One evening, I went to get Abi from school, and I saw a sign; it was a daycare. It was right there in the school; the man ran the program, and his wife did a daycare in the morning at 6:30 a.m. The good news was that it was across the street from her school. I went over and asked him for all the information. It was about one hundred and eighty dollars every two weeks. I didn't have any choice; I did what I had to do. This was good because I didn't have to race home to get her, and I could do my errands as well.

I had to cut back on a lot of things, like the home phone and the cable. It was a lot, but we got by. I wasn't getting any money from her dad; he was not working; on the weekend, I would have to take her to see him at his mother's place. Sometimes when I couldn't make it to Edward, I would take her to another church sister's house for her to take her to church. She was getting big, not like before. I would call Mother, and then she would take her.

This was our life story; Abi knew our routine; at least no one could curse us out about the early bus ride. If only people would understand what it meant to be a single parent. I was really tired when I got home from work.

Sometimes, I would cook pasta. It was the easiest thing to prepare. That was just life for Abi and me. We would check her homework together when the daycare helped her.

During the summer, my cousin called me and told me that she was coming to help me paint the house, and she wanted Abi and I to go to Disney with her and her sister. I needed a break from life itself; we went and had fun. As I watched this child on one of the rides, she didn't look happy at all. She was so bored that she almost fell asleep. I could not believe it; I told her that children all over the world would love to be there, and she was sleeping on a ride. She looked at me and shook her shoulder. I guess she was bored; I tried to get her mind off things. I only hoped it was working. That summer went by fast. We would do our daily routine; she was my little company.

I would call her my pocketbook; sometimes, when I got sick from the lupus, I would ask another church sister to keep her for me. I didn't want her to see me like that or when it was during the school week. She would help me a lot; it was too much for her, but God helped us.

We had our good days and bad ones; one day, I went to her parent-teacher meeting. While I was there, I went to talk with her teacher; just to see how she was doing. Then he told me that Abigail told him that she needed a dad; I told him that she already had one. I didn't even wait to hear anything else. I just walked away. When I got home, I asked her if she told her teacher she needed a dad. She looked me in the eyes and said yes; she told me that he was her teacher and she loved him very much. She knew that I didn't have a husband right now, so he was right for me.

I just walked away. I could not win with this kid. I was so embarrassed; I didn't know if I could face this man ever. I didn't know what she was thinking, but she was looking out for me and herself. I just shook my head and went to my room, the place where I spend most of my time. I cried there and prayed there; I talked to God there; it was my place of rest. I didn't know what else to do with this kid; I had to find something for her to do. On Halloween, if it fell on a school day, I sometimes took her out. She didn't go to school that day. We could go to the movies; she didn't understand why, but I didn't want to get her used to having candy and celebrating a holiday for the devil.

Most of the time, she would ask me for a baby brother, and I would tell her no, or when I went to the store, I would pick up one. She just looked at me to say, "How dare you!" This child did not know I was told by the doctors that I should not have any more kids. If I had decided to have one, it would have cost me my life. I always felt the pain over that sometimes, but she never gave up, but I would tell her the same thing over and over again. I would ask her dad if he wanted her for Thanksgiving. He would take her. If I was off, that could be it.

Christmas was the same. If I was off from work, she was mine; if I had to work, she would be at his mom's place. Then I would get her after work; if he wanted her for that day. I would have to back off; we got along with these holidays, and she loved it too. She got her gifts and was good with everything. I always dreaded going to work on Christmas Day, but the day went by really fast.

The holiday came, and now it was a New Year; my life was the same ups and downs, and we didn't argue much. I knew when to walk away and when to just smile. I did what I knew best, but I was still missing something in my life. I didn't know what it was. My church sister called me and told me that she had just graduated from ministry school; she gave me all the information I needed, so I went and filled out the application and did the class.

It was interesting; there was a lot I thought I knew about God. I was getting tested and tempted. When I got to work, that was when my real trial began. The patient was on a trip, and so were my co-workers; we all had problems.

Chapter 31

Some of the patients' problems were even bigger than mine: their children, bosses, and family members. I didn't know if there was a sign on my forehead, but they always came to me for advice. I would ask God to answer them, which he did.

My biggest test was one of my patients; he was a man that didn't have any manners at all, and every word that came out of his mouth was bad. He would tell me things like to clean him up with my tongue or just racial things. If you were having a bad day, he was not the person you wanted to see. I would go to the supervisor and tell her that the patient had just fired me from my job; she didn't care at all. I would have to go back to the room. I went back in and told him, "Until death do us part, you are not getting another aide. This face you will see in the morning; I would be your wife. I will bathe you, dress you, and feed you. The only thing I won't do for you is cook. If you poop, I will have to clean you. I am your all and all." That made him mad. He told me I didn't have any ambition.

He sounded just like my ex-husband; sometimes, I would make him get the best of me, and sometimes, I just wanted to hit him over the head; but I had to walk away. Whenever he saw me, he would give me a hard time. I just sang and blocked him out of my mind; I guess he was right. This was one of my tests if I wanted to be a minister. He got so used to me and knew what I was all about; I tried to not let him get the best of me, and I just started to sing. He didn't like it one bit; that was when I sang more.

When he finally gave up, he asked me who I was. I told him, "I'm Angela." He looked at me and said, "You are different from the rest." Then he started to cry. He told me he did everything for me to hate him, and I kept showing him kindness. He couldn't stop crying. Then he told me if I knew what manner of man he was in his days; that's why he wanted to die; I told him that he was okay and that life would do this to him, but he had to hang in there. I went and told the nurse; they took it to another level.

Now my patient was on twenty-four hours watch; I had to stay with him at all times. When I went to see him, he would tell me to stay with him. If another aide had him, he wanted me to feed him and clean him up; even on my days off, the aide would call me and say that he wanted to see me. I could talk to him and tell him to behave himself. On Monday morning, when I got to work, they didn't shave him at all, and his clothes were not washed. I had to take care of him as if he was my husband.

Wherever I was, he would be at the top of his voice calling me; no one wanted to go in his room because he would tell them to get out. Our friendship was good; I would call him my husband, and he knew I was his wife. One day, he gave his heart to the Lord; that day, he cried like a baby. I was so happy for him. It seemed as if we all needed love; some did, while others didn't. The next test was another patient I had; she was racist. She didn't like black people at all; she rang her bell for help, but I was with another patient. When I got to her, she was upset, so I asked her if she needed help. She looked at me with evil eyes and said, "Do you know what we do with people like you? We hang them upside down and skin them." I looked at her and said, "Really!" She was so mad that she told me to get out, screaming at the top of her voice.

I didn't know that the social worker was outside the door and heard everything; she went to the administrator, and they came to me apologizing for the patient's behavior. I told them that it was okay. I didn't know that white people treat human beings like that, and when they are finished, they call other people animals. The administrator told me not to go into her room at all. I was happy; one less stress for me.

As an aide, it was a ruff job because you had to watch out for the therapist, the nurse, and the family members, and when they wanted to cut staff, it was even harder. You would have to do double work. Whenever the bell rang, and it was not their patient, they would not answer it at all. It was hard working on that floor; no matter what you did, it was never good enough.

I was asked to work over one evening; it was a totally different atmosphere. The workers worked together, like my old job did. I saw the supervisor with a toilet plunger; I asked her what she was going to do with that. She then told me to fix the toilet. I was surprised to see that kind of teamwork. The only problem I had that night was with one of the aides. She was there talking, and I brought up God; she didn't like the idea that I spoke about him. She told me that she used to be like me. Then she realized there was no God at all. "Where is God when so many people are being killed?" And she went on and on. Now she was using her education on me; she was going back to school for psychology, and she made me look small. Two of the other aides were laughing; I just asked God to fix this. He told me to let her read 2 Colossians. When she was finished, she told me that I was good. I said to her, "No, God is good." And walked away. I did what the good Lord told me to do; that was how I got my job done.

One of the things that I hated at work was when my patient died, you would come to work, and then they would die just like that. It was hard to deal with most of the time; they didn't want you to get close to the patient, but how could you not? You saw them every day. One of the scariest things was to clean them up when they passed away. It was scary, at times, to look at a dead person. I remember one day doing this with one of my co-workers; when we turned the patient on her side, she made a sound. We both ran out of that room screaming. We went to the nurse, and she was just laughing at us; we both looked at each other and shook our heads.

I remember a nurse once told me that I could not work at a place like that because I was too emotional. I took her advice, and it almost killed me; I didn't have any compassion at all because everything was routine. When the patient died, I came like nothing to me until a mother died one day. Her daughter was waiting for the nurse to come in the room to pronounce her dead, but he fanned me off when I told him that her daughter was waiting on him. He didn't see the young lady, but she saw him.

She was at the top of her voice crying; she told him that it was her mother, she might mean nothing to him, but that was her mother. It felt as if she had ripped out a piece of my heart with her. I was just crying with her for her loss and her pain. I didn't even know if I could handle that one. I knew when my dad had passed how I felt. When we work with these patients, we don't look at them as if they are someone's loved ones; it's just a job to us, which is not right.

I went home that night and poured out my heart to the Lord and told him that I didn't need to be a nurse if it meant that my heart was going to get hard. I didn't want to hurt people like that. I've seen a lot of aides being mean to their patients, and if you report them, they call you a snitch.

Things were not always the same whenever they didn't have enough patients at my workplace. I was being sent home a lot; I didn't say much. It was happening too often now; I asked them if they could rotate the aides to be sent home because this was putting a hole in my budget. No one wanted to do anything about it, so I had to because I had too much on my plate.

I stood up and told them no. I was not going home; I had a lot of bills to pay, and my daughter needed all the help I could give her. So they did the next thing, they sent someone else home, and that left us working with less help. The patient and the aides suffer as well. It never gets any better; management always wants to save money while their workers suffer. You will do the dirty work while they get the credit.

I could not complain; I had to do my work and take it with a smile. I was still going to school for minister. It was a lot on my plate, but you do what you have to. The patient that loved me so much had died; I missed him a lot; even when the nurse got me upset, I would go into his room, and he would tell me not to let them get the best of me. I would look at him and ask him who told him all of this; he said, "I learned it from you." He was right in a lot of ways, but sometimes the nurses would talk to you as if you were a dog with no respect.

I saw patients come, and I saw them leave, both home and the other side. I would ask some of them if they knew the Lord. Some accepted Jesus, while others told me they would rather go to hell. I didn't think in my lifetime that anyone would want to go to a place like that, but we all have to choose where we want to go. Some of them were of different religions. I could only help those who wanted to be helped.

One thing I wanted more than all was to heal my patients; I prayed for all of them and asked God to save some. They were people with many problems; I had some of my own. I was told once never to take home all this stress with me, so when I left work, I would leave it right at the time clock. I brought home with me pain and heartache; this went on as always; someone needed my help, and I was there to help.

My life went on as always; my aunt told me that she was planning to move back home to England. I didn't believe her at all due to the fact I was alone in Connecticut. She stayed true to her words; once you make your plan, stick to it. She left three months later. I missed her so much. Edward was the same as always; he would call me whenever he needed anything. Abi would make sure I stayed to my word. I would take him to the supermarket if he had a doctor's appointment.

One day, I got a call from my sister Marlene; she wanted to know if she could come and stay with me for a while. I had space, so it was not a problem at all. When she came, Abi was happy because she would go into her room and talk. She didn't want to talk to me too much because I talked a lot about God, and my sister didn't. I did what I knew best, but it seemed as if I was just too much in God. I was not going to compromise at all because he brought me a mighty long way. My sister came, and she put on cable; she loves to watch TV; not saying I didn't like it, but it was not in my budget.

She told me to put it into my name, which Abi loved; now she could watch her program once more. Things were going on fine until the car started to act up.

When it was not one thing, it was another. It seemed as if the car was always in the shop. I would call one of my church brothers, and he came and looked at it and told me he could fix it, but it was gone once more. My sister told me not to give him the car at all because he was using me. He didn't like the idea at all, so they both had an argument. She didn't like church people.

I didn't use him anymore to fix my car; it was getting to be a lot of problems, so I asked her if she thought that I should get another vehicle. She told me that it was a good idea, and I thought so too. I did get another vehicle; it was not a new one, but after two weeks, it was acting up as well. I took it back to the dealer. They told me that there was nothing they could do about it; now I had a vehicle that was shutting off on me in the middle of the road.

I got it back to the dealer, parked it in the parking lot, and called a cab. The people at the dealer thought that I was crazy. Now Abigail and I were taking the bus once more. I told them I would only come for that vehicle when they fixed it.

They refused to do so. I did all I knew how; I even wrote DMV, but they would not help me at all. After all, everyone was friends with each other. No wonder you could drive a car off the lot without going to the DMV.

Things were so bad I even asked the daycare worker where Abigail went too. I asked him if he could talk to these men for me because I was a woman, and they treated me as if I was nothing. I thought that if they saw a man's figure, they would get scared. That didn't move them at all; they still turned me down; they even threatened me if I didn't come and take the vehicle off their property... What were they going to do with me? I did the next thing that came to my mind. I called one of the men from my union; he's an Italian like them. I told him the whole story; I gave him the information, and he told me not to worry.

He was right; I got a call to come in the next day. I was told to pick anything off the lot. I was so happy. I saw one I had liked a lot; when I went over to the dealer, he told me not to listen to them. They only wanted to hurt me; he told me I had to take out another loan to get that vehicle. He told me that they were all crooks, and they wanted me to pay. His advice for me was to take back the vehicle and let them fix it. I didn't know if he was telling the truth, but I had no choice. These men were just plain evil when it came to women, and to think that they had wives, daughters, and mothers too. I drove off the vehicle and asked God to put his hand on it for me. He did, even though I was tested more than once with it, but I kept saying it in Jesus's name. His name is powerful.

I had my ups and downs with life itself. One day, while I was at work, I didn't hear when the call had come in. The receptionist came to me and told me I should call home. I asked her what it was; I asked her if it was my daughter. She didn't know. When I called home, it was my sister Marlene; she told me to come home right now.

I asked her if everything was okay; she told me to come home. I asked her if it was Abi, Mother, or my brother;

she insisted I come home. I went on the phone and called my sister Althea, and that was when she told me that my nephew had gotten shot and died. My sister Karen's son lived in Jamaica. I was driving and had to pull over. I asked her what had happened to my sister; she told me that she did not know as yet; she only called me so that I could comfort my oldest sister. She told me that she thought that she was going to die.

I got home, and then I called my sister once more; she told me they were at my sister's house; I listened on the phone when my sister got the news about her son. I could hear the scream and wheeling; my heart dropped once more. Another mother cried for help; I listened to my family tell my sister the most disturbing news.

I kept seeing my co-worker; I could not cry. I heard something in my head burst, and blood was gushing out of my nose. I had to sit down and hang up the phone.

Marlene came into the kitchen where I was and told me to go to the emergency room. I asked the daycare lady, Mrs. Jenkins, if she could bring Abi home for me, which she helped out a lot.

When I got to the hospital, they asked what had happened. I told the doctor; his advice to me was less stress; he was sorry that I was going through this, but I had to be really careful. When I came home, I told Abi about what had happened; she didn't know Leon at all. This was another thing that was on me, the guilt that I was facing with my own problem; I was more focusing on my own thing and forgetting about others. I was the one you would call. Out of sight, out of mind.

Shame on me. I didn't know what to say to my sister. When I got home, they had to take her too with my mother to the emergency room. Seeing her child in so much pain was hard on the mother. I called back my sister Althea and asked her what had happened. She told me it was a drive-by shooting. He was at the wrong place at the wrong time.

It is so funny, you would hear about these things, but you take it lightly; but when it hits home, man, it hurts. I started to pack up my things, and I called Abi's dad. I told him that I needed a suitcase for Abi and a plane ticket as well. I didn't have any money to buy a ticket for myself, but I was packing my suitcase. Edward didn't say no at all; he told me to come for the money, and we could get the suitcase the following day. He helped out a lot, and I called my brother about the tickets. He asked me if I had money, and I told him no, but God would provide.

I went to work and told my scheduler about my situation. She gave me extra hours and some sick times with my bereavement days. I had almost two weeks off, but I took days off without pay. Marie helped out really well, as well as the scheduler. I was grateful for the help.

I didn't plan this at all, but who plans for death? I got everything, and I was ready to take off with my daughter and sister. We had to meet our brother with his girlfriend at the airport.

My mother and sisters went down two weeks early. They had enough time to do what they had to. Althea was out of work for some time now, and Mother stayed home and took care of her grandkids. They were okay, so they went with Karen. When we finally reached the airport, I greeted my niece and brother with his girlfriend.

It was always a situation to meet each other like this. Then it was time to get in line to get checked in; another line was open, so my brother ran over to the agent first. He had cut a white man in line; he got upset, and everyone was mad. What he did was wrong, but I got so mad in the airport and told everyone I was sick and tired of the hatred and cursing all over the world. I told them as it was. I said, "We are all going on the same flight; does it matter who gets checked in first or not? The pilot won't leave any of us; we all will be on the same flight at the same time. What we should be doing is praying to God to let us reach safely."

I heard one of the workers say amen; at this time, everyone was quiet; then I told my brother to wait his turn next time. I didn't care who wanted to hate me; I said it, and that was final. We got on the plane, and it took off. When we reached Florida, we had to connect to another flight to Jamaica; then, we got a taxi to the house. Mother and my sisters were out; they had gone grocery shopping.

When they came home, my aunt, who had gone back to England, was there too; I hugged her so tight. She was just looking at me and Abi. I was happy to see everyone, but it was a sad occasion. We greeted the neighbors and family members; our home looked so small. I remember it so well; this is the place where our lives have changed.

I had to get a hold of myself; the house looked like crap, but no one wanted to fix it at all. Everyone wanted to claim it, but to fix it was another story.

I was once told that it was not my birthright, so I didn't care at all, but it brought back memories. I went over to my sister Karen; I didn't know what to say to her. I asked her if she was okay. She just shook her head; her daughter was sad as well to lose her brother like that.

The only person that was missing was my brother Gary and Karen's boyfriend. My brother Gary could not deal with what had happened at all. He still thinks that it was my sister's and her boyfriend's fault that our nephew was dead. They didn't have time for the kids at all, they loved to party, and the kids would have slowed them down. It was sad, but that was an everyday life for a lot of people.

The funeral was in two days; my aunt from England and my mother with their other sister were all there. It was the first time that Aunt Audrey met her other sister. I knew that I was not that bad; as I watched my sister Marlene with her children and grandkids, it was like I was watching a movie in slow motion. Before you knew it, the place was getting packed with people from all over. I didn't remember most of them because we were living with my aunt when we came to America.

The evening went well, then Karen went missing. Mother found her in the room all by herself, crying. We all came in to see her. Everyone was talking and telling her that it would be okay.

I knew that it would take some time right now for me to tell her that. I would be lying to her. I sat beside her and was just asking the Lord to comfort her. I begged him so hard, just for my sister's sake.

She poured her heart out that night, and Mother stayed with her. The day of the funeral was the day to remember; tears and more tears. I could not cry at all; I had to be strong for her and myself. Althea was just standing by herself; Karen was gone; she was lost. Marlene, on the other hand, was crying so loud and hard. She sounded like she was going to pass out. While my nieces were crying too, Abi didn't know any better. She was crying as well.

When I looked around the place, the devil was having a field day. I was running back and forth; I went over to Marlene because they told me that she was going to pass out; I got so angry and slapped her across her face and told her to get a hold of herself. "Karen is not doing so good, and to see you acting like this... Stop it!" I told her.

She did stop and look at me; then I went to my dramatic niece and told her to calm down with my eyebrow mad. I was just getting upset that I told the Lord to let this place be still. Now everyone was in their little world. Everyone was crying louder than the other one. I knew that they missed him, but the way they were behaving was as if they loved him more.

I know that everyone grieves differently, but this was over the top. Abigail had written a poem for my sister and my aunt as well as I read a Bible scripture. Althea didn't want to sing, but I told her to. So we both went up, and she sang the most beautiful song.

When everything was over at the church, we took Leon to the burial ground to say our goodbyes. That was when my sister Karen gave out a cry. That cry I will not forget. It was the cry of a mother who had lost her child. That sound goes to your heart and soul; it burns deep into your innermost being. To know that you will never see him again; she didn't even know if he had called out to the Lord when he had gotten shot.

He didn't die on the spot; they said that he ran inside the bathroom and died on the floor. My heart goes out to mothers who have to face these pain and thoughts in their minds and hearts. When we got back to the house, I told Mother that it was best that we went away from the house. My sister Marlene and niece, with my brother and his girlfriend, went back to America. I was with Mother and Karen and Abi, and Althea went with us too. We went to Abi's godmother's house and went all over for a while.

I didn't know if this was helping her at all; one of the places that we went to was dolphin court. Abi wanted to swim with the dolphins, but it was too much money, so we went to where the caves were. While Abi and I were standing near the cave, my sister Karen told her to pose for the picture; then I heard her. "Oh, my God!" I asked her what was the matter. She said that she saw a light come over Abi and me. I asked her what kind of light it was. She couldn't explain herself, then Althea said she didn't see a thing. I guess it was only for Karen to see. Sometimes, that's how God works. She didn't even take the picture; then we would know what really happened. We went to Dunn's River Falls; this time, Abi did swim. This child wanted to swim that badly; while we had climbed the falls, Karen and my niece went and sat down on the river bed; they were talking.

Then Abi went over to them and sat down. In the middle of nowhere, a gush of water came down and took Abi away. I stood by and saw the water take my baby away. I could not move or talk. Everyone was trying to help her, but the water had her going, and there were a lot of rocks, so I could not run to even save her. Then came a man that was climbing the falls and grabbed her. He had saved my baby and brought her to me. Then she had the nerve to tell me how much fun it was and that she should do it again. I just grabbed her and told her to go to the beach area. This child did not know the danger that she was in. I had to thank the Lord for helping us. We went for fun, and this happened. I had to be on my guide with praying because the devil was not kidding.

We had fun for the reminder week; we said goodbye to our family members once more. Abi and I were on different flights; I had to wait on Mother to get home. I left the following day and went back home to Connecticut. It was a long drive home, but we got home safely.

Marlene was not happy that I hit her at the funeral, but I finally got a chance to hit her. I told Abi to get ready for bed, and I did the same as well. We went on with life as always; everyone was still talking about the funeral. I just wanted to remember the good times with him, even though I didn't have many happy ones with him. I can only pray for my sister and hope she keeps him in her heart.

Life was okay and going well; I would go to work and pay our bills. It seemed as if that was my life in general; one stress after another. As the months went by, the holidays were coming; Marlene asked me if she could invite our cousin from our father's side to visit. She told me that she would invite our sisters as well. I knew that Mother was out of the picture because they didn't like her at all. I didn't mind; due to the fact of my nephew passing, I didn't want to hold any grudge; I told her fine.

The holiday came, and my sisters cooked, and I went to work. I invited one of my co-workers over as well. It was fun, and we all enjoyed ourselves, except my other sister Althea. We didn't see eye to eye; with every event, we would argue a lot. It didn't feel good at times because the dinner would be over. This was one of the reasons God sent me to Connecticut; they still treated me like a kid.

It came and went; the next thing was Christmas. That event went even better, even though I could not drive to New York because I had a lupus flare-up. My nephew Derrick came down and drove us back for Christmas dinner and then took us home. He then took the bus back home to New York. I thought that was the best gift he could have given me. I knew that I had to take it easy, but I couldn't.

The holidays came and were gone; now we had to start all over again with our routine. It seemed as if you knew what to expect with life itself. Then my sister Marlene came with the news I didn't want to hear. She told me she was going home to visit her children in Jamaica. She didn't come back at all. I didn't know if it was the slap I had given her or what, but she left me in a lot of debt. My sister came, and then she took off once more. I was so upset with her. Every time I tried to help people, they always hurt me even more. I was left with all the bills and a car note, too much for me, and they were still cutting my hours at work. I was stressed, but I still did not throw in the towel.

I had to do my best with all of this; I had to cut back on some of the bills again. I needed the vehicle to take me to work and Abi to school. It was a mess, but I trusted God, and he brought me through. I was always there helping my co-worker back and forth, wherever they wanted to go.

Chapter 32

I always look out for people who need my help. Even Edward called me for a ride to go to his doctor's office as often. I did, of course, even though we were not married. I would look out for him. Sometimes, I would tell him I was not a cab driver, but he still called me.

One day, he asked me to take him to the supermarket to get him some groceries. He told me that he wanted all these things and that I should get what Abi wanted as well.

I helped him get his groceries, and I picked up stuff for Abi, as he told me to; then, he said that he wanted to sit down. I just looked at him, and he then gave me his food stamp card. I looked at him; I told him that I did not know how to use this, and he told me that they would tell me how to do it. I was so embarrassed to use it. I didn't know what to do. I always used cash and did what I had to do. I was in the line praying that I didn't see anyone I knew.

I was so embarrassed, and he went in the car, not to be seen using his card. I went in the vehicle and told him, "Next time, do your own shopping yourself." I didn't want people to judge me at all, saying that I was living after them with the state money. People can be cruel at times. I know because I hear them talk a lot at work and even in the stores at times.

He didn't understand it at all; I was full of pride and self-righteousness; who would think that Angela would be using food stamps?

Then another time, he did this to me, it was even snowing, and he didn't have any food at his place. He was moving from house to house; his family had told him he had to move out of his mother's apartment, but Edward didn't. So they took her to one of her daughter's homes.

Edward had to find a room for himself, and he didn't keep the place clean; that was the reason he kept moving. I wasn't there to clean up after him; I still had to take Abi to see him.

It was his right, and I had to follow the court's order. When I took him to the store, there was so much snow, and his landlord didn't clean up the driveway yet.

His foot was not well, so I had to take him through the snow to the back door so that he could get inside. I told Abi to keep the door closed as I took this two-hundred-and-change pound man to the house. We both fell into the snow; I could hardly get him up.

Finally, when I got him to the door, I had to get his grocery to him once more. There was a lot of snow, about eleven inches or more. I remember crying to the Lord and asking him to please let Edward find a wife to help him. I was getting tired each day. It was too much for me. I was divorced and still was taking care of this man. I did it for Abi as well; he needed help a lot.

I could do so much; my poor heart was killing me; my life was a mess. I wasn't trying to prove anything to anyone because if people found out what I was doing, they would think I was crazy. I did the best that I could do each day. When I didn't have problems at work, I would have it at home with the tenants.

I don't know what it is with people; they have no respect for me. Whenever I stand up to them, I am called all kinds of things. I knew I had a lot of enemies, but I had to be strong. One day at the house, I was doing my daily thing as always. When I heard a lot of cursing and loud noise, I took it upon myself to find out what the problem was; when I went upstairs, it was the tenant's son with his baby's mother fighting; I tried to stop them, but I could not.

I just took their child and went downstairs; I didn't think that he needed to see all of that. When they were finished fighting, they would come for him. He sometimes would tell his mother he didn't want to go with her. I tried to show him kindness, which kids need.

I had so many things to hold down; I was almost finished with school as well. I was so happy with myself to have accomplished what I loved. I knew I was tested and tried, but I still held on to the Lord.

The months went by really fast; now Edward had found a woman. This was the happiest time of my life; he had moved on. I was thanking God so much for what he had done. Now I could move on with my life and find someone for me. I was not searching, but I was looking. I saw a lot of men, but I remember the promise I made to God about the divorce; I told him that I would not date again. Even though I was trying to be faithful to my words, the devil had a plan for me.

It was at my workplace when it was not my boss. It was a patient or a family member. I almost fell, but God kept me in his hand and told me not to go down that road. I cried out to God because my flesh was trying to put a strong hold on me. I remember crying out for Abba to give me the strength; my flesh was getting the best of me, and I didn't know how to handle it. God always was through.

The devil was so bad; he would tempt me in everything possible in any way he could, in movies or even songs I would listen to. He knew the promise I had made to the Lord, so he wanted me to break it. God had a strong hold on my life; he took me through it. So he went to another test. This time, it was racism with the nurses at work.

There were a lot of white nurses and supervisors who thought that they were superior to us, black aides. They would talk to you as if we were dogs and nothing else. I knew in my heart that God was my Father, and there was no way on Earth that I would allow anyone to treat me as such. I am a child of a King, and no devil in hell was going to put me down. They tried in every way to write me up or even get me fired, but God showed up and showed himself to them.

This walk I had to take was a hard one, but I only had to trust in him. I had to stop going to church for a while due to the fact of what that pastor was doing to me, but I was going to Bible school and was getting fed with the Word more than ever. I did the best I could with life itself; I tried to live a Christian life, but it was hard.

Wherever I went, I always felt like an outcast. I didn't know if people understood me or not. I didn't always listen to God, but when I did, I was called crazy. I remember one of my co-workers telling me that he could not talk to me at all; he said that in any conversation I had with him, only God knew, and he asked me something about politics. I would answer him; only God knew. He was upset most of the time, so we never talked too much about anything. When I was at school, it was the same thing.

I loved school a lot because I was surrounded by a lot of elderly people. They are wise, and I needed that right now; no time for idling. I was on my way to becoming a minister; I was even more focused than ever. That was what I was taught; I had all the tests I could ever have.

The first one was with a church brother; he told me that he loved me very much. Now this man was married and had children. I didn't love him like that; I had to let him know that God was the only man in my life right now; he still didn't take no for an answer, so I told him that we could not be friends anymore. He didn't like it at all, but he did back off. I'd learned my lesson well about other people's property.

Then the devil kept tempting me. This time, it was one of the bosses at work. He was always there wherever I went; one of the times, I thought that he was stalking me. Then I felt that it was cute. I would love the idea that this man liked me like that, even though he didn't tell me that at all. He was always around; he was not married, which was good. I never tried to mix busy with pleasure. My flesh, on the other hand, had the best of me. It would tell me I was all that and could get anyone I wanted.

I could not see what was happening to me; I was being led by my flesh; now I was going to school and studying the Word of God, but I was being tempted, and I didn't notice it at all. This went on for a while; I was faced with a lot of things in my life right now.

I remember I went to the lord in prayer and asked him what was wrong with me. I wanted to know if I was going crazy or what. I didn't go out on a date with this man, and I was having feelings for him. Was it because I saw him every day at work, and he was always around us?

I saw the side he wanted me to see, which was loving and caring, but other workers told me he was crazy. The answer I got from God, I didn't like it at all. He told me that this man was not for me, even though my flesh didn't like the answer that it got.

The Lord let me know that not everything that appears to look good is good. I'd been through too much not to pay attention. Even though the flesh was upset, I had to listen to God because he knows best. I asked him to take away the feeling that I had developed in my mind for this person. It took some time to get over it. The next thing the Lord did was to get rid of him. I did not realize that the enemy was tempting me so much. I had to be more careful because this walk was no joke at all. Christian life is really hard. The enemy wanted me to fall so badly, but I thank God for Jesus Christ to be there looking out for me.

The months went by, and graduation was here. Time waits on no one; that weekend, my family came down to celebrate with me. They could not wait until the ceremony was finished, so they left me all by myself. They even took Abi with them before the graduation was over. I was all alone when I came out; my mother, brother, and cousin left me there, and to top it off, I had gotten the valedictorian for my class. No one to celebrate with me. I took a picture with my teacher and was just walking around and looking at students with their loved ones embracing each other.

Here I was, with the most accomplishment and no one to share it with. I was angry and mad at the same time. I was so disappointed. I wanted to tell them a piece of my mind. When I got home, they were at the house getting ready to leave to go back to New York. I just took some pictures with my daughter. As I watched them take off, I kept wondering what was wrong with me. This day was so important to me, and I needed my family with me. They didn't care at all; it was not like either of them had to work the next day because it was a holiday. I knew that what I did for the Lord was not important to them, but for God's sake, it meant a lot to me.

I was so mad at them. I didn't let them know how I felt because they had to drive home to New York. I did to let them know how I felt a couple of days later, and then I hung up the phone. I knew my family was upset about what I told them. My sister told me I was ungrateful that they even came. I still could not understand it at all. She came as well and did not even come to the graduation at all because she didn't feel good.

They still would have to wait for me to get home to the house to get Abigail. This was the moment when I felt that I had accomplished something for the Lord, and they didn't stay to share that happiness with me. I still didn't understand that at all; I was upset for a couple of months, and to top it off, God told me not to finish with the ministry school. I almost died when I heard these words.

He told me that he didn't call me to be a minister; I did it because I heard someone talking about it. I didn't ask him at all. I went and did the class, due to the fact I wanted to look good. I cried so hard that I felt like a failure once more. I started something, and I could not finish it. He told me that he wanted me for another mission, and I was to wait on his calling.

I didn't mind at all; I still didn't lose out on anything. I still had the Word, and it was in me. I got to understand a lot with God. It was not on my timing but his. I knew I was not perfect, but I tried to listen to him most of the time. To serve Jesus in the world today, you are going to get ridiculed.

People, in general, don't know that the enemy is fighting them each day. He knows what button to push and what to pull. I had to just keep focus on the Lord. Sometimes, I did get lonely, and Abi was set in her ways at times. I think it was my fault with her. I always pushed her away due to the fact of this lupus, and I knew I could leave this earth at any time. I always thought that if I died, she would not miss me as much.

I know what it felt like when your parents died, and you loved them so much. I taught her everything I knew she would need to survive. Abigail probably thought that I didn't love her, but the world in which we lived was not pretty at all. I saw too much pain and hurt with everyone.

I taught her to only trust the Lord because he would never let her down at all. Even when it seems God is letting you down, he is always there to help us through the good and bad times. People can never be trusted due to the fact of our sinful nature. One minute they got your back; the next, they wanted to stab you in it. My motherly advice was not good at the time, but I was trying to do what I knew best.

The next thing went wrong was that Edward was in the hospital. They didn't know what had happened to him. His sister, too, was in the same hospital as well. She had a stroke, so I went and visited them.

Chapter 33

I didn't know if it was right to have visited his sister. After all, she didn't like me. Edward's brother Paul saw me and told me she was on the other floor. I went with him to see her. She didn't look that great, but I still prayed for her, then I went and looked for Edward. I would take Abi and my church sister to visit him at times. This kid would be in bed with her dad and just smiling while I watched her with him.

I remember Edward asking me when I was going to finish my book. I just looked at him; then my church sister asked me when. I didn't have words at this time; we visited him day after day, then they took him to a nursing home. He didn't like it at all; it seemed as if Edward was not taking care of himself. He was eating what he felt like eating, but the next time I went with Abi, he was cursing everyone at the home. I felt so embarrassed. I just went into the waiting room and waited until Abi was done visiting. He was cursing a lot of bad words, and his daughter was there. I went and took her. Then he told me he wanted to go home. I told him that he needed help first; of course, Edward didn't stay at the nursing home; he took himself out and went back to this apartment.

He was home and was just calling me a lot for help; his new girlfriend was gone as always; he asked me if I had seen his other daughter. I saw her now and then, and I tried to keep her in Abi's life. She had two children now, and I wanted Abi to know her niece and nephew.

One night, I dreamt about Edward. He was in a store with a lot of people, and he was there, giving a lot of problems. He had on black pants and a red shirt. I told him that he needed to just chill and behave himself. He just looked at me; I thought that it was strange.

I got a call from Edward; it seems as if when you think of people, they call you. He told me that he was looking for a place to live at this time. He told me that he had heard from his other daughter. She was somewhere about the place. He wanted to stay with her, but she didn't return his phone calls. He gave me the number to call her, which I did.

She spoke to me and told me she was fine; she asked for her sister. Which I didn't have a problem with at all. Abigail wanted to see her, so I took her over to her home to visit. She was happy to see her niece and nephew; Abi asked me if she could stay with her sister for a while. I didn't mind at all; she was old enough to handle herself.

Abi wanted to spend some time with them; I asked the young lady when was the first time she had spoken to her father. She told me for a couple of days. I didn't get involved with their situation at all due to the fact Edward was looking for somewhere to live. I let Abi stay with her for three days; I didn't want to put her in that uncomfortable situation with her dad.

Edward was still calling me and asking me about his daughter. I told her, but I didn't know what was going on with both of them. I went to work, and then I would visit the kids. I was spending most of my time back and forth with them. I always send Abigail to her dad's place. When I called him that Thursday and told him that I was going to take her over to her sister's house once more, he told me fine, so I did just that.

I took her there, and she stayed a while with them; we went and saw the fireworks; it was a lot of fun to see all of that. The kids enjoyed themselves a lot; I asked Abi if she wanted to come home, and she told me no. I let her stay with her sister once more; then, I called her dad to let him know because I had to follow the court's rules. He didn't mind at all; I went to work on Sunday, and then I came home.

While I was getting ready to go and visit the kids, I got a visit from Edward's sister. She told me to sit down; I knew this look; it was the look of death. She told me that Edward had passed away. I didn't know what to say to her. I was just shaking. She told me that she had gotten a call from his landlord. He had died in the room where he was staying. I wanted him out of my life, but not this way.

How was I going to tell Abigail about her dad? I asked her if she had told Edward's daughter about it, and she said yes. I called her as soon as she left and asked her if she heard, but she was just crying. I told her I was coming over; she did not tell Abigail yet.

When I hung up the phone, my whole life was a mess once more. I cried and could not stop. Then I called my mother; she was there with me on the phone. She told me to try and stop the crying due to my lupus. I told her I didn't know how to tell a ten-year-old child that her father, whom she loved so much, was dead. My heart was racing, and I was so nervous. I called Edward's mother, and we were both talking. She was sad; I told her I didn't know what to tell her. She told me I should trust God; he would give me the strength to do so. I took both of their advice and went to see the girls. Abi still didn't know what had happened to her dad.

I went into the room to see his daughter, and she was just crying. I tried to console her. Then I had to do the biggest job in my life. I asked the Lord to help me with this one. I took her into a room by herself and asked her if she had called her dad all weekend; she told me that she had spoken to him some days before. As the tears rolled down my face, she asked me what was wrong; I didn't know how to tell her.

I told my baby the saddest news that no mother should have to tell their child. That child held me so tight and screamed. I felt it to my belly button. I just held her as she cried; the tears just rolled down my face. I didn't know what to say to her; I could not tell her that it was okay and she would be fine. She loved this man so much, and now that he was gone, it seemed as if her whole world was ended. I just held her and let her cry out her feelings. She fell asleep in my arms.

When she woke up, I asked them if they wanted to see their grandmother; they both said yes. I couldn't drive; I was in the backseat with the kids. Edward's niece was with us at the time, so she drove over to his sister's house.

When we got there, his mother and two of his sisters were there, with his nieces as well. The kids went over to their grandmother and embraced her. These ladies didn't waste any time. They wanted to bury him on Wednesday. I could not believe it.

His mother wanted them to hold off for a while to let the rest of the family know; then, one of his sisters was upset. She jumped up and said that he was a problem-maker and that he needed to go and get some rest. She said that he caused everyone pain and hurt, then she turned to me and said that I should know that. I just stood there with my mouth open; I could not believe what she said about her own brother and his children were there.

She was mad with him and didn't care to show it; she was the one who took him to court to get the house from me and was the same one who had a stroke. I looked at the kids, then Abi told me that she was ready to go home; the other sister told me that they were going to bury him in red and black. The dream I had flashed before me; I told her that I would get him a shirt. I didn't know what was wrong with them, but a lot of anger was there, so we left. On our way home, the kids were just talking about the comment that their aunt had made.

I could not have said anything. After all, I was the one who divorced him. I was the one who ruined his life, and now I was coming to them with my condolence. I felt really bad to think that his own family was like that, but I was an outcast, so I just held it by my ears. I could only do what I could do. I didn't have any money to help them at all, but they didn't need my money either. One of these sisters called me and told me if I had a pastor I could use. The only one I knew was the one that hated me so much, and Abigail knew him pretty well.

I gave her his number, and then I told her I would pick up the shirt for Edward. She called me and told me their mother had convinced them to hold out for another week. I then asked Abi what Bible verse she was going to read; she didn't know, so I found one for her. One of his nieces is a social worker; she told me what I needed to do to get help for Abi. I was grateful for the information from her. I did my part, and I stayed away as much. I called my mother and told her when the funeral was going to be. I even called my co-workers from my late job and the ones at my present one.

On the day of the funeral, my mother and brother, with my sister, came to support me, as well as my co-workers from Hamden and Hartford. The same day, I got a call from his daughter; she could not get anyone to come and pick her up, so I left Abi with my mother and went to get her with the kids; her cousin was with her as well. When I got to the house, she was still getting ready.

I told her that she needed to hurry up cause I needed to get dressed as well. She finally got the kids ready and herself with Edward's niece; we all left her house. I told them to take my van and go ahead while I rode with my co-worker from Hamden. My brother took my mother and sister with him.

While we were in the van, Miss Smith was there talking to Abi. She told her that everything would be okay. "God knows best, and you still have your mother with you." She told her like it was; she made Abi see that she would always miss him and that he would be watching over her, but she had to be strong for me as well. Miss Smith knew most of what I went through with this man; she told me not to cry too much but to be strong for Abi.

I loved them so much. Even death didn't keep them away from me. When we reached the funeral room, they had already closed the casket. We were late; all eyes were on us. I felt so ashamed. I sat in the back; while I watched the pastor say his words, he didn't know Edward at all, but he knew me. I was always his sermon most of the time; I just held my baby girl as she cried once more. Edward's brother was the one that spoke over the funeral, the one who wanted Abi.

As I watched them as they made their speeches, one of Edward's ex-wives was there. She introduced herself as wife number one; that didn't shake me at all. When they all said what they had to, it was time for Abi to read the Bible verse for her dad. She asked me to follow her, which I did. I could feel all the hatred and anger on me, but I stood proud for her and myself. I knew this pastor was having the time of his life to see me in pain, but I didn't let him once get the best of me.

Abi did well with the Bible reading; then, I took her back to the seat. She just looked at everyone and held me tight. When the funeral was finally over, his brother took the microphone and said that he wanted to give much credit to Edwards's wife number four.

I was just laughing within myself. I was even looking around to see that wife, only to know that the joke was on me. I was that wife, number four. Edward did get his way; I did feel embarrassed, but I knew that he could not hurt me anymore. I said goodbye to him at the burial ground, but Abi was just crying.

Mother told me that I needed to go now; she had cooked some food for us. Marie had stopped by earlier and had brought me some fried fish. They ate, and we talked about the good and bad days; it was mostly bad ones with Edward. I was hurt by the fact I was number four, and he didn't tell me at all. His family could have let it rest, but they wanted to get back at me, and this was how they did it. I was thankful for all the support I got from my family and co-worker from both jobs.

One of our church mothers from my old church came as well. She had helped us a lot while I was going through the divorce. She would call me to come and get food from the food pantry from the church; she was always looking out for us.

Marie, on the other hand, was there all the time; she strengthened me; when sometimes I felt like giving up, she was not afraid of telling me what she felt. She helped us a lot with monetary gifts, and she was always there when my lupus would act up.

God always puts people in our lives to help us when we need help. She was just straightforward with everything; you could not be weak around her at all. Sometimes, she would tell me things to hurt me, but then I was no better at all. We still kept it real; she was there for me even more than my sisters.

As the Bible says, you will find a friend that sticks closer than a brother. When everyone had left, I was so afraid to be in the house all by myself. This went on for months. The fear I felt, if I saw a shadow, I would be rebuking it. I listened to what everyone had to say. People told me that I should put onion under my bed, I should put tape measure over my door. I did all that because I was afraid of Edward's spirit and the fact that I had dreamt of him a week before he died.

I was not having it. He was in black and red in my dreams, and his sister wanted to bury him in the same colors. I was not going out like this; evil spirits were there, and they were real, just like angels. I was paranoid a lot, I didn't want to stay in the house at all, but I had to be strong for Abi. I didn't let her know at all; she was there crying for her dad while I was there rebuking him.

I didn't want any form of spirit in that house, so I would call my other church sister, who knew the Word well. The ones that I went to church with Abi were too much in the world, but there were some church brothers and sisters that were in the spirit.

I finally got into the word once more and started to rebuke things myself. I was now trusting God once more and getting to know him. Abi went to church every Sunday with that same pastor; she asked me why I didn't come back to church with her. Which I did, but it was the same thing over and over again. I was sick with lupus, so, therefore, I was not living right. I took his abuse, but I was not told to leave the church. I told Marie about the behavior of this man. She would tell me to leave his church and come visit the one she went to. I was always told to go to that church because it was near my house.

I didn't want to visit that church at all due to the fact it was the same church in my aunt's home back in Jamaica. They didn't like to wear jewelry, and I loved mine a lot. I just loved to look good in the eyes of the Lord. I always thought that I was his child, and when people saw me, they should know that I was his kid. I had it all wrong.

What I thought about being a Christian was all wrong. It was not the clothes I wore or the things I did, but it was the relationship that I had with the Lord.

It took me a while to understand this, but I had to get back to the Lord. This was not some kind of game I was playing; it was a real-life thing. There are good and bad spirits out there in this world, whether we like it or not. It is real; they tell you how to think sometimes and what you should do as well. If you don't know the good Lord, the enemy will take you for a ride. That was one of the reasons why he wanted people to think that there was no God.

There are a lot of gods, but only one, Jesus Christ, and who was this man, the Son of God? We know that God did not have sex with the Virgin Mary but found favor with her. She was chosen above all women to do this job for him. Jesus is the ultimate sacrifice for all of us if only we believe. We do not have to work on being holy but only believe that he is the Son of God and that he was risen from the dead. I always tried to be holy, but I would always fall on my face.

I did all that I thought that I should have done just to be his child, but all I needed was to accept him into my heart, and he would do the rest. He knows we can not do things without him, so he sends the Holy Spirit to help us. I sometimes held the Holy Spirit down, but he would come through. There was a lot I needed to learn, but it took a lot of trusting and believing in his words and the inner voice inside.

This was my time now to just let the Lord lead me. He told me what I should do and when I should do it; sometimes, I would be obedient, and sometimes, my flesh made me do crazy things. I still went to church with Abi. The church was having a revival; they would get different pastors from different churches to preach. So I did not expect anything at all. I had gotten a call from my nephew in New York.

Chapter 34

He wanted to know if he could come and stay with me, as he always did. I told him yes. I even called Edward's daughter to come and stay with us as well. She knew Derrick also; it was like a little family reunion. I was just looking at both of them; I asked them what they were doing with their lives. I told my nephew that he needed to go back to school, and then I told Edward's daughter the same thing. They both agreed on what I was telling them. My nephew didn't waste any time; he went to New York and got his things.

While Edward's daughter did the same, she got her son in the same school Abi went to. I remember these two kids told me what they wanted to be, and now they were just wasting their time. I hoped this would work for both of them. I had Abi in the room with me, while my nephew had Abi's room. Edward's daughter was in the other room with her children. It was a lot I had taken on, but they needed the guidance. Now she was going to school, and my nephew was looking for work. I told them to go to church with me, but they had all the excuses. I didn't bother them at all. I did what was best.

I was getting ready for the church revival that night; I didn't want to go, but I went anyway. The evening I went to church, the pastor and his members were with him. I saw the guest speaker and his wife; everyone seemed well and fine. I took my seat with one of the members. I knew she was with her boyfriend. When the guest speaker started to preach, it was a different atmosphere.

He started by letting the pastor know about the congregation. He started by saying that some of us in the church were sick due to the fact of our lifestyle. He went on by saying that people were not right, and that was why they were going through it. At this time, the pastor got up out of his seat and was at the top of his voice. He looked over at me and was just praising God.

Then the guest speaker called me out of all the congregation; when the pastor and some of the members got up and were just thanking Jesus and saying, "Hallelujah! Thank you, Jesus! Glory!" I didn't let what they had to say get to me. I went straight to the altar. Now all the members were waiting on the man of God to tell me what I was doing wrong, but to their surprise, he told them what the Lord had said. He told them that I was the only good spirit in the church.

The whole church got quiet; then he went on by letting them know that I was covered with God's hand and that whatever they were doing to me, it couldn't harm me; I didn't take what he said at all. I asked him who told

211

him that; I had to make sure it was coming from Abba. He said yes, then both of us began to talk in tongues. When the two spirits met together, I felt a load come off me.

He told me to continue to do what I was doing for the Lord, and he will see me through. I was just saying hallelujah and thanking Abba, Jesus, and the Holy Spirit.

That's when I went back to my seat and sat down, then one of the members gave me her money to drop for her, which she never did before. The pastor was upset all night, he thought that the man of God was going to embarrass me, but God is good all the time. I had enemies all over the place. I have them at work, in church, and even at home; living for God is no joke because the devil knows who you are. He wants to get rid of you, but I am in it for the long run. When service was over, I went over to the guest speaker and his wife; they let me know that the church was full of demonic spirits, and they wanted me down. I just shook my head and thanked the good Lord. I was upset about the whole situation because some of these sisters I did a lot for by helping them with what I could, and to think that they wanted me down and out... May God have mercy on their souls. I would continue to live for Jesus, my only true friend. When I went home, I told my nephew what had happened. Then he asked me if I was going back to the church ever, and I said yes.

God didn't tell me to leave; no devil in hell was going to stop me. I did go back the next night. When I got there, he had a line of people waiting for him to pray for them. I went in the line myself. Then he told me to go and sit down. Too much evil spirit was in the church. I did as I was told; then it came to me; I knew that my time was done with this church. I sat down and was just thinking on how these people let me feel as if I was a sinner and they were holy. He showed me all the members who wanted to hurt me, and I was so naive to ignore the spirit that was in me.

I will never do that again; now I really know that it was God that was with me. I was just thinking on my past when the patient called me, "Hallelujah, kid." Even Edward's sister told me once she would know if I was serving God or not. Then she told me that I was serving the Master. I didn't know all of this due to the fact of my unbelieving; now I knew.

The revival was over, and so was my time with these people. I told my daughter that I was not going back to that church because those people wanted to hurt me; I didn't get it at all with our pastor. He wanted me to take out a loan on my house so that he could get a church; when I told him no, he was upset with me. Even when I bought my car, he had a problem with me. Then he wanted me to give the church my whole paycheck; I only got paid twice a month. Owning a home, people think that you have money, but you don't always. I had more bills than ever before, and with one job, it was really hard to get by.

I had to leave that church and fast; I didn't know how this world was operating at all. The man of God wanted me to feel as if I was an evil person and that God was not with me. I went on with what God called me to do. When I was at work, this was another story. I would do the best I could for my patient; some of them loved me, while others hated my guts. Not to mention some of my co-workers; they hated me without a cost. I didn't let them get to me one bit; I did what the Lord had told me to do.

This job was not at all good for me, but God wanted me to be there. Whenever a patient was dying, he would tell me to cross them over. They would accept Jesus Christ before they died; not all of them wanted to. I had a homosexual who told me he would rather die before he accepted Jesus Christ. Then I had other ones who accepted the Lord. I realize that you can only help those who want to be helped.

I didn't mind crossing patients over; even some of the nurses would tell me to pray for them. One day, my nurse called me and told me to do her a favor. I asked her what it was. Then she told me that she had a patient who was suffering. The nurse had given her morphine almost a week now, and she was still there.

She had no family at all, only a daughter who didn't care to visit her at all. I looked at the nurse and asked her what she thought I could do for her. She told me to just pray for her because they went fast when I did it. At this point, I felt like the angel of death, not of life. When I went into the room, I could not believe my eyes. It was the same racist woman who wanted to skin me and hang me up.

I went back to my nurse and told her that woman she wanted me to pray for wanted me dead, and now she wanted me to pray for her. She said, "Angela, what was the difference?" She was dying and needed my help. I felt really bad; she was right. If I was doing God's work, no matter what people did to me. I should forgive them; I went back inside the room and asked God to forgive me, and I went to the patient and sang a song for her.

I didn't know if she could hear me, but I told her that Jesus loved her, and I forgave her as well. I didn't know I felt that way toward her, but I felt a peace came over me. I told her, "Goodbye! God bless you." I went home and felt good in my spirit. The following day, I went to work, and I asked the nurse what had happened to her. She told me that she passed a few hours later that day.

It was a good thing that I had forgiven that lady because I would have an extra burden to carry with me. Things were always the same with me and Abigail; we would have our moments. She would be fine one minute and the next upset with me. It was more my fault most of the time.

She didn't like the fact that I was always talking about God; I don't know if I embarrassed her a lot; to be honest, I didn't care at all. I know the God I serve; he's been faithful to both of us. She didn't even invite her friends to come over, but she would want me to let her go to visit them. I used to let her go to my church sister's house, but when she got married, I had to think twice. I didn't let her go back to sleep over; she was upset most of the time; she told me how she hated me and wanted her dad. I felt really bad about what she had said.

I just went on; she didn't know the danger I was taking her out of. I didn't want anyone to hurt her at all, but I was the one that got the end of it. I sometimes tell her things that really hurt her; in the middle of what I said, it was too late to take it back. I would sometimes tell her that she was just like her dad, which made her mad. She didn't like being around me at all. I did what I knew best.

It was too late for me because I had pushed her away so many times. I didn't want her to miss me too much when I died, so I would let her know how life was and what she needed to survive. My parenting guide was not that good. I tried to live by the Word of God. I didn't want her to go through ruff life the way I did when my parents were separated. I didn't date at all; I didn't want a man to treat her the way I went through with my mother's man-friend. I had needs too, but I sacrificed it all for her—the things I lived without so that she could be happy—it was not working out at all. I sometimes would tell her to shut up, or sometimes I would just right beat her.

She would take it and then tell me she didn't care. I saw so much of her dad in her, and that made me mad, but I love her so much. I knew I could not divorce her, but I still had to show her God's love. I sometimes wanted his love to guide me and keep me. I, too, wanted his arms around me. The only thing I could do was just pray and ask God to help me through it all. My life was a mess.

I knew in my heart that God would take good care of me, but my flesh would give me a hard time. I was always wrestling with myself and the spirit of the Lord. I wanted to do good, but when people got the best of me. I wanted to get even with them; whenever I got even, I would feel really bad, and then I would have to go back and apologize to them. Now I weighed the situation a lot before I jumped to any conclusion. I knew I'm not perfect, but I loved God so much that I didn't want to disappoint him.

My life was always the same until something else happened to me. The next thing took place in my life; I didn't expect it at all. One day, I was home with my nephew. I was sleeping. When I got a call from my brother, he told me that a lot of police were coming to my home. I just listened to him as he explained; he told me that they were looking for our nephew. I asked him what for, but he told me he didn't know at all. I should give him the phone.

I got up and gave him the phone, then I took off my bedclothes and put on something else. My nephew came to me and said that he didn't know what was going on. He didn't know why the cops were after him. I looked at him and asked him if he had killed someone. He told me, "No, Aunty, I did no such thing." Then my house phone rang.

It was the police. They wanted to know if my nephew was in the house. I told the officer yes; they wanted him to come outside the house. I went and put olive oil on him and prayed with him before he went outside. I gave him his Bible and told him that God would work it out. I was okay until I opened the door; the street was full of policemen. They even blocked off the street. This was when I got nervous; they told him to put his hands in the air and walk backwards.

He had his Bible, which they told him to drop; at this time, all the police had their guns on my nephew, and I felt blood rush to my head. I heard a small voice telling me to get a grip on myself. I didn't go outside to my nephew at all. I felt so embarrassed and ashamed. I was weak, but I did not cry at all.

Then they took him, and one of the police came to the door. I told him to come in, but he said he was waiting on a search warrant. I just stayed in the house as they took my nephew to the bottom of the fence. I didn't know if I should pass out or just run away. Where could I have gone? A lot of things were going through my head; what in the world had this boy done for so many police were at my home? I was thinking all kinds of things; I knew he was a good kid. If he was not one, then I would have known what to expect.

I called my mother and asked her what was going on, but then they got the warrant to come in. I could not believe my eyes. When they came into the house, they all sat down. I asked them what it was that my nephew did. They told me that they could not say, but they needed to search my home.

They did search my home. They went into the garage and the room that he was in, and they were on the street searching. There was not a place they didn't look through; I told them that they could not search my tenant's apartment, which they knew. When they were finished with the search, one of the cops asked me if he had a laptop; he said that he noticed the cord in his bag.

I told him I knew he had one; then he asked me if that was the one. I told him I didn't know, so he asked me to bring it to him, which I did. He took it and went outside. Then finally, the cops from New York came; they were all there; high-fived each other for a job well done. I just watched them.

There was a female, one who came in the house first, and then the others followed. She asked me if I was Angela, and she knew that I was sick with lupus. She told me she didn't want to upset me. I asked her how she knew I had lupus. My sister had told her that I did. Then Mr. Big Shot came in and asked me who told me that they were coming. I just looked at him and asked him, "Who do you think you are?" I told him that my brother called me and thank God he did. Moreover, we were a close family. I was so upset with him, showing all authority as if he was God.

Then the female cop came over to me and told me she knew what I was going through. I looked at her. She asked me why my nephew was there with me. I told her, "I'm his aunt, and he always comes to visit me." Then she asked me why he had his things with me, whether he was running away from something. I looked at her and asked her why he would run and come to Connecticut.

I told her I was the one who told him to come and stay with me so that he could start a new life because they were only wasting time and money in New York while he could get a job and go back to school. Then Mr. Big Shot was acting up; I just looked at him and was annoyed with his behavior. I was not afraid of what he had to say. Then she asked me if I could testify about what I just told her in court. I told her yes. I asked them again what he did, but no one told me.

When they left, I was just asking God what in the world had just happened. I ran to the bathroom and had a bowel movement. I was just shaking all over; I was so alone and afraid, I felt so ashamed for the fact that I could not help him at all. I went on my knees and asked God just to help him at this time; they took him back to New York. Then the phone rang, it was an attorney, she wanted to know if my house was paid off.

She said that my nephew was in a lot of trouble and that he needed a good lawyer; my poor head was hurting. I told her to just stop; I could not handle this at all. Then I got a call from my sister Marlene; I asked her what was wrong, but no one wanted to say anything to me. I felt like a fish out of water; then Althea called me as well, and she told me she was sorry. I asked her, "Sorry for what?" She said that the way they came to her house and searched it, she knew that they had done mine as well.

I asked her what her son did, but she was clueless as I was. One thing I didn't like was that she didn't call me and let me know what had happened to her. She said they told her that if she called me, they would have arrested her. I was so mad with her, but thank God my brother did, we had nothing to hide, but she was afraid. I was so glad that the kids were not at home. I had to call out from work the next day; my heart could not handle all of this.

When Abi came home from school, the first person she asked for was my nephew; I told her that he had gone back to New York. I didn't want to upset her; she was upset that he didn't tell her that he was leaving. I just looked at her and shook my head; my throat was burning a lot due to the fact I wanted to cry. That night, I was just thinking about my sister. She was brave and everything; now, to save our lives, she could not handle it.

She didn't want anyone to know what had happened, so I got a call from my mother. She wanted me to tell no one what had happened. I asked her what this was about, so I could not tell my daughter what had happened to her cousin. I didn't have a good night at all. I was so restless.

The following day at home, I just stayed in the house; I was so ashamed to go outside. I didn't want to face the neighbors at all; I could not handle the question most of all. My life was a mess, and still, no one called me and told me what was going on. I felt betrayed once more, just used and left.

While I was letting the devil get the best of me, the doorbell rang. It was the police that had come to the house yesterday. They gave me a paper and told me that I was being served to go to court to testify. I felt as if I was going to pass out; I didn't know what was happening to me at all. I went on the phone and called my mother; then she told me that she would call me back. Then in a few minutes, I was on the phone with a lawyer we all knew. He asked me to read the letter to him, which I did.

He then told me that they wanted me to testify for what had happened. I asked him what I should say, and he said, "The truth." As the weeks went by, I was so nervous. Now I had to drive to New York and go to a courthouse to testify for what had happened. The whole time, I was so upset; my body was telling me all kinds of things. If I went what I was going to say, I didn't know anything at all.

The day finally came, and I went with the lawyer and my sister to the courthouse; our lawyer friend told me that I was not under arrest. When the district attorney called me, they took me to a room to ask me more questions. I went with them. They asked me who the young man was. I told them he was my nephew, then I asked her. I thought that she knew that already. The police officer told me they were only asking me these questions first before I went into the courtroom. She then asked me why my nephew was with me, and I told her the reason why already. She then looked at the policewoman and said that was not what she heard.

She heard that my nephew was running, so he came to me. I looked at her and told her as it was; she wanted me to tell lies to say that my nephew was hiding from the police. I looked at both of them and was just thinking to myself, *Why in the world would he want to hide at my house?* He knew when it came to God, I was not having it at all. They knew how I felt with the Lord. They were asking me the same question but in different terms. I still told them the same thing; I could see that they were both annoyed with me; then the district attorney went over to the policewoman, and they were both talking to each other. I just sat there; I could not hear what they were saying.

Then she told me they would need me in a few; I went back to where my sister was. They took me to the courtroom to testify against my nephew. I was called to go on the stand; this was way different from the divorce court. I stood up and had to swear on my father's book.

It was so weird; they wanted me to tell a lie on the Holy Bible. I did what they told me to do. As she approached the stand, she told me to state my name and what I did for a living. She was asking me more questions about myself than about my nephew. She then asked the same question: why was my nephew with me in Connecticut; I looked at her and said I told you already upstairs when you had me in the room, questioning me. She cut me off really fast and told me that I was under oath and everything was being recorded. I told her that I was sorry, I didn't know. She came back with a slap in the face. She wanted to know why my nephew had so many numbers changed. I told her maybe he didn't pay his bill. She was so upset; then she took it personally. She went as far as trying to belittle me; she asked me why I didn't go back to school and better myself because the job I was doing was not at all good.

This was when I got so upset with her. I told her, "For your information, I went back to school for ministry not to tell lies for people, and I see what some of the nurses do to keep their job. I would be fired already." She realized that she was not going anywhere with me; then she said, "No further questions about, Your Honor." She looked at me as if I was garbage, but I was not going to tell a lie for her to look good.

This reminded me of a nurse who wanted me to tell a lie at work, and because I refused to do so, it was a big thing. They called me all kinds of things; who do I think I was? I was acting holy as thou; I was told that the nurse could have lost his license. I, too, was threatened to lose my CNA license, but that was nothing at all to him. After all, the aides were nobody in the sight of the medical field. If I have to keep a job to take away my integrity, I would rather stand up for what is right.

I knew that I could not be a nurse or doctor, not for the fact that I had to study so hard but for the fact that they would do anything to cover up their dirty act. I saw it so much at work; I know that some of the nurses hated me for this. Patients would be so drug up due to the fact that they made a mistake, then you hear that they went to another job.

I could not play with people's lives like that. Some jobs I would not do to make money; if I knew that it was hurting the next person. I saw it every day, how management would rob the workers who did the dirty and heavy work while they took the credit. This was too much, and it needed to stop; if only we all stood up for what was right. I knew that this lady was mad, but I did what I was told—tell the truth. They wanted me to tell a lie that my nephew was running away from New York. I don't know if he was or not, but Connecticut… That was like going to my neighbor's house; I don't understand people at all. After the court, I had to get back home; this was too much for me, and now they left me thinking on a lot of things. This thing went on for some time; my sister was back and forth with my nephew, and sometimes, she would call me to pray, which we did. Then she told me that they were letting him go. I told her to just thank God for that; she was so happy. She didn't want him in New York at all. He came back to me once more.

Chapter 35

I was happy because Abi was happy to see him, and I was relieved over the fact that the neighbors saw him once more. I didn't need to explain anything to anyone; I looked at him and told him that he needed to give his life to the Lord. He told me that he was not ready as yet. I was only helping these kids in life; they thought that they knew everything. I wanted to ask him what had happened, but I was afraid too. I didn't want to ask any questions, and when they asked me, I would have to tell them the truth. I was afraid of lying, and at one time, I was the master of it, but God meant so much to me. I always thought I was letting him down if I went out of his way.

Thanksgiving came, and we went to New York. Everyone seemed so happy. We ate and laughed and had fun; after the holiday, we went back home. My nephew stayed back because he wanted his driver's license and his paperwork from the cops.

When we went home, we were doing the same thing once more. Abi's sister had gone back home to visit. Then she came back to us. She was going to school, and so were her kids; I went to work as always. Things in life are so strange, but you have to do what you have to. Then one day at work, I had an accident with one of my patients. She was acting combative with me. She then came down on my arm while I was cleaning her up; she started with her racist remarks. I don't know what was wrong with these people. The nurse heard her and came in. She asked if I was okay.

I told her that she came down on my arm really hard; she told me to fill out an accident report, she told me that she told the director of nursing about the patient's behavior, and they did nothing about it. I went and filled out the report. Thank god I did; at this point, my arm was hurting me a lot. They sent me out to their doctor. I didn't like the way they were treating me. The lady wanted me to do things that I could not do, just to fill out her paperwork.

I let her know that I was in a lot of pain and needed to know what was going on with my arm; she acted as if I was crazy. I told her that she was rude, and I walked out of their office. I went to my own doctor; he sent me to do an X-ray and everything, then my insurance got involved with the case because it was a worker's compensation problem. Now I was out of work due to the fact that my bones were brickle. They told me that it was not work-related, and they told me all kinds of things.

They told me that it was my fault, that the patient was an assistant of two, the therapist that had the patient's case did not update her record, and now everything was on me. I still stood up for what was right. Now I was out of work, they told me to come and do light duty, but I told them that my arm was sick and I needed rest. This didn't go too well with me; they wanted to go to their doctor so that they could tell lies and then tell me to go back to work.

They denied my claims and told me that I needed to go to their doctor once more. I did not; now, I was home, not working, and in a lot of pain. I had no insurance due to the fact I was not working to pay the copayment. Now I was home, and no money was coming in. I could not go to my own doctor because I had no insurance. This was too much for me. I didn't know what to do. I called one of my patient's daughters. She was an attorney; she told me that she could not take the case, but she could recommend someone to me. I didn't waste any time; I called the attorney whom she recommended. She didn't know me at all, but she knew the other lawyer very well.

She took my case, and that was it. I brought all the paperwork that she needed and then left her office. This was no picnic in the park. I then got a call from my sister; she told me that they had taken my nephew back into custody once more. I was so upset and mad; I didn't know why the enemy was on my back. I knew I had to do a lot more praying than what I was doing. When it was not one thing, it was another.

Now Abi's sister was acting up; she would leave her children with me to take care of. This girl knew that my arm was not feeling good. I would have to get her son ready for school and then take them and then pick them up once more. This was too much for me. I could not call anyone for help at all. I would have to pay my bill plus the mortgage. It was too much for me. Marie told me about a job I could do. I didn't have to lift the patient up but assisted her. She still helped me to find something to do. I would call the lawyer, and she still didn't hear anything at all. I was frustrated with my life at this time; I didn't know what to do. I called Abi's sister and told her to come and get her kids.

I could not handle all the stress and burden with all that was going on. I called my job and asked about my short-term disability. They told me they were looking into it. It was a mess. Then I got a call from the worker's comp. They told me that I needed to get back to work or they would fire me. I told him that I needed to see a doctor or get an MRI of my arm before I got back to work. They called me from work and told me where to go to get an MRI on my arm, which I went and got done.

Things couldn't get any better; Abi told me that she wanted glasses. I told her that I didn't have any money right now due to the fact that we didn't have any insurance. Now another bill was upon me; I remember crying out to the Lord and telling him that I needed his help. I was in tears. The devil was having a field day with me; he told me that God didn't love me at all. I should just stop believing in God and go back to my old self.

Everything was on my mind: my nephew, Abi couldn't see well, and all my bills were over due to the point of disconnection. Even the house was in trouble. I didn't know if I was coming or going. I was only getting help from Abi's money from her dad and the rent. This was still not enough.

The first call I got was from Abigail's teacher; she wanted me to come by the school. I asked my daughter what it was that she told her teacher. She said that I didn't have any money to pay for her glasses; I just looked at her with my mouth open. I didn't know what to say; I went to school the next day. I thought that I was going to see the guidance counselor to discuss my daughter's eyesight.

I could not believe what the teacher had done; she gave me an envelope with money to buy Abi glasses. I didn't know what to say. I just hugged her and told her thanks. When I went home, I was just crying and thanking the good Lord; my heart was full. He went this far by helping me. The next day, she called me and told me not to spend the money on glasses but to go to the store and get some groceries. She told me to come back to the school and fill out paperwork so that Abi could get her glasses for free. Now I was just thanking my Savior. The teacher loved Abi, and she noticed that she was getting behind with her schoolwork. She told me that everything would be all right and I should continue to trust God. This woman was hearing from God; she knew everything I was facing. I didn't tell her, "No, thanks," due to pride; I just thanked her and accepted every bit of God's blessings.

Then I got a call from my workplace; she told me that the MRI had returned and I had pulled a muscle and should do what I was told. I asked her if she could send the report over to my doctor to look at it. Then she hung up the phone. I was still waiting on her. Then I got a call from my friend Marie; she told me she had gotten a job. Her sister couldn't do it at all, so she called me to come and do it while I got back on my feet. I had to know what it was all about because I could not lift up too much weight.

I didn't have to do much, but I had to work in the morning while Marie came in at night. We did this for two weeks; it was not hard work like the one I did at the nursing home. This was a little old lady that was very sweet. She loved to tell her story about herself and her family. She had a son, and he was going away for two weeks. He needed help to take care of his mother. So Marie called me, and I was grateful for the work, so we went and did it. The little lady was very sweet; she was sharp like a knife.

She knew everything about everything. She told me what to do and how to do it. I didn't complain at all. I was happy that I was getting paid and I could pay my bills. Working for her was a lot of fun, and she would give me good advice. I knew I could not be with her for too long; I had to get back to work before I lost my job. I had to go back to my doctor to give me the release form to fill out; he didn't waste any time at all. While I was just getting my things together for work, I knew what I needed to do this time. I put my trust in the Lord and did what I had to do.

I got a call from my sister Althea; she asked me if I was going back to work. I told her I had to do what I had to do to save my house. I knew that my body was not well. I didn't want to be homeless at all; my sister had gotten hurt on her job as well, and she was out of work too. I asked her how her bills were being paid, and she told me that she did not have it at all. I could not have helped her myself. I did what was best for me and my daughter; if it meant I had to go back to work, that was what I had to do; now I had finished all I needed to be done, and I was able to go back to work without any problem at all. When I got back to work, everyone was happy to see me, but I kept to myself. I knew all the hypocrites that worked at that place. They acted as if they cared about you, and they hated you with a passion. I learned a lot about people who would help and who wouldn't.

I tried to do my best and do what was right. When I came back to work, they had us enrolled for insurance. They had Aflac; I took that insurance so fast. I didn't want what happened to me to happen again. I walked around the building, telling the worker that they should take it out so that it could help them.

The next surprise I got when I got back was one of our union delegates was quitting from her pose. She told me that it was too much for her and she was not well to handle everything else. I asked her what the whole idea about this union thing was, and she told me that a lot of workers needed help, but I would be hated by management, and I couldn't disgust everyone's case with each other. She told me that I was fit to do the work. Wrong move, but I gave her my word; then she called the office from the union and told them that I was taking over. They came in and took my information; I had more things on my plate to chew on.

It was a lot of work; sometimes, I would be doing my job, and I was called by the administrator to come to their office. When they didn't fire one employer, they wanted to suspend them from work; everything you could think of, even just to write them up for anything. Now all the stress was on me.

I had a worker coming into my face and threatening me due to the fact they didn't like management; then, management would be against me. This job was no fun at all. I had to be very careful. I could not trust too many people at all. I was constantly watching my back with these people I was helping as well because if they didn't like the result, they would threaten me, not thinking that I had to play by the rules.

It was not an easy job, and with all this work, I was not getting any pay at all. Things I did for these workers and got no respect in return; I did what I had to do with God's help. Sometimes when they came up with problems I could not solve, I just turned to God and asked him to help me; he never failed me yet. Some of the workers had problems with reading, so the management took advantage of this with them. I knew this from the reports I had to write for most of them.

I would sometimes help them with their in-service as well; I would be on the computer with many of their ID numbers. I would make sure to help the ones who didn't know English that well; even the nurses gave me their number to do it for them. They had too much work to do. I don't know why they made all the workers take the same test. I don't think that each person had the same job description.

I was only the worker; I tried to help each and every one of them with everything I knew best. Some of them even brought their own life issue for me to help them with, but I just asked God to help me in Jesus's name. He always sees me through.

Not before long, my sister called me with another bad news; her landlord was putting her out. She was not working, and she didn't have any money at all to find somewhere to live. I told her she could put her things in storage and move in with us until she got a job to help herself. She found all kinds of excuses you could possibly think of; she told me she didn't have any money to put her things in storage. I then told her she could take them to Connecticut and put them in my garage. Now she didn't have any money to do that; I then called my cousin in New York to see if she could help her with transportation; she helped with the monetary gift.

Now she needed a driver, whom she didn't have. I took it upon myself and called my brother Edson and asked him. He didn't think twice; Edson went to Queens and helped her move her things to my house. I don't know how she felt being here in Connecticut; her other son went back with my brother and then came back a week after. Things were different now.

I did my best to try and help my sister with a lot of things, but her mind was on her other son. Nothing I did made her happy. If I told her about a job, she would let me know that she didn't drive, so I suggested that she get her license. Then she told me that she could not see at all. She made all kinds of excuses not to work; I didn't bother her anymore. I just did what I could to help her. Things were good and sometimes bad; I tried to keep it real. I can't say I know what she was feeling, but her action was loud and clear. My other nephew didn't let anything bother him at all; he did his own thing and was just enjoying life.

Abigail loved the company too; as I said, she was with them most of the time. I was glad that they were there; now Abi could stay home more often because being a single parent and having to take her to my church sister's house was no fun for me.

She could sleep in her bed and be at rest; as the months went by, it was almost the same thing. Whenever my friends came by, they would ask me if she was not working. I told them not yet; I knew what she was facing, but they didn't at all. I remember one of my church brothers came by and asked her if she didn't want a job; she told him yes, but she couldn't find one.

He told her to check the mall and other stores, and she told him that she didn't know her way around. He told her that she was lazy and that she didn't want to work. My mouth was open; I didn't even tell him that it was wrong. I was more shocked by what he said. Then I noticed her face change; when he left, she didn't say another word to me. I know that I should have told him to stop, but maybe he was right. She needed to get up and shake herself and try to help the boys; it was not like her son was dead, like my other sister's.

This went on for a while; she would isolate herself from me. I still did my best with all of them. I didn't show them any sign of negativity. I always welcomed people to my home, whether strangers or family; that was me. I did what I knew best, but my sister was hard to please, unlike Marlene. She did what she could do; the only problem I had with her, she talked a lot about politics and hated church people, and I was one of them. She always told me that I was wasting my money on them, and then they turned around and used me.

She was right in most things she said because I can look back and see where they really took me for a ride. Althea was not like that. She was more independent and did her own thing. Now that her son was locked up and she was living with me, only God knew what she was feeling. I tried to help until another friend stopped by; this lady was from my job. She never did this at all; she told me that she came to see my sister. I told her that she was in the room; then she asked her if she was not going to look for a job.

This woman came out the same way as my church brother said. My sister just looked at me and said, "Not yet." It dawned on me that she said it in the same place he did. I should have rebuked her, but I didn't. I went inside my room and asked God if that was him letting her know that I needed help or if it was the devil making mischief in my life at this time.

My sister was drawn to herself; she didn't say much. I invited her to church, but she told me that she was not ready. I didn't force anyone to the house of God because I was once told that I think I am holier than thou.

The week before Thanksgiving Day, I asked Althea if she was going to cook, and she told me yes. I went to the fish market in New York with Marie. I bought salmon and snapper fish. I knew that they loved this, but she didn't get to cook. She was hospitalized for a few days. So I had to cook that day. I did what I could, and I still went to J. C. Penny and got some good sales.

Then she called me and told me that they were going to release her. When I went to get her, the doctor came into the room and told her that he looked at every possible angle and could not see what was wrong with her. He asked her if she was stressed or anything; she told him no. Then he asked her if she worked, and she told him no. He asked her who took care of her; she looked at me and said, "My sister did." He asked her, "Who do you live with?" "My sister." The answers to each question he asked her were the same: "My sister."

I could not say another word at all to her; I felt like crying when the doctor looked at me. God knows I was trying with her, but nothing I did made her happy. I just trusted God because I knew that he would touch her heart. She actually came around; she went to church with me on New Year's Eve with her son and Abi.

It seemed as if she liked it because she was going a lot, even when I didn't go. I thanked God for that because she was getting her mind off herself. This didn't last too long. She complained about everything; even the knife to cook with was too dull. She would complain; she didn't know that she could sharpen it for it to work. I was getting tired of her complaining and fault-finding. She never one day thanked me for anything at all. I talked to God most of the time, and he told me just to show himself in me. He loved to tell me those words, which I had too.

I could not please her at all, so I just did my own thing, and she did the same. One day, it went far. She called me at work to buy coconut milk for her to cook rice and peas. I got off work at 3:00 pm, and it was about 2:45 p.m. I asked her if she didn't have two bucks to send her son to the store to get it, but she didn't say another word. After work, I just went to J. C. Penny and bought myself something. When I got home, she sent her son to the store that was only a block away.

I took my shower and went to bed; I knew that Abi was okay until later. I don't think people knew how hard I had to work; sometimes, my fingers were swollen from the hot and cold water. I was in a lot of pain with lupus; only God knew how I did my work. Whenever it snowed, that was the next thing. It was too much snow, and my nephew would complain too; it seemed as if I was the slave master with both of them. I would be there helping to shovel the snow as well. I tried to be fair and do my part, but it was never enough. I only complained to God; even when my family asked about her, I told them that all was well. One day, a squirrel was in the garage; due to the fact that the boards were rotten on the gutter, it fell through the roof. She went into the garage and saw the squirrel and told me to call 911; she didn't want it to bite her and then get rabies. I did what she said and called the fire department; they came and told me to call animal control next time.

Then she told me I needed to fix my house because it was falling apart; I knew that, but I was more concerned about paying the mortgage first. She told me that she had a friend that knew how to fix everything; I told her to call him and ask him how much he would charge to fix it. When he came, it was a different story. I don't know what she told him, but he didn't do a thing and wanted money. I told her to tell him I didn't have any money like that he wanted to be paid, and she knew I didn't have it at all. So I had to take him to Sears and use my credit card and get him a tool that he needed for his pay.

I could not believe this at all; she knew that I didn't have it like that. I had to pay all the bills, and she didn't want to help at all. She didn't want to work to help her other son. I knew that she was stressed out over her other son, but she still had to live. This went on and on. I just kept my mouth shut and listened to her as she complained about Connecticut; I knew it was not New York, but I had to live where I could afford it.

As the spring approached, things were the same. She was not happy, and I could not make her get to the point of life itself. One day, she came with a suitcase and told me that she was going to New York to visit for a week; I don't know if she thought that I was stupid or what. She never came back, and she didn't speak to me at all, but she left her son with me. I didn't mind; as I said, everyone was welcome. He stayed with me for two years; he didn't let anything bother him at all. Althea's two sons were like that. They were good kids. I used to take care of them in the summer when I used to live in Hamden, so I knew them pretty well.

I did my best with him; I would still go to the fish market and get snapper fish and salmon. I knew he loved it so much; he would even cook it for me when I was at work, and it came out really well. I did the best I knew how; the only difference we had was over church. He would come sometimes, while other times, he would play soccer or just ride his bike. I remember one Sunday, I was running late for church, and I always cooked before I went to worship. I ran out of the house; then I remembered that I didn't turn off the stove. I knew that I would be late for church if I turned back. I didn't take my phone with me either. I was upset in my spirit, so I rebuked the spirit that was bothering me and telling me that the house was going to burn down.

I remember that I just looked up and told God to wake up Raymond and let him turn off the stove, so I went to church and just worshipped, but that spirit of fear kept telling me to go home; of course, I didn't. When church was over, I heard the fire siren going off. Then, the spirits told me the house was burned down. I still rebuked the spirit and went home. The house was still intact. My nephew opened the door and asked me what had happened. I asked him what he was talking about. He asked me why I left the stove on. He said he was sleeping when he heard a voice telling him to wake up and turn off the stove. He even thought it was me who was telling him to check the stove. Then he realized that I was not in the house. I just laughed and said that was the God I served. Abba did wake him up to turn the stove off.

I don't know if that was faith or something else, but I stood my ground with the spirit of fear. I don't think I would do it again; I wasn't sure if I had turned the stove off or not, but God showed up for both of us, for me to believe in him more, and for my nephew to understand that he is God all by himself. I just worshipped him like never before; I then called his mother and told her what had happened. We were talking at this time. She just listened to what I had to say; then, she asked me to continue to pray for Derrick. I always did; he was on my number-one list. I think that my nephew in prison understood more what I was talking about because he saw what God was doing for him in that place.

I keep praying for my family, but they always think I go too far with Jesus. He is always there for me even when my family is not; God sometimes sends people into our lives to help us. I have Marie, who helps me more like a sister, while my flesh and blood think I'm crazy.

I'm not putting her above my family, but I have to give credit when credit is due. When I'm sick with the lupus, and my family knows, no one comes to help me or even help me with my bills. Marie never asks you if you need money; she just gives you a friendly handshake and walks away. That is what I call looking out for each other. Like my sister Marlene always says, we are not her family but her relatives. Her kids are her family, but Marie put her to shame.

Chapter 36

The next person that helped me was Mother Dell; she didn't have much to give, but she always prayed with me or encouraged me when I fell in and out with my family or the sickness. Sometimes, I wish my mother would come and help me, but it was too much to ask her to do. She had her own life to live, and I was too much to deal with. I know that my daughter had too much of me as well. Abi would leave me a lot; she always wanted to visit our church sister's house. I didn't blame her; I was too much of a handful. This is the reason why I can't put anyone before Jesus because he never leaves me or forsakes me at all.

When I'm sick, and the pain gets really bad, I just ask him to help me. The enemy always comes and tells me that I'm serving a God who doesn't care. This is why I don't like the devil; he always kicks you when you don't feel well, then I would go into a pity party and feel sorry for myself. I never stay in that mood too long because I know the Word, and I know that I have to fight that feeling.

I would go on with my daily life, trying to live for God and not give in to the evil that surrounded me, but it was hard to do, especially when I had to work with people who hated Jesus so much. I could tell my family about Jesus; some would take it and tell me when they were ready. I would know, but at work, I could not; it was forbidden. I was not going to deny my Lord, even if it cost me my job. I guess that they knew who I loved and who I served.

It was really a challenge in life itself because they were always watching me to see if I was going to mess up. I know that I'm not perfect, but I represent my Father, so I have to do my best. When I watch the Olympics and see how these people represent their country, they do such an excellent job, so why can't I do the same thing for my Father? I got a lot of testing and criticism from people, but God told me to just sing, and it helped so much. It's like a shield that protects me very well. I sometimes don't even tell them about Jesus, but they watch my behavior or the pin I wear on my uniform. It says that Jesus loves you, but I am his favorite. Some of my patients would laugh, while others would ask me questions I could not answer, but I asked God to answer them for me.

I sometimes didn't even think that Dad would answer them so soon. I try not to take the credit at all because I know in my heart that there was no way I could answer them or even know what they were going through. This was how I knew he needed our bodies to do his work; if only we would let him. I did what he told me to do, but not all the time. I know he must be disappointed with me because I do get into the flesh most of the time.

I just love God so much, I don't want to ever disappoint him, but like I say, living in this world, you would question yourselves a lot. The devil would always be tempting me, but I have to be on my guide with my eyes, ears, mind, and heart, not to mention my mouth. God helps me even more with that body part; this is what my life consists of.

When I say that, I see where I ask for things, and it happens, just like my mother called me up one day and told me that her boyfriend was sick, and the next news was that he died. She was lonely and sad, so she decided to come and stay with us; of course, I was happy, and Abigail couldn't wait. The only problem was that my mother was back in the world; she had given up on most of the Bible.

I had to still honor her as the Bible told me to do; I still stood up for what I believed. Now my daughter was always on my mother's side with everything she said. Now I was really being tested. She didn't want to hear too much about God anymore; Mother didn't want to go to church with me either. She would stay home and cook, the same thing she did when we were kids.

I made sure Abi went to church; even though she didn't want to come with me, she still went to the same church that wanted me gone. Now I was the evil mother who didn't understand my daughter; we fought a lot, and when I say we "fought," I would hit her really hard. My mother never once told her to stop disrespecting me. She would keep quiet and let this child talk to me really badly. I would watch them watch TV together, things that my spirit didn't like. I don't know if I was jealous, but it hurt really bad, but I was not going to bow to the devil. I had to stand up for the Lord, even if it meant to show my daughter and mother that they were wrong.

They both watched the cursing movies and laughed. Abi knew that I didn't like it. She didn't respect the Lord anymore. I was so upset; I felt as if her dad was once more in the house; even when my sisters and nephew were here, it was the same thing with this child. I can only pray for her and believe God will show her the way because I did my best with her. She knew the Word, and if she wanted to act stupid, it was on her. I still hold my ground when it comes with the Lord; as the Bible says in Romans 8:38–39, who will separate me from the love of God? Nobody! That is why I have to love God with all of my heart, soul, mind, and strength. It is hard, but the devil will use anything he catches his hand on.

Now he was using the two people I love, but if it means to turn my face from them, I will not put God down for them because he loves me more than they did. I never give up on Abi; we have our ups and down. I would listen to my mother with my sister, cursing bad words, and the spirit in me would cry out. I pray that one day the Lord will bring her back to him because she was the one that taught me about him. She was always on her knees praying and asking Jesus to watch over her kids and grandkids; now she is on Facebook and social media life too much.

I'm not saying that I don't do these things, not to the point that it lets me think evil and curse everything that moves. This is why I have to pay attention to what I watch and listen to as well. As my sister would say, "I'm too holy, and I am just like the hypocrite that I went to church with." I don't know why she hates church people like that.

When I think about my family, they didn't want to live for God, but when they were sick or had some kind of problem, they would call me to pray for them. I never stop praying for them and friends, even people I don't know. My life was on a roller-coaster ride. One minute I was up; the next time, I was down, but I've been through a lot, so this, too, will pass.

Out of the ordinary, I got a call from Abi's school. It seemed as if she had hurt her foot. This was not something new. When she was at her other school, she was always spraining her foot. This time, it was more than just a sprain; the doctor told me she needed surgery. He told me that Abigail's foot was missing a bone that connects to the ankle; this was the reason why it was always spraining. He told me that the surgery would take two or three hours, but she would be able to run and do normal activities. I was still in shock, but for all these years, no one knew that. My mother told me I should go ahead with the surgery, which I did.

On the day of the surgery, I was on my knees, praying to God to watch over her and guide the doctor's hand. Mother reassured me that everything would be okay. We took Abi into a room where they gave her anesthesia to put her to sleep; this child fought five of us; she didn't like needles at all. I knew that she was not going to be a doctor at all; finally, we got her to take the shot; it was a fight, but she gave up. Then we had to wait for her to fall asleep; finally, they took her into the other room to wait until it was time for her surgery. I was just praying and asking God to watch over her. I fell asleep as always, then I woke up. It was only a few hours. Then the doctor came into the waiting room and told me that the surgery was successful. He took me and my mother into another room to show us what he did. I was so grateful for what he found out and did.

Now we had to go into the recovering room to be with her, she was a miner, and we had to wait a while before we woke her up. We stayed for an hour and a half; this child didn't want to get up, so I went over to her and was waking her up; Mother told me to let her rest some more, but one of the nurses told me to try and see if she was all right. That was my "okay" to wake her up.

The nurse gave me all the instructions on what to do, who to call, and so forth. I filled her prescription; even that was a problem for her to take. She didn't like pills at all; I wonder if it was a trauma that she remembered when she overdosed on Tylenol. I did all I was told to do; I even had to take time off from work just to be with her. I didn't want to hurt her foot at all due to the fact how I slept, so I gave her something to eat and her meds.

She fell asleep, and I went into my room; at about 2:00 a.m., my mother came for me. I was out, really tired; she was crying and telling me that I had left her by herself, why I did that to her. She was in a lot of pain, and she would not stop crying. I tried to comfort her, but the pain was unbearable. My mother gave her the meds, but it was a fight, as always; I told her that she had to take them if she wanted to feel better. When she couldn't take the pain, she gave up and took the pills.

She told me not to leave her again, which I didn't. I had to sleep with her, but I could not move at all due to the fact that I didn't want to hurt her. I watched her as she cried herself to sleep. I knew that I had to get some rest as well to deal with her in the morning. The following day she had a temp, so I called the doctor, and he told me that he would prescribe something else. Of course, this was another problem. I had to call someone else, which the doctor told me to do; it was an ice machine. I had to order it to put it on her foot every so often; the man came and showed me how to set up the machine and told me when to change it and so forth. I had to do all this work.

This went on for about a week or two with her; she would be in a lot of pain, but I did what a mother had to do. I couldn't wait to get back in my own bed. This child had so much mouth, and when pain inflicted her, it was another story. I had to get back to work, but my mother was home with her. She was out of school for a while. When she went to the doctor, he told her that she could go back to school only on crutches. Now this was my difficult task because I didn't know how she could manage to go to school without my help. I did what any mother would do; I went to the social worker at her school and told her I needed help. She didn't waste any time; she helped me a lot.

Mrs. Clark had gotten the school bus with the lift to pick Abi up at the house, and I would get her from school; we did this for some time. Then she had to do physical therapy; now, this was another task for both of us. It seemed that Abi was not paying any attention.

The bus that took her to school had stopped; I didn't know what to do with Abigail. I had to get a ride for her. I didn't know what to do, but I went on my knees and asked God to help me, which he came through as always. I asked Abigail's hairdresser; she took her two times a week in the morning.

I gave her money for gas, and she was fine with that, so this was my story. This was a lot of work, but God kept me. It was a long road to recovery, but we went through it with the help of God. I didn't know what else to do, but he kept me rooted and grounded.

My mother was at the house helping us as always; I thanked God for her as well, but she was more on the negative side of things. If I said anything about God, she could say something else; she was too much in the world. We always had a problem with God, I talked too much about him, and she wanted to hear less about him. As the months went by, Abi was finished with therapy, and I was on another mission in life. When I didn't have to face my mother, I had to face the people at my workplace, not to mention my church members as well. I was fighting from every angle.

I loved the church I was attending then, but it seemed as if everyone had their own opinion about me. Our pastor and his wife were having their fiftieth wedding anniversary, and they invited the whole church, which I thought was so nice. As they prepared for their special day, they said if anyone wanted to help, they could help. I went to see if they needed my help, but one of the church sisters told me that they were okay. I didn't take it personally; the day of the event, it was so beautiful. Everything went great; when the service was over, we had to go downstairs for refreshments.

When I went downstairs to the church hall, it was so crowded; I could hardly think. I took it upon myself and went upstairs again; I didn't drive my vehicle, so I had nowhere to go. I saw Marie, and I told her that I was going over to the tent to sit down for a while; she went with me. Unfortunately, they were still fixing the place; due to the fact that I had worn new shoes, it was killing my foot. I went over to the tent door to sit on one of the chairs; I was told by one of the sisters to leave. I was not going to stay too long, but she got rude to me. I just wanted to take off those shoes.

I lived two blocks from the church, but the fact of walking home on these heels would have killed me. I felt so embarrassed; I wanted to go home at this time, but the spirit told me that she did not invite me to this function. I stayed and went back to the church building, where I saw a couple of people waiting. This time, I made sure to ask them if I could stay in the building; so Marie and I went in. It was so good to sit down and take those shoes off; I stayed until they called us this time.

When they finally opened the tent, we went in; I could not find my table for anything. This place looked like it seated about five hundred or more people. This pastor was a generous person to invite even strangers to his wedding anniversary. I thought that it was very nice of him; the pastor and his wedding party had to wait until everyone was seated for them to enter. I found my seat and sat down. As the bridal party came in and did what they do at weddings, the host of the reception was getting ready to call the table for their meal, but the God I served called my table first.

Everyone was surprised that the same lady who told me that they were not ready as yet ran over to the host and told him that the head table should be served first; I didn't mind at all. She was right about that, but our table got up already, and we just stood there and waited on the head table to be served. The look she gave me was not right, but I just said to myself, "Eat your heart out. I'm Abba's daughter." The young lady behind me kept saying that she could not believe it because other bishops and pastors were there, and he did not call their table.

When they were finished with the head table, we went and got our dinner while the others waited. I even won a gift for the best shoes, even though they were killing me. The anniversary party went well, but then the rain came down really hard. The pastor and first lady enjoyed themselves a lot. I got a ride from one of the church brothers. He thought that I lived somewhere else; before he could say amen to me, I was home. It seemed as if he was upset; I didn't care one bit; I was happy that I was home; it was a night to remember.

The brother got mad because I lived so close to church; there was no way I was going to walk home in the rain with those shoes killing me like that. I could not call a cab because they would not have come for me either. I just thanked God for what he did for me tonight; that lady let me feel bad, but God turned it around, and I enjoyed myself after all.

I know that I was not loved at that church, but the good Lord told me to go there for almost ten years, but I told Dad that I knew that Prophecy Church didn't wear clothes that I loved. They are a strict church that has rules and regulations that they always see through. The Lord would tell me to go, and I would tell Dad that I loved to dress up and look good.

When I was growing up, and the church that was in my aunt's house, where my uncle was the pastor for it, the way the members dressed, they looked like saints; I was far from that. It took me a while before I went there. When I went to that church, I didn't take out any membership until two years later; due to the fact of my record with pastors and members. I kept my guard, but God wanted me there for some time now.

I was doing everything Abba told me to do; I would go to church every other weekend due to work and then Bible study. I did this for some time well; Pastor Hume is a funny man at times, not to mention his wife. He would always talk about going to Israel; I wanted to go to that place where Jesus was born. It was too expensive for me; I had other things to do with my money. I had to pay my bills and so forth; when it was not one thing, it was another.

When I didn't have a problem with the tenant, it was at work. I had to wear Jesus Christ well; sometimes, I failed him, and I told him that I was sorry because these people were driving me up the walls. It was a lot of stress on me at times, but I would help those who wanted my help.

I did what I could to help them; after all, I hate when people take disadvantage of other people. Now, I had a lot of enemies for the fact that I looked out for the worker. I didn't care at all. I had problems with the head nurses and the supervisor from different departments. I never had a problem with the administrators; they always seemed to like me. I don't know what it was. I guess it was God's favor when the devil thought that he got me in some kind of trap; God was right there to get me out.

I saw so many things at that place; if you didn't know the Lord, you would sin your soul. There were times when some of the bosses were okay and somewhere from the pits of hell, but nothing happened before the time. The worker could get out of hand, so they needed a bad boss to put us back in check; it's the way of life.

Sometimes, I would go to another unit to get the blood pressure machine. On this particular day, I saw a patient I once knew, so I was there talking to the patient. She was reading her Bible. Of course, I had to get involved in that. She was reading Psalm 46; I knew it by heart, so I recited it loud while she read the scripture. I closed my eyes, and when I was finished, I opened them just to see my administrator at the door looking at me. She wanted to speak with me, but she waited until I was finished with the patient. I took a deep breath and went to her; I was waiting for her to ask me what I was doing in the patient's room because I was far away from my unit. She took me into her office and told me that she had a problem with one of the workers.

Man, I felt so relieved; it was one of the nurses that she wanted to talk to me about. I didn't know what to do at this time, I just asked God to help me with the answer, and he did. She gave her a second chance; she didn't say anything to me about what she saw, and after all, I was doing my Father's work. This administrator was firing people left, right, and center, and I was there to witness it.

Some of the things they did were just silly, and some of them had to reconsider. I had my own work to do, but she loved to see my face. She even wanted me to help her with interviews. I asked the scheduler why me. She told me she was the boss and wanted me in the room with her and the director of nursing. Now I had to write down a question I was going to ask the aide they were hiring.

It was very knowledgeable; they both taught me what to look out for and then told me to ask the aide my questions. I did; some answered well, while others... I don't know what they were thinking. The way some of them dressed for an interview was no joke; jeans with sneakers and their head wrapped with a hair cover. One came in, and I thought she dressed well, and so did the administrator, but the director asked her a question, and she could not answer. She then told the lady that they would call her back when we were finished interviewing the rest of them. When she left the room, I asked her what was wrong with that one; she didn't understand the question that I asked her. She went on by saying if the patients wanted something, she couldn't help them.

Chapter 37

There was a lot I needed to learn, and I thanked them for the experience they taught me. When we were all finished, we only agreed with one person; the rest were not qualified for the job, and this was something different for me. I remember one of our administrators once told me that I could not treat every worker the same; some are from different cultures and backgrounds.

What you think would be offensive to you will not harm the other person, while the next man would think otherwise. I tried to always keep this in mind. While I was in the break room, I saw one of the workers; he was looking for me. He told me that he wished to speak with me. He took me in the hallway; then he told me that he just got fired; I asked him what had happened. He started to explain. When he got the job, he knew that he had an anger problem, but he was working on it; but he knew that he was changed. He kept telling me that even his worker was making fun of him because he was gay; I didn't even know.

I asked him if he wanted his job back or what he wanted to do, and he told me what he felt like doing to everyone that messed with him. I told him, "No one deserves your life; you are better than this job. You are young and can go back to school and become anything." I asked him if he wanted me to get to the bottom of what they were saying about him being gay. He didn't want the rest of the workers to know about his situation. As I watched him walk away, I was angry. I went to the department that he worked in and confronted the guy who was making fun of him.

I told him that I could get all of them fired for what they did; I told them, "What is fun to you is death to another. You owe him an apology before he leaves." You could see the guilt on his face. I was even upset with the administrator for letting this young man work his shift and then letting him go like that.

This was one case I would have fought for. A lot of people don't know their rights and the system, so they just let the devil tell them a lot of negative things, then they come back and kill innocent people. If only these bosses knew how to handle certain situations before they fired their workers. There are a lot of people in this world who don't care at all for other people, and this is so sad.

I have to deal with racism as well as religion and cultural matters. People, in general, don't care at all for each other; they are only for themselves. I know that I can't fix everyone or even change them, but I know that I can show them the love of Christ. I never had this love before. I was once like them; then Jesus taught me how to love and respect others.

Every day was a different story with my mother; she told me that her boyfriend from Jamaica was coming to visit, but I didn't have a problem with that. I didn't know that she had one, but when he came, the Holy Spirit dealt with me really well. He told me that they needed to fix what they were doing. I didn't know how to tell my mother what she was doing was wrong, but if I was going to do God's work, I had to let them know, but I didn't. I know God was upset with me, but he was gone, and I know I didn't have to hurt anyone's feelings.

The following weekend at church, the pastor announced that he was going to Israel again. I wanted to go so badly, but I knew I could not afford it, but I asked the good Lord if I could go, and he opened doors for me to get started. I didn't dare tell my mother at all, so I paid down on my ticket month after month.

Pastor told us that we could do that. Marie too was going with us, so I had company with me. I picked up overtime at work and the part-time job I went to whenever she needed me. This helped me a lot with the things I needed to take with me to Israel. The next thing happened: Marlene's son also came from Jamaica. He asked me if he could stay with me as well. Of course, I told him yes.

He stayed with us for some time; he knew this girl he met in Jamaica. She lived in Connecticut, so that was one of the reasons why he came to stay with me. One night, he brought her to the house—at midnight. He told my mother that it was her birthday. He didn't ask me if this girl could come, but he just brought her to the house. My mother thought that it was okay, but I didn't think so at all. I still didn't say a word at all. I just kept my mouth shut, just to let everyone be happy. This happened very often now, she would come when they thought I was sleeping, but the Holy Spirit would wake me up. He told me to put a stop to it, but now I was compromising again because I didn't want to hurt anyone's feelings.

My daughter was doing her own thing; we were arguing more than ever before. She felt that what I was telling her about the Lord didn't matter at all. I was not doing anything for her to think that God didn't matter in my life. I wasn't sleeping around with anyone; since I left her dad over ten years now; not saying that I was not tempted to look at other men, but I didn't want anyone abusing her. I did my best to show her all that I had learned. She wanted fun, and I was boring; I just let it roll. I needed to go to Israel and see what it was all about.

I didn't let my mother know until I had almost paid off the ticket, but she knew I was going somewhere because I was buying things to travel. When she found out, she told me all kinds of negative things, I had to rebuke her at times, but I still put everything into her name if anything happened to me.

One day she came into my room and told me they were killing people in Israel. I still didn't listen to her at all because they were killing people everywhere, especially in Jamaica and America. I knew that God was not going to let anything happen to me; after all, I was going to his country. I went to my doctor and got my check-up, and I asked him if it was okay for me to travel to Israel with lupus. They told me that it was fine. My lupus doctor even told me to take the flu shot and checked out everything for me.

I got the okay from him, so I was ready to go to my Father's country. This was the happiest moment of my life. It was like a dream come true. The lady I took care of told me that she was going to miss me, but I let nothing or no one stop me. Abi was fine with it, she had her grandmother with her, and my nephew was with them. The only thing that was getting me upset more than anything was this girl coming into the house at night as if it was okay.

My brother Edson used to do this a lot with his girlfriend; I asked him when he was going to get married, and he told me not yet. I always wonder why they were wasting their time. They finally got married, and now they have a baby girl. I still think this young man should do the same; he was not getting any younger at all, but who was I to tell them? Mother always tells me that I talk too much and I should let my family do their own thing.

She was right, but there was no way this kid was going to make my house into a sleeping den for him and his girlfriend. I didn't say anything at this point because I was going to Israel; I didn't want to let anyone get me down right now. *When I come back, then I'll see to it that he does something.*

I couldn't wait to leave; I was so excited. To think about Israel was the greatest pleasure for me. One day, Marie told me that she had to go to New York to change her passport. I kept wondering what was wrong with it, and she told me that the pastor wanted her to change the name to match her green card. We went to New York, and she took her picture and put it in the form. Now all she had to do was wait for it to come back; she had less than two weeks to get it done. She paid extra money to get it back in time; as the week went by so fast, we were all getting ready for our trip. I didn't go to church that Sunday because I had to go to work. I had gotten my hair done on Saturday; now, my mother didn't say anything at all.

I told her all that she should do if anything happened to me. Even though I knew that God would not let me get hurt. I respect my mother very much; I am not afraid of her, but sometimes she tests me a lot. Marie still didn't get her passport as yet, so she took the bus to New York that same day and went to the passport office to get it. I had to take her luggage to the airport with me. I took the four pieces with me to church; then, I had to drive my vehicle back home. I then told my mother and my nephew bye. Abi had already left for school at this time. When I got to church, I saw all those going with us. It was six of us, and Marie would be the seventh.

Then the bus was late, which made me happy. This would buy Marie some time. We loaded our luggage onto the bus; the pastor prayed before we left. I knew some of the church people in the bus with us. There was more than one church that went; because this was the church I used to attend, one of the sisters came over to me; she wanted to know how I was feeling. She knew about my lupus. I told her I was fine as ever; she told me that I was looking great as ever. I thanked her, then I went to sleep. I knew some of these people, but I didn't know all of them from our church. You would think I didn't even know the pastor that well, but no one would ever know.

I am the kind of person who just stays by myself because I know my luck with church people. I was more interested in going to Israel than anything at all. Not too long afterwards, I got a call from Marie; she told me that she had gotten her passport. I just thanked God for that; she told me that she was going to the airport to meet us, so I would see her there. I went and told the pastor that she got through and was on her way to the airport. He, too, was glad to hear that, when we got there, everyone took their luggage and left me with the four suitcases. I called Marie on her phone, but I could not get her. I had to struggle to get one of those carts; then, I put them on one by one. When I looked around, everyone had gone and left me all by myself; this is why I am skeptical about church people. I finally saw Marie; then she came over to me.

I told her that they all left me and didn't care at all, but when we got near all of them, the pastor was busy looking for the rest of the churches that were going with us. It was about four different churches and other people whom he knew were coming with us. In total, it was about thirty-five of us who went. I knew I was not a baby; I had to catch up with the group. Marie was there to carry her own things.

The pastor was in charge of everyone, even though they had their pastor with them. We had to tell the Israelites why we wanted to visit their country. When all of that was over, they searched us, and we were off for the rat race. We had to do that long walk; the pastor was ahead of us, and I could not keep up with them.

When I got to the point where they were sitting, I heard the pastor calling me. I just sat down next to him; this was a different story. I didn't know too much about this place, and I wasn't going to be left behind. They called our flight; as we were going on the plane, I just took my time. I was so tired; this walking was too much. When I boarded the airplane, I was seated in a far place from Marie. There was a couple that wanted to sit together, so I gave up my seat so that they could sit together. I sat with one of the ladies from the church in New York, who was traveling with us. I didn't mind at all; we talked for hours, and she was telling me about her life story. I just listened; I was used to that. Then these young ladies had their seats all the way down on us; this woman was not all that saved because she let them have it.

I told the lady if she minded if I could put my head on her shoulder, and she told me to go ahead. I fell asleep for some time. Then they woke us up for something to eat. I thought we were halfway there, but it was only three hours. We had seven and a half more hours to go. As I watched the Jewish people get up and pray, they did this about three times on the flight. It was interesting to see; I just watched them. I only asked God to let me not pass gas because it would not be pretty at all. I knew that my stomach was killing me with gas; my good friend was not there as yet. I got up and went to the bathroom, I needed a shower, so I went and took out my toothbrush and brushed my teeth, then I used my wipes and cleaned up a little. I could not wait to reach Israel so that I could take a shower. We still had four more hours left; this was torture because the plane was tight, and those ladies didn't want to pull up their seats so that I could get some ease. Then I heard the pilot announcing that we would reach Tel Aviv airport in one and a half hours. I was so happy. My legs were happy too, then Marie came over and asked me if I was okay.

I told her that Mommy was taking care of me. Then she went back to her seat; we finally reached our destination, we landed, and we got our luggage. They didn't do too much to us; they gave us this little passport card to take around with us. I put mine into my passport book. Then we had to wait until the rest of the churches came out.

Everyone was taking pictures; I was more fascinated by what their sign meant, but no one could answer me; they themselves didn't know what it meant. I always wanted to know what it meant with the eye on the pyramid. Then one of the sisters from our church was calling home in Connecticut, I asked her to hook me up, but the tour guide came and told us that he had been waiting a long time.

I looked at Marie and said that this one was something else; he was not friendly at all. When we went outside, it was so warm, so we all took off our jackets; it was November 27. When we got into the bus, he introduced himself to us and the driver as well. He was talking really fast, with an accent. I got some of what he was saying. As I sat on the bus, everybody was all together once more. I sat with Marie in the back; she didn't want to because of the bumps, but I didn't like to be all crowded too much.

I love space, a lot of it. When we were on our way to the hotel, I was just watching everyone as they talked; some were taking pictures while some were sleeping. I told Marie that I needed to take a shower first, which I did; when we got to the hotel, our pastor told us to get some rest because tomorrow was a busy day. He was not kidding. We had to get up before 6:00 a.m. to take a shower before we hit the road at about 7:00 a.m. My body was still crying out for rest, but I did most of this in the bus. Now that was another story; it seemed as if most of them wanted the front seat as if they were driving the bus. I told Marie I was going to the back of the bus, but she didn't want to; then she came.

I sat at the back itself; then, one of our church sisters asked me if she could sit next to me. I told her that it was fine, but she should sit on the other side. She asked me why; then I told her that I needed three seats to be mine, and she asked why. I said for the Father, Son, and Holy Ghost; she started to laugh and said I was funny.

Then Marie told her that she would find out soon; our first tour was a boat ride on the sea of Galilee; this was so awesome. I felt like a kid in a candy store; Marie and I went to the front of the boat, then it started to rain. Now everyone was running to get shade from the rain; Marie and I took out our raincoats, and we got them down. One of the sisters asked me how I knew what to bring. I told her I read the small prints on the brochure; when the rain stopped and a rainbow came over the boat, it seemed as if God was telling us welcome. We went into a place that looked like a museum. They showed us all kinds of boats. One that they used to use back in the days of Jesus, we came out and took group pictures of our church members.

Then our next stop was the Mount of the Beatitudes. This is the place where Jesus gave his sermon. They had built a church in honor of what he had done there. When we went into the church building, there was another church there. They were singing "Amazing Grace"; I felt every hair on my body rise up. I could not control the tears in my eyes; they rolled down my face. Then we went outside the building, and our pastor asked a young lady to read the scripture of Matthew chapter 5. I can't believe it; I was actually standing at the place where this took place. The place where he fed the five thousand with the two fishes and five loaves of bread. God is so awesome.

We then went to Peter's house and where Peter, too, did his miracle; this place was real and full of life. We then went back into the bus; then another sister from our church came and sat on the other side with us; she, too, had two seats as well. Then the pastor saw us and was laughing because we were all from his church. I would see him counting the passengers in the bus; he wanted to make sure everyone was there.

When we came off the bus, I asked the driver if he could open the back door so that we didn't have to wait on everyone else. He smiled and said yes, now we had our own entrance; we didn't wait in line because our door was open and ready for us at all times. Then another sister and her mother came to the back as well. She was from another church. I told her everyone was welcome; sister McDonald told me I was crazy. I just laughed and kept on taking pictures as the bus drove by. We then went to King David's tomb. This was where all the men had to go to a different place while the ladies went somewhere else.

In the tomb of King David, I saw a big coffin, and three women were praying there; then I heard Sam's voice on the other side explaining to the men. One of the ladies who was praying got up and told him to shut up, but they both were arguing. Then she put us out of the tomb, I thought she was rude, and I asked Sam if she was allowed to do that.

He told me she was wrong and that I should go back there. I went with the other church sisters, but she would not let anyone in. We had to wait until she was finished with what she was doing, so I told her that she was wrong, and then everyone started to curse because they wanted to move on to the next sight. It started a little riot to break out, and one of the ladies who was praying had her glasses come off. The older lady looked at me, but I didn't care at all. She had no right to run me out.

Then we went to the upper room where the Holy Spirit came down on the disciple; at this time, everyone was praying and crying. Pastor was singing as always; I just closed my eyes and was just thinking about what had taken place there. On our way back to the hotel, our tour guide Sam was telling us that they had had a drought for a couple of months now. As we passed the Jordan River, we could see it as well. He asked our pastor to pray for rain, which he did. I really wanted it to rain as well because the river didn't look full at all. That night, it rained all night; we should be careful what we ask for. It seemed as if it was a storm.

The next day, we went to the River Jordan to be baptized. The morning was cold, but I got up and was ready to go. If I didn't come to Israel for this, I would not have come at all. This was my moment as we went into the bathroom to get dressed for our baptism. I was so excited; this was the moment I waited all my life. We were standing in line waiting to experience history being made, the River Jordan where my Savior got baptized. I could not wait; I was the first one into the water.

My Lord, the water was so cold. I looked up to the sky and told him if it was not for him, I would not have done this; I gave one of our brothers my iPod to video this for me. When the three pastors asked me a couple of questions that I once took, I was so happy to repeat them once more. It was like I was getting married once more. As they held my hands and merged me into the water, they put me really deep. I came out with a smile and a clap; I then collected some of the water for a couple of people who wanted it.

I then went and got dressed. When I came out of the bathroom, I went over to our tour guide Sam and the pastor with my church brother. They were talking. Then my church brother told me to look behind me, which hit me really hard. I saw myself being baptized. I don't know what it was. I was just crying; it felt like a burden was lifted up from me. I could not explain it at all. I could not control myself. I just went and hugged them. God knows how to work into our lives. That feeling was something different from the one I felt when I was first baptized. This was one moment no one could take away from me. Then Marie and the rest of the sisters came over.

I didn't know what to say; I was just thanking Jesus for loving me. We then left and went to different places. They even took us to their shopping area, but the price was too high. Sam took us to the marketplace, where Jesus had to walk with the cross. He told us that it was a long walk; while we were walking, I was tempted to stop and buy something for my brother Edson. Sam got upset and was telling us that we were selfish, buying things while other people were waiting on us. I felt really bad; then, our pastor told me not to feel guilty. I spent my money to come to this place, and he could wait on me like anyone else. I felt better, but I didn't want to get on Sam's wrong side again.

Chapter 38

I went over to him and told him I was sorry, but I had to get something for my brother. I told him that the place that he was taking us to was too expensive; I needed a place like a flea market, where you can get things reasonable to buy, not five hundred or a thousand US dollars. He looked at me. Then he asked me what it was that I was looking for. "Prayer shawl, caps, scarf, and souvenir," I told him. Things you can give people when you get back home.

He told me to wait, then he went on his phone and called one of his friends. This man had a store in his van, and we went in the parking lot, and boy, did we shop. Pastor just watched us; everyone was happy. Sam asked me if that was fine. I just gave the thumbs up. He then told me we had a day to shop all by ourselves. I just smiled because I knew what I was going to do with my day.

I had gotten most of what I wanted to bring for families and friends. The following day, we went to the Dome of the Rock and the Western Wall and museums. We left and went to sites like the old Roman City of Best Shean to visit the impressive Roman ruins. We even stopped at Jericho, it was not on our itinerary, but we convinced Sam to take us there. I guess by now, he knew that we were not easy people at all. We went on camel rides and to the Dead Sea; this was even more fun to swim in the dead sea. If you didn't know how to swim, it didn't even matter at all. The water kept you afloat because of all that salt. Sam told us not to let it get into our eyes, but I paid by not hearing.

This was another life moment for me; the sun went down so that I could enjoy myself. I swam and danced in the water. Then I put a lot of mud on my body, places that didn't need it. We left and went to a different place. When we got to the hotel, I went and took my shower to get all that salt from my hair. Then Marie told me that our pastor was going on Skype to talk to the congregation at church. I told her that I was not coming. I was going to wash my hair. She said fine and left.

When I think about how far Jesus and his disciple went on foot. I respect him even more; it was walking from Connecticut to New York. Man, that was a lot of walking, and they did not complain once. We went to the tomb and the garden of Gethsemane; this was another point for me. It was such a peaceful place, even though Jesus was carrying the burden of the world.

We went to a lot of places. I can't say I didn't enjoy myself. One night, a couple of us took a walk out of the hotel. We took our church brother with us for protection. If our pastor ever found out, he probably would get mad. He didn't want anything to happen to us while we were in Israel.

The following day was our day off; I didn't know who went shopping, but I stayed back too fast and prayed that day. I prayed and asked the Lord to use me in any way he wanted to. I know that sometimes, I can be a handful, and I know that I get on people's nerves as well.

Marie can give a testament on this; this was my day to do anything and everything, but I gave it back to Abba. That evening when Marie came back and was packing up her things, I had a lot of stuff, and I knew that I was overweight. I had sand from the dead sea, water from the Jordan River, and all that I had brought. I packed a lot of my things up; I didn't know anyone to give away some of my stuff to. If I was in Jamaica, I would have left a lot of things with family or friends. I didn't know what to do with them, so I took them with me. On the last day in Israel, we went back to the Dome of the Dock and Western Wall; this was where I wrote a prayer for everyone I could remember. I was told they would take them out when the wall was full.

We went back to different places, and then we had dinner before they took us to the airport. Sam came in with me, and he stayed with me until I went over to the counter, where I knew I was overweight. He then told me where to go and paid the money for my luggage. I didn't walk with my credit card, but I walked with cash. I went, and I told him bye and hugged him. I told him I would call him when I got back to the US. As we went upstairs and waited on our flight, it felt like I was leaving something behind.

I didn't know what it was; I just felt sad. While we were waiting, I saw our pastor get up and walk over to the place where they checked you before you entered the plane. Then he started to run; I ran too. The next thing, everyone was running.

Another riot at the airport, then one of the hostesses told us to please wait. Sister McDonald asked me why I ran; I told her that I was following the man of God; she then asked me if I didn't know that they would search us again. I didn't know that; to check my ticket, yes, but to search again... "No," I told her, "I was just following the Shepherd." We all went on the flight. I was just laughing as I sat down. To think that I could have gotten arrested over this. On my way back, I was placed in another area all by myself, not one of my church people. I sat down beside a professor; he asked me how I liked my visit. I told him I loved it very much; then he asked me if I had seen the new temple site and where they were planning to build it.

I just looked at him. It seemed as if he was in another place from where I was. As he spoke, I just listened to him. This was a lot of information I didn't know. We had only gone to the places that Jesus went and a couple more stories in the Bible, but this man was telling me something different. It was good to know; I then offered him a pack of gum. I had too much with me; I loved my seat. I had a place where I could lead back and even put my feet up; this flight was good, and I found a new friend. One that was not telling me his business but was telling me what was taking place in Israel. I knew that they might think that I was a little bit nuts, but I see the way our pastor behaves when he doesn't see us near him. He gets paranoid. I think it is too much stress for him to be looking after so many people.

While the other church pastors sleep or take pictures, this man needs a week off from everyone. I remember we were at a place, and some of the members told him that they would soon be back, so he told us to wait for them. It seemed as if they had forgotten about us, so the pastor let us wait for them almost any hour. They were having fun while we were waiting. I remember asking him if I could use the restroom; he looked at me and said, "Not another one leaving!" I just stood there with my mouth open; then he realized and told me to go and get back in five minutes.

I shook my head and went to the bathroom. I kept thinking that this man thought that he was my father, but I guess that he was a caring man and was responsible for all of us. I came back, and he shook his head. This man would do the same thing my dad would have done. He told you no, then he changed his mind, and you better hurry up before he changed it again. On the flight, I got up three times to use the restroom, then went back to sleep. I saw some of the people who were in the hotel with us, not on our tour, the same ladies who had their seats back on us.

I was comfortable, and I was not giving up my seat this time; when we got to New York, we had to wait on our ride for almost two hours; we were all tired and wanted to go home. I told the pastor I would soon be back; out of respect. Would you believe the man told me I could go anywhere in the United States? I just looked at him and said, "Well," to myself.

I guess he was tired of us; when we finally got on the bus and came back to our church, Pastor's wife was there waiting for him. My other church sister asked me if I loved my new church. I told her yes; then she asked me if that was our first lady. I told her yes, and she was waiting for us. Then I asked her if her first lady was waiting for them. She said, "I guess not."

I know the pastor's wife was waiting for her husband, not me. When I came off the bus, the first thing she said to me was that she didn't know I went with them. I just smiled and walked home to get my vehicle while Marie stayed with our luggage. She called me while I was home and told me that her daughter had come for her, so she came by the house and dropped off my suitcase. I greeted my mother and nephew; Abi was still at school. I could not wait to take a shower.

You would think that I was sleepy, but I went to the store with my mother. I was not tired after all; I was so grateful and thankful for that experience in Israel. The following day, I was packing out all that I had brought. I was just looking at what I brought back. There were a lot of things. I didn't need all this sand, and I should have listened to Sam when he told me to catch water when I reached America because I would not have paid for overweight.

I guess that was it; I had two more days before I went back to work this weekend. My mother and I were talking about Israel. I told her that one day we should take a trip to Israel; she just looked at me and said, "No, thanks." With all of those killings that I saw on TV, I told her that it was not like what they showed us on TV; it's like when you are in a different state. She told me she was fine and would stay in this state for now. I just looked at her and shook my head; you can't win with her.

When Abi came home, I could really talk with her. She was looking at the pictures. She put some of them on the computer for me. Then, I took out what I bought for my co-workers. Mother had my family's things already. I took out for my church sisters and brothers as well. I could not wait to get back to work just to tell them about Israel. The reason for this, I always tell them I am a Jew, and they think that I am crazy, but if you think about it,

God made Adam and Eve, and we are the descendants of them. He didn't create any more than the human race; that I know of, I don't even know about this thing racism came from. He made some black, brown light shade, some fat, some skinny, some tall, some short. He made all kinds of shapes and sizes, but we take it to another level and think we are different from the other person.

If we were all blind, would it really matter? I don't think so; it's really what we see that causes so many problems in this world. If we could only get our hearts right with the Lord, but without Jesus Christ, it is impossible to do so. As the scripture says, the only person who can really change our hearts is that man, Jesus. God was the one who told us that; we can't love anyone without the love of Christ in our hearts. I know this well. If I didn't know Jesus, there was no way I could love or forgive anyone. If you don't believe in him, he can't enter your heart to change you, but if you believe in him and believe that he is the Son of God and that he raised him from the dead, then you are saved. God can do anything; that's why this is so impossible for people to believe.

God said, "Let there be light: and there was light" (Genesis 1:3); God can do anything because he is God. Then he said, "Let us make man in our own image" (Genesis 1:26a), who was with him, while he was making man, his Son. We just have to believe in him because we watch the news and the weather and believe it as well. I know that there is a lot I need to know about the Bible, but it is the Word of God, and if the devil could stop it, which he is still trying today. I love you, Jesus, I love you, Abba, and I love you, Holy Ghost. You guys rock.

The day came for work, and I went to see my patients. I gave some of them their gift, as well as my co-worker. I told them all about Israel and told them that they needed to take a trip. I went around and told everyone about Israel until they were tired of hearing me and my experience. The day went by really fast. I was off from work for two days; then, I went to my other job on Monday. This was with my lady, I gave her a gift as well, and her son had gotten a key chain. I was telling her the same story as the others. I didn't know what it was, but I was feeling some strange pain in my right hand.

Then I had to go to work the following day; my body was not up to it, but due to the fact that I just came back. I didn't have any more time left, so I had to push myself. I knew that I would be off on Thursday, but that night, I thought that I would have died.

On Thursday, I took it real easy. I didn't think that it was lupus acting up because I knew the symptoms for that. I told my mother, and she said that I should call my lupus doctor. I told her I would. That night, I had a dream that I was walking into a field; it was so beautiful and peaceful as well. It seemed as if I was still in Israel; while I was walking, I saw this black man; he was digging a hole, and he had a box that he wanted to put into the hole. It was a huge box, so I asked him if he needed help. He then turned around and looked at me with his mouth open.

The same look I would give when something was wrong, I jumped out of my dream. On Friday morning, I felt the same way; but my lupus doctor was near my workplace. I knew that I could have seen him after work. I got up, showered, got ready, and went to work.

When I got there, the numbness had gotten worse, so I went to one of the nurses and told her what was happening. She told me to sit down, and she took my blood pressure; that was okay, but the numbness was getting worse. She told me it was best for me to go to UConn Hospital and get checked out.

"It's better to be safe than sorry," she told me. So she took me to the emergency room; then she told me I should call her back or the scheduler to come and get me. This was a usual thing with me at work. Whenever my Aupus acts up, they help me out a lot. When I went in, they didn't waste any time at all because of what I told them I was feeling. They took my vitals and then blood work; I just felt as if I was going to pass out.

Finally, they put me into a room while waiting on my blood work to determine what was wrong with me. When they got back the results from the blood work, the doctor told me it was fine. She was the same Jamaican doctor that I saw most of the time when I went to UConn. She always seemed angry with me, but I didn't let her get the best of me at all. She then told me the blood work was okay and that I might need some fluid. She sent for an IV and told me she didn't see anything at all, even though I told her I was not feeling well. She told me that she was going to do a CAT scan to determine if I was fine.

I didn't say another word to her; she thought that she owned the hospital. They came and got me, and we went and got the test done. The thing that hurt me was this doctor had a big problem with me, and I had insurance. I could just imagine if I didn't have insurance. I was in the room for almost four hours and still felt the same way. I called my mother and told her what was going on with me.

She asked me if I needed her to call Marie, I told her no because it was her day off, and I knew she was busy. Not before long, the doctor returned to the room and told me that she did not find anything wrong with the CAT scan and that she was going to discharge me. I told her that I was not feeling well, and she then told me that I should go to my rheumatoid arthritis doctor for him to see what was wrong with me because she did all that was to be done with me.

As she walked out of the room, the nurse came in with my discharge papers. I was just crying on my way out; I felt as if I was going to pass out. I went into the lobby and was about to call my job when I saw my lupus doctor. He was coming from lunch and decided to walk that way; he saw me crying and asked me what was wrong, then he asked me what was wrong with my face. I told him what had happened. Then he told me to come to his office. I knew I could not have walked that far, so I took the hospital shuttle.

When I went to his office, he told me that my face was lean, and he then went on his phone and called another doctor. Then he told me to follow him. At this time, I was so tired that I wanted to pass out. We went upstairs to the neurologist to check me out. I was with her for almost two hours, asking me questions, then she called another doctor to see what was wrong. They told me it looked like I had a stroke, but they were not sure, so they called my doctor once more and told him they thought it was a stroke.

He told them to send me back to the emergency room, but they refused me. Dr. Laks could not believe that they could refuse patients, but they did. Now I was sick, and the UConn hospital didn't want to take me back, and I had insurance. The other doctor told Dr. Laks that he should let me try another hospital, Hartford Hospital. She told me that she worked there as well, and she could call her friend to let him know that I was coming.

They told me to let someone take me to the emergency room; I don't know why they didn't just call an ambulance for me. I was lost at this point, I called my co-worker, and she came and took me to the ER. I told my mother what I was going through, then she called Marie and told her what was going on with me. Marie asked me if I wanted her to come, but the schedule told her that she was there with me already. Marie told me to keep in touch. I knew that something was up, but I didn't know that my face was lean as well.

Dr. Laks told me, but no one else saw it; I knew he knew me well; I was going to him for at least twelve years for lupus. Now I had to go through all of this once more, sitting and waiting for a long time due to the fact that this was a new hospital for me. They didn't have my information about me. If I had gone to Saint Francis Hospital, they would have known my history. I don't know what was happening to me at this point; I only asked God to take care of me.

They told me they were going to keep me overnight, but they didn't have any beds at all, so I had to wait in the emergency room until a room was available. My co-worker stayed with me until they got me all ready for that room; she told me to call her if I needed anything. I told her thanks, then she left. I then called my mother and told her what was going on, she didn't have a ride to get here, and I still had to wait until they ran more tests.

I called Marie and told her what was going on as well; she asked me if I wanted her to get my vehicle from work. I was grateful for that; that night was awful. They didn't want to give me anything to eat due to the fact they didn't know what was wrong with me. The doctor came in the room and asked me a lot of questions; he asked me how I didn't know if it was not lupus acting up because this disease mimics anything. I told him that I didn't know at all, but I was not feeling good. This was why I came to the hospital so that he could tell me what was wrong with me. It seemed as if no one wanted to give me an MRI that I knew would determine the problem.

Finally, they came around 3:00 a.m. to get the MRI done and then asked more questions. I just wanted to go home at this point, but I had to wait and see what was going on with me. As I lay down, my thoughts were just going crazy. I kept thinking about what was happening to me.

The doctor came back and told me that he was waiting for another doctor to read the scan results, and now I was seeing another doctor as well. The next doctor had left; they gave me some medication for lupus and my other medications as well. I didn't take any of my meds all day; now, I was on the next day.

I didn't ask one of them what was wrong; a new doctor came and told me that she could not see what was wrong with me, so she had to discharge me once more. She told me to make an appointment to see a neurologist once more. I could not wait to leave; I called my co-worker, and she came and got me at 3:00 p.m. Saturday evening. She asked me if I was okay. I told her no, so she took me off the schedule for the week. When I went home, I took my shower and went to bed. My mother asked if I was fine, but I was hurting all over.

My head felt as if it was going to explode; Marie came by with my vehicle, and she asked another co-worker to help her. She told me that everything would be fine, but I knew that something was wrong. I know my body, and this was not a lupus flare-up. When my mother gave me the food, I could not eat it at all; I just stayed in bed and cried myself to sleep, which I could not do too much because my head was hurting so bad.

On Monday morning, I called and made an appointment to see the neurologist. They gave me one for Wednesday morning; during this time, I felt pain that I don't think any human being could have taken, not even animals. When my mother took me to the appointment with a cab, it was the same as always. He asked me the same question; then he told me to squeeze his hands and walk a straight line. I did what he told me to do; he then told me it might be lupus.

I didn't want to hear this at all; I knew my body needed help. A couple of days were the worst; my head was pounding really badly. When I cried, it could not stop. The more I cried, the more pain I felt. My mother felt sorry for me that she called a cab once more and took me to Saint Francis Hospital as well.

They, too, didn't even run any tests at all due to my going to two hospitals, and they didn't see anything wrong with me. I just lay there, and my mind went all over the place. I knew at this point everyone had given up on me. I, too, had given up on myself.

When I got home, I cried so hard; my daughter didn't want to see me like this. I remember asking God to please stop the pain; I could not handle it anymore. I called Dr. Laks, and they told me that he was away. The next day, I felt the pain move from my head right through my eyes and then through my entire body. The pain was not that bad; the only thing that was wrong now was that I could not see through my right eye.

I didn't know if I should cry or not, but I told my mother. I don't think she understood what I was telling her. So I was home blind in one eye; I didn't even go back to the hospital at all. I didn't want them to think that I was crazy. Whenever I was talking, it didn't make any sense at all. On Wednesday evening, I got a call from Dr. Laks. He told me to come in and see him on Friday at 2:00 p.m. I could not wait; I told my mother that I would go with my nephew; she, too, didn't believe me at all.

We took a cab and went; Dr. Laks called me into the room; he was so shocked to see how I had looked. He told me to follow his finger with my eye; I couldn't at all. He had me rush over to the eye doctor. They had me there for three hours running tests and more tests, then another doctor came into the room, and he checked me out when I told him what had happened. They left and spoke with Dr. Laks. After a while, they both came back into the room and told me that I did have a stroke. He told me where they were looking was not the place the stroke took place. Now they had to put me back into the hospital, and this time, they were going to admit me.

As I heard the doctor tell me what had happened to me, the tears just ran down my face. I called my mother at once and told her what had happened. I had called one of my friends to come to the hospital to take us back home, but now I told my nephew to go with him. They stayed until they brought me up to the room; my mother was a nervous wreck. She was calling and wanted to know what to do. I told her that they were going to run some tests and see what was going on. I told her to get me some things for the hospital. She didn't need to come and wait to hear what they were going to say. They came in and took more blood work; then, they had some nurses draw blood. She didn't know what she was doing.

At this point, I just wanted to give up. They ran test after test. I did another MRI that night; they did all kinds of blood tests as well as a CAT scan. I didn't like the MRI; I felt as if I was in a coffin. I was scared most of the time; I kept asking God to take me through this. As I went into that death trap machine, it made all kinds of sounds. I asked them if I could listen to some gospel music. I just closed my eyes and let God take over. When they were finished, I was back in the room once more.

The following day, Marie took my mother to the hospital to see me; she was on her way to work. Mother came by herself; Abigail didn't come with her because Mother was going to stay until Marie left work. I know I was always sick, and she was tired of seeing me this way, but I wanted to see her. I just sat there as they came in and did their thing. It seemed as if I knew what they were going to do.

When Marie came, they stayed for a while, then left. I tried not to call the nurse too much because I knew the nurses would get tired of them when patients called a lot, so I tried to do as much as possible for myself. I was very tired most of the time; I didn't know what they were giving me at this time. I was taking too much medication that my body could not manage at all. In the morning, I would take my own shower because I knew what to do. I thanked God for what I knew; it took a lot out of me, but I got the job done.

I always remember what Wendy, one of the therapists, told me. She said that you can't feel sorry for yourself; you have to push to reach your gold. That Sunday, I got a couple of visitors, those from my old church: Brother Jackson, his wife, and two of the sisters who took care of Abigail when I was at work every other weekend. Brother Jackson brought me some fruits; he was always looking out for Abi and me. My pastor and his wife came as well; I can't say I didn't see anyone even though I could not see out of my right eye. Mother would let Marie take her to the hospital on her way to work; this time, Abigail came with her as well as Marie's niece. The kids were both bored, so I told them to watch TV while they waited until Marie left work at 11:00 p.m.

I didn't get any calls from my family at all. They would tell my mother hi. When Marie came, everyone was ready to go; after all, they had done a full shift with me. I knew that the next day would be another day in the hospital. That night, it was the same routine; they would come in and do vitals.

The next day was all a different ball game; doctors were coming everywhere. They wanted to do another MRI. I just wanted all of this to end. That morning, they took me to run some more tests, and I did not get back to my room until 5:00 p.m. I called my mother and let her know that I was going to have tests done. I went and had a camera put into my nose to my stomach. It was painful; then they took me to another part of the building. I gave up on what they were doing with me. It felt as if I was some kind of experiment. One of the rooms was so cold as ice, while another one was just different.

When they brought me back to the room, I could not believe it. My co-workers were there, about five of them, and one of my church sisters as well as my mother. I greeted all of them, but I was out of it, so they didn't stay too long because they were there for two hours waiting for me. Then Mother and my church sister were talking; she then left. I asked my mother to help me in the shower. I was so tired; I took my shower and ate what she brought for me.

When I looked at my arm, I started to cry because I looked like I was using drugs. Then two of the doctors came in and told my mother what they thought was wrong with me. As she listened to what they were saying, I could not believe I could not see out of my right eye, and when I stood up, my legs were so weak.

My body felt as if someone had entered in and taken over. I could not fight this at all, but I knew that God would not leave me at all. They had me on one thousand milligrams of prednisone and all kinds of meds. I felt like a drug baby.

Chapter 39

I could not control my body at all; I felt weak and tired a lot. It seemed as if my heart was always racing; I just wanted to just scream out for help. They had me in the hospital for four days filling me up with steroids so that I could gain my eyesight back, but still, nothing happened.

I didn't get any visits from my family in New York at all. I didn't have the time for animosity at all. I just wanted to do well; I know that I was in Connecticut, and they lived in New York, even if they all put together and rented a car. I know that my brother would have driven them here. I thought to myself, *If I wasn't that bad of a person, why no one wanted to see me?*

I know that I told them a lot about God, which, at times, they didn't want to hear. I told my mother as well, and she sometimes shook me off. I always knew that everyone needed to know about God, especially in times like these, but no one cared at all. Even my own daughter didn't come every day to see me at all. Why should other people care? I just watched and listened to my mother go on and on.

I wouldn't tell anyone that I didn't feel hurt over the fact that my own daughter treated me like this, not to mention my family, but it was not the first time they had abandoned me. I didn't question it at all, but these thoughts were coming up so often. When they discharged me from the hospital, this was another story. The house felt heavy and needed to be prayed out. I know that this was not normal; I wanted prayer really bad, but I had so many enemies around me.

The tenant was getting on my last nerves; I could not control what was taking place. I used to live well with my tenants; now, everything was wrong. I knew that something was wrong, but I could not put my hands on it; my spirit was angry most of the time. The same way I felt when my ex-husband was around. I knew that I had to focus on getting better, but something was just sucking the life out of me.

I would pray and ask God to help me. The more I prayed, the worse it got.

Now I could hear everything that my mother was saying about me; it seemed as if I had lost my eyesight, but my hearing was stronger than ever. I could literally hear her talking about me to my siblings. She was telling them how I had changed and how she could not live with me.

I was being difficult with everyone in the house; even my own daughter could not stand me at all, not to mention the tenant. She let me sound as if I was going crazy or something; at times, she would give me my meals with all the wrong things or even pack up my plate really full.

I could not see to help myself at all; for breakfast was the same thing. She gave me raised toast with tea, and I had to take fourteen pills each morning. Sometimes, I wanted to call Marie and ask her to bring me something else, but I didn't want to hurt her feelings. I know that I was not my mother's favorite, but I was not well, and I needed her most of all. She was talking more about my nephew and how depressed he was living in the country. I knew it was not like New York, where he could go out and party and so on.

He knew that I had given up on that lifestyle long before he got here; after all, I was not my sister at all. I guess he didn't want to hear about God; I knew something was wrong in this house, but I knew the good Lord would clean the house. As I went back and forth to the doctor's office, then test after test. When I went to see Dr. Laks, he was running all over the place; I was angry at the time. I was not myself and wanted to get back on my feet, but I kept getting bad news, and my mother was not helping at all.

One morning, my mother called me and told me that my breakfast was on the table. It was the same thing over and over again. I know it was hard for her to get up and give a grown woman breakfast in the morning, but I could not see to do it myself, and you would think that my daughter was old enough to have helped me. My stomach wanted more food, for all these medications that I was taking were not good at all. I could not handle what was wrong with me; when I looked at the breakfast she had prepared, I just went and fell for the cupboard, got a pot out, and put an egg on. I bumped my head on the cabinet door; then, I would cry. I could not see out of my right eye; I was not used to this at all.

My mother asked me what I was doing. I told her I needed something else to eat because the pills were too much. She didn't say anything else; I sat down and did what I had to do.

I felt most of my way around the house. I was not used to this at all; I know I was not completely blind, but this was something new for me. I had to know how to control my balance at times, as well as to see where I was going.

My daughter didn't care at all. I could see her father in her; this was how he used to treat me when I was sick. I guess it was me who had the fault because everyone was unhappy in this house. I could not find a place to sleep at all; the child upstairs was getting the best of me; he would run and jump, and the noise was unbearable; and if I told them to hold down the noise, they would get louder and louder, I just wanted to leave this place and not come back, but I had nowhere else to go.

Mother told me she had to go to New York for her doctor's visit; I could not wait. She told my nephew to fry me some plantain for my breakfast. I don't know what he did, but it was the worst I had ever tasted. He didn't even make me a cup of tea with it. I just smiled and asked God to see me through this. Then it came to me to ask Marie to make me some banana porridge.

I didn't want her to know what I was going through because I was not a bad person for all of this treatment that I was facing. I tried to live for the Lord, but I was getting all the fights that I could not handle. My heart was full, and I could not take it anymore. At this point, I had to do something with my tenant. The more I talked to them about the noise, the more loud they got. My mother was not loving to me at all; we were arguing most of the time; I don't know what she told my siblings about me.

One day, she had my sister on the phone on speaker, of course. She was asking my mother about her crazy daughter, that is, me. I just said, "Right here, listening to you calling me crazy." My mother took her speaker off so fast, then I got up and went into my bedroom. This hurt me so badly, and my nephew and Abi were there too. I went into my room, put on my iPod, and listened to my gospel. As the tears rolled down my face, no one called me from my family; now I know why.

I was crazy; that was what my mother had told them. No wonder no one came to visit or even called me. I was sad most of the time. I did a lot of crying, and I did a lot of feeling sorry for myself as well. I could not have gone to church due to the sound of the music; it was too loud. I needed God right now; he was nowhere to be found. As the weeks went by, I knew that I had to make a plan on everything in my life at this point.

My job was asking me a lot of questions when I was coming back to work. These questions I could not answer at all, so I had to wait until I went to the doctor for him to fill out the paperwork. I knew I had to get rid of some of the expenses that I had in the house. I was not working, and I knew that the bills were coming so much. I decided to get rid of my vehicle; I had offered it to my brother, but he told me to sell it and pay some of my bills.

So I asked the tenant upstairs, and he liked it. He even got his mechanic to check it out, then he told me he could give me $2,500 for it, but I asked the lady's son whom I took care of. He told me that if he didn't have his mother's car, he could buy it from me. He told me how much to sell it for. He said that I could get it for 3 thousand dollars; I didn't know when I could drive at all. The van would have been sitting there and rotten.

I called Abi's hairdresser and asked her if she could get Abi and do her hair for me. She told me to bring her to her house. She didn't know I was sick like that, but no one told her. She came by the house and told me that she had moved from her shop. Most of her clients had left her, and she was struggling to make ends meet. She even lost her apartment as well. I felt sorry for her. I guess I was one of her clients, and I, too, stopped going to her due to her behavior. She felt as if I needed her; she needed my business.

She would talk to you any way she wanted to, and now it seemed as if people didn't like her attitude at all. I had still let Abi go to her. So she came to the house and did my hair for me, it was falling out, but I could not put any chemicals in my hair at this time.

I was on too much medication, and my hair was falling out, so she came and washed it; then she braided it for me. She told me that she would come and get Abi whenever it was time to do her hair. This girl was not even driving, and now she had only a few clients to do. I really felt sorry for her. I got a call from the lady that I took care of. She wanted to see me, so I asked the hairdresser if she could take me into my vehicle to see her. My nephew came with us. I saw the way she looked at him, but he was in another world by himself.

When I got to the lady's house, it was a mess. I could not believe the condition of the place. As Mrs. Brown hugged me, she told me how much she missed me; I could see that the house was a mess, and she was sad. I asked her why didn't they get someone to clean the place up. She looked, but no one stayed at all; I looked at Abi's hairdresser and asked her if she needed me to look for someone for her; I knew that Marie didn't want to do her house at all; she had another job herself.

Then I looked at the young lady; I knew that she wanted a job; this would do good for her right now. It could help her with some of the stress she was going through. I asked Mrs. Brown, and she told her son. I called the young lady and asked her if she wanted a job; she looked at me as if I was crazy as well. I guessed she needed it more than I thought. I left them to talk and went outside to my nephew, and we were just talking. I told him I saw the way she was looking at him; he didn't notice anything at all.

I knew that he was bored, and I knew that Abi was sad about what was happening to me. I tried everything I knew how. I would call the hairdresser to take them to the movie so that they could be happy. I was once told that he was unhappy. Then Mother told me that she was going to New York again.

I didn't mind at all. At this time, I got this idea for my nephew to marry this girl. He needed someone as well as she. I know it sounds crazy, but it came up in my spirit, and he needed a girlfriend. I didn't waste any time. I asked her if she would marry him, and she thought I was crazy, as well as my nephew. I was just trying to help both of them. He needed help, and she wanted a husband as well. They both looked at me. I didn't want to waste any time because I knew my mother would stop it.

I just had to ask; this would stop that girl from coming to my house at night. I told them to think about it until my mother came back. I knew this was not right, but she needed a man, and he wanted a lot of things. She was still taking the bus, back and forth. Then she called me and told me that Mrs. Brown had called her and given her the job. I knew she was going to get it, but then her son William called me one day and asked me why I didn't sell her the vehicle. I didn't even think about her, she was taking the bus to work, and it seemed as if she was having a hard time.

I asked her if she wanted to buy the van. She knew how it looked and how it felt. She told me she didn't have that kind of money right now. I told her if she married my nephew, she wouldn't have to pay me for it. I knew that I would not have a problem at all.

When my mother came home, I told her that my nephew was going to get married, but this woman didn't say another word. She just looked at him. I knew that this was a dead deal, but Mother said no with her eyes.

Now the house was full of tension; I didn't stay in the house too much. When the hairdresser came over, Mother would get upset, and so did my nephew. He could not look at her, so I told her that his mother and grandmother didn't want him to get married. They wanted to find him a bride. I don't know if they were looking for a virgin. Once more tension was in the house, I didn't like staying around them.

They would be talking, and when I entered the room, the talking would stop. I just smiled and walked away; then, one day, she called me and told me that Mrs. Brown had fired her. It seemed as if William had called me and told me she was nothing like me.

I don't know what had happened to them; now she was on her face once more. I had already told her that I was going to sell her the vehicle, but I could not go back on my words. She had promised to take me to any doctor's appointment whenever I had one; that sounded even better to me. Taking a cab to my doctor's appointment was expensive. Marie had to go to work, and it was too much for me.

I needed help, and I had to try and help myself. When my mother came back from New York, she brought back a bag of peppermint for my nephew. His mother had sent it for him due to the fact I know Abi loves sweets, and she would eat them. I gave them away to my co-worker to give to the kids at her church. My mother asked me where the candy was; I told her what I did with them; she started to scream and tell me how I was an idiot. She said it seemed as if the stroke hit my head and let me get crazy. As the tears rolled down my face, my nephew just laughed, while my daughter didn't say anything.

I told her that I was not crazy, but I had a stroke, and the doctor told me that my brain was crushed up like a foil paper. I got up and went into my room once more and shut out everyone. I was waiting for my daughter to come and tell me how sorry she was to hear what her grandma said to me like that. I guess she was right; I am crazy. I am lost and crazy; I just called the young lady to come and get me. I told her to take me to the motor vehicle to get the van out of my name.

I called my insurance guy and asked him what I needed to do. He gave me all the advice I needed. I did a bill of sale, and she did her part on the van. Now I was with this girl, trying to get it turned over to her; everything was not working out too well. She would be cursing God, and this girl went to church. I don't know if I was blind or what, but I guess I was crazy, as my entire family thought.

I called my brother and asked him if he was coming down for Mother's birthday; he told me that he didn't have any money at all to even rent a car. I told him to take the van, but he told me no. I guess no one wanted anything from me; not even my own child wanted me near her. Whenever I went into her room to sit with her, she would get up and go into my mother's room.

I didn't know what kind of hold my mother had on her. I was her mother, and I didn't even treat her in any way I could not understand. Why was she treating me this way? The love I had for her was what I knew how; I remember what her dad had told me, that my family didn't like me at all. I was always trying to prove my love to them, but they only used me, and that was all; he had told me a lot of things, but I was always quick to forgive people too much. He told me to be like the Bible says, to be gentle as a dove but to be wise as a serpent.

As I sat down and let all of his word rush through my head, I would cry most of the time. I went into the garage and emptied out the van and went into my closet and went through my clothes and took out dresses that I had bought and gave them to this girl. I was just giving away things I didn't need. I called Marie and gave her curtains and a pot that I didn't need. I knew my mother thought I was crazy, but that was okay.

Now Abi had a thing with my nephew; she was always in his room playing games on her Xbox. I told her that she needed to go to her room and do her homework, and now she was upset with me. I could not wait for my brother to come and talk to them. I even noticed that my nephew didn't want to do anything for me again.

He would pay most of my bills because I couldn't see that well. Now everything was a problem for him. Whenever I asked him, he would get upset. I knew that I could not see that well to do my medication as well. I was taking pills that I should not have been taking. I was afraid to ask for help; he didn't want to do anything anymore; he just wanted to listen to his grandmother and mother.

I kept out of their way; I was not getting any rest at all. I called my brother and told him that I would send him the money to rent a car, to come down and visit his mother for her birthday. He did just that. I called Marie and asked her if she could get a cake for me at the stop and shop. They had a nice fruit cake; I knew that she loved

Boston Market food, so I even got a meal for her. I knew it was her seventieth birthday; I tried to make it special for her.

When he came with his wife and daughter, it seemed as if her world was open, and I was her nightmare. I asked him to take me shopping to get her something. He told me that he didn't have any money at all. I told him that I got this, and he asked me where I got the money from.

I just told him that I gave back to the Lord, and he blessed me, plus Aflac was sending me my money. We went, and he got her a plant, then we went and got her balloons and a banner. I sent my nephew to Boston Market, and we got her a card, and we all signed it for her. I was still trying my best to love her, but she just hated me so much. I don't know what I have done for her all my life. I had killed my own baby so that I would not bring shame to her name. I was just dying inside for her to love me. It seemed as if everything I buried was surfing back up. I had buried all these things, but my brother was not the good choice to help me because now my mother's favorite was here. I felt like an outcast; the only person that let me feel that I was worth living for was my dad. He was long gone, and I was left with people who wanted me dead. They just didn't love me at all.

Her birthday was on Saturday, and Marie came over with Shan and her grandson, my brother and his daughter, and his wife. Abi and I, with my nephew, were there just to make her feel special. She was happy, and she called everyone and told them how her son came from New York and gave her a party.

I just smiled because her crazy daughter would not do anything for her. I just let her give him all the praise. She was happy. I tried not to say anything at all so as not to get her upset. I took all that she was doing to me; I knew that I was crazy, and I didn't want to get anyone upset.

My brother and his wife called me into the garage and asked me what was happening inside my house. My brother told me that blackness was over the house, it felt heavy, and this was not my house at all. I just looked at them and asked them if they felt it too.

His wife said, "Yes, girl; something is not right here." I just looked up and thanked God because I thought I was getting crazy. I just went down and started to cry. I knew I was not getting mad. I just started to tell them how I was being treated in my house.

He looked at me and told me that it was not me, the house was heavy, and I needed to clean the house. He told me that I should do what I needed to do; then, he did not like the idea that my nephew had Abi in his room playing games. He told me if I needed his help just call him. I felt good because I really thought that I was losing my mind. He told me that he was going to bring my nephew back to New York for some time.

The following day, Mother cooked food for all of us, and she was sharing dinner for my brother to take home. I asked if she could share some food. She told me, "No, do it yourself." I wanted to cry, but I just held back the tears and shared the food myself. My nephew couldn't want to go to New York; it seemed as if I was killing him. I didn't care at all. Now I knew that I was not getting crazy. When they left, I had to get back into the Word of God, so I listened to the Bible when I was not listening to gospel music.

I needed the spirit to lead me once more. It seemed as if I had gone cold with the Lord. I made the devil have me under his feet, and now I had to raise up at once. When my nephew went to New York, I don't know what he told his mother; she called me and asked me about the girl I wanted her son to marry. She told me that the girl was a temptress, to which I said that all of us were once that, too, until God cleaned us up. I said, "Even you, too, were one." She called me all kinds of things and cursed me. Then she told me that she was going to call immigration on me; for them to lock me up.

She even told me that I was no Christian; I just hung up my phone and called my nephew and told him not to come back and that he should stay with his mother; maybe she would give him his virgin wife he needed. Now all broke loose, now my mother hated me even more, and my daughter came into my room crying and telling me that he had an issue with his mother.

I looked at her and said, "You too... They need to work it out." I was in the house with all of this. The tenant was getting out of control, and the Lord told me to give them notice. My mother told me that I was crazy. I should put a stop on this for a long time. I did not care at all; if she wanted to go, I didn't care at this point. I had to clean the house now. I was just letting the Holy Spirit lead.

You could feel the tension in the house; I didn't care at all. The next thing that took place was I went to the hospital to do a procedure. They wanted to capture some image of my heart at a different angle, so they had to put a camera in my leg. They did what they needed to do; I was out for a while. My mother came with me for that procedure; when I was over with it, I called a cab, but I could not get one, so I called the young lady to see if she could come and get me. She let me know that she was going to Bible study and I should call a cab.

It served me right. I was always helping people, and they always hurt me. I was in a lot of pain, and no cab was available for me. I called another co-worker, and she came for us. I gave her the money for gas. When I reached home, I was in a lot of pain; I had to take a sponge bath.

Chapter 40

This was just a setback on my part. Now I was getting so tired. I could hardly move, but I still push myself. Some days were bad, while others were not any better. I still had to fight the good fight of faith. I would watch TV a lot; it was on TBN. I would watch this preacher by the name of Joseph Prince. He was talking a lot about the Lord's Supper. I would follow him as he went on. I took the Lord's Supper for eight days straight; I would read the Bible verses as well, which was in 1 Corinthians chapter 11. I had crackers I had in the house, and I used syrup for my wine. I would anoint my head as well. I had to believe what the Bible says about Jesus; by his stripes, I am healed. I was more in the Word and was praying a lot.

Then I got a call from my cousin; she told me that she was coming for my birthday. I was happy to hear that; at least she would be here to remind me of my dad. She was my dad's niece. When my cousin came, she brought me a lot of things; she saw the condition I was in. She would not believe it at all. My mother didn't let anyone know what I was facing at all.

My birthday was in a few days, and my cousin would talk about my dad, which made me feel good. Mother was upset, but I knew if he were here, I would be fine. I didn't have to prove my love to him, he knew it, and that was all that mattered.

The day before my birthday, Mrs. Brown sent me a bouquet of red long-stem roses. They were gorgeous; I had to call her and thank her. Marie asked me what I wanted. I told her a cake. She bought the same cake I had gotten for my mother. She didn't come because it was her weekend to work, but my cousin Tina was there. She never left me out for nothing; my mom and Abi and Tina sang me happy birthday songs; to top it off, the tenant moved out that night. I could not ask for anything else; that night, I was just eating and drinking water so much. I told her I felt as if I wanted coke, and she went and got it for me.

That night, I felt so thirsty; the more I drank water, the more it came out, and I still didn't quench the thirst. My body was not right at this time. I could not understand what was going on with me. I felt very different and didn't know what was wrong with me. I was so happy that my cousin was with me for my birthday; I didn't make whatever my mother was dishing out to me affect me at all.

Tina had to go back to New York; she helped me fill out paperwork for social security disability, and she helped me with my medication as well. I didn't think that I would need someone to help me with all of this.

It seemed as if whenever I read something, it wasn't registering to me; I didn't want them to think that I was stupid.

I cried a lot because I felt like someone was taking over my body. I still didn't ask God what was wrong. I just trusted him with everything; it is very hard not to have control over your own body. *I've been taking care of myself, and now I feel helpless.* I still didn't question Abba about what I was feeling, but I could feel my thoughts crying out for me to question God.

I even heard the devil telling me that I trusted God, and he let this happen to me, but I had to rebuke the devil and still trust God. I remember one night, I got up and was writing a letter to my daughter, telling her goodbye. Not saying I was going to kill myself; the way I felt, it seemed as if I was dying. There were a lot of white things in my mouth and my private area. I didn't know if I should tell my mother; it didn't seem as if she cared at all.

The treatment was not right. I still tried to honor her as the Bible says, but sometimes, it was difficult. I just trusted God. I went on my knees and asked God what was really happening to me and why I felt like this.

I heard his voice so clearly; he told me that I needed to go back to the emergency room. I even packed my bag just in case they decided to keep me, but I didn't take it with me. I woke up in the morning and told my mother that I was going to the hospital. She asked me why. I told her that I was not feeling well. I knew in my heart that she was tired of going to the hospital, so I told her to stay. I went with God and did what he told me to do. I asked Marie to take me on her way to work, which she did. When I went in, they thought I was crazy. I didn't care at all; I was just listening to what the Spirit told me to do; they saw the thrush in my mouth, and they did some blood work while I was waiting in one of the rooms. It wasn't long before I saw a couple of nurses and doctors come in. The doctor came over and questioned me. He wanted to know what was wrong with me and why I came to the ER; I didn't let him know that God told me to. I didn't want another person to think that I was crazy.

The doctor told me he was glad I came in, or maybe I would die. I just looked at him as he explained what was going on with me. He told me that my sugar count was 699. I didn't even know what that meant; I just listened to him as he went into details. Now they admitted me once more, and I had to do more tests. I just sat there and waited until they tried to get another needle into my arm; the young lady didn't know what she was doing. The doctor even noticed the nurse was having a problem with the needle; she had it all over my arm.

She was just poking me like a rag doll. I don't know if I should have just hit her out. I know that she must have known that she was hurting me as well. He asked for another nurse to come in and do the procedure. I just sat there and was lost for words, but in my thoughts, I thanked God for telling me to go to the hospital.

I called my mother and told her what was taking place. She was silent on the phone. I then told her that I had packed a bag and when she was coming to bring it for me. I then called my church sister P, who told me to call her if I had need of anything. I had a need right then; she did come, and she brought my mother to the hospital. I didn't have time to feel sorry for myself; I had to focus on getting better. While I was in the hospital, I knew what to expect. They came in and took my blood every morning. Then I had these pills I had to put under my tongue and one in my private area as well. I didn't let the nurse do that at all.

I told her that I would take care of myself; I tried not to let them do too much. Now this thing called diabetes was a new thing for me to handle. My body was definitely not my own. One minute, it was shaking; the next, I just felt like my eyes were going blurry. I could not see a thing. I could see good out of my left eye, and now both eyes were doing their own thing. The nurse would come in often and stick me with that needle to check my sugar. Sometimes, it hurt, while other times, I did not feel a thing. Whenever I was finished with a meal, she would stick me once more in my stomach for the insulin.

This was too much for me; I really didn't need another sickness at all. I was getting used to not seeing too well out of my right eye, and now both my eyes were acting up. I had to watch what I ate; this was something I had to be really careful of. I used to complain about my arm being black and blue from the blood work; now, I had to get shots in my stomach.

One night, the aide came into the room to check my vitals; she noticed that my temperature was high. The nurse then came in and told me what was going on. She told me that she had put it into my record so that the doctors could let her know what the matter was. I just wanted to go home at this time; too much was going on in my life. She came back and told me that they were going to give me Tylenol, but I had to do more blood work.

I was used to this by now; they did the usual thing at night, but I had a terrible headache. The Tylenol was not working after all. I didn't want to eat at all, but they told me that I was now a diabetic and needed to eat; if not, I could go into a diabetic coma. I didn't care at all; I reached the point of giving up at this time. I really didn't want my mother to come to visit me due to the fact that she wanted me to eat, and I just didn't feel like eating at all. She did come and tell me the same thing they were telling me.

One day, I looked in the bathroom mirror, and I could not see Angela at all. I looked totally different. It took them two days to realize I was off the prednisone medication. I don't know what was going on, but Doctor Laks sent another doctor over to see how I was doing. He never came once, but he sent other doctors to check on me. To my surprise, Dr. Weighmen, the doctor who told them I had a stroke, came over to see me.

He brought another doctor with him; he told me that no one was monitoring my sugar level, which they should have done. He checked me out and asked how I felt; then, I told him what I was feeling. He just looked at me and said, "It seems as if they wanted to kill you." I didn't say anything because I worked in the medical field, and I knew what he was talking about.

The next day, one of Doctor Laks's assistants came over. It seemed as if he told Doctor Laks what was happening to me, so he sent his assistant doctor. When she was going through my chart, she was making jokes on how I got fat. Then she realized that they had stopped the prednisone. She asked them why, but I told her that another doctor thought that I had too much sugar in my system. She told me that was the reason I had a high temperature. She told me I was going cold turkey; she then told them to put me back on the meds, and she filled out more things I needed to take. It seemed as if each doctor I saw was doing their own things. I was taking a lot of meds in the morning as well as evening and at night. I felt like CVS pharmacy, which I had to pay a co-payment as well.

I was still getting letters from my job. They wanted to know when I was coming back to work. I could hardly keep my head straight; I was tempted to cry, but I asked God to just keep me strong so that I could keep the faith. My pastor didn't even know that I had gone back to the hospital again. They had a death in their family as well, but sister McDonald came to visit me. She prayed with me and left; I was trying my best at this point not to give up after all that I was going through.

It seemed as if they wanted to kill me; I had to keep my eyes open and ask a lot of questions. When they started to give me the prednisone back, I felt my appetite coming back, and the fever was gone. The following day, I got up, showered, and had breakfast. Then one of the dietitians came into my room; she wanted me to know a lot about the sickness. She gave me a list of what I could and could not eat.

Then she told me that I could only eat in portions; if only she could tell my mother that. When she left, another person came in, the nurse as well. She wanted to show me how to give myself the insulin shot. I took my lesson, and then I called the young lady to whom I had sold my van.

I called her to find out if she was going to pay me my money for the van; I don't know why I called her, but she told me a lot of bad things. Then she made me feel even worse than before. I don't know if she would ever pay me at all, but I put it to God. It seemed as if I had to go through this to know who was for me.

When I was okay, I would go above and beyond to help people, but now that I was down, no one to help. If Marie weren't there to take me to the hospital for my doctor's visit, I would have had to take the cab, which was expensive. I didn't know if I was coming or going. Sometimes, sister P would take me.

When they finally discharged me, I knew that I had a lot of work to do with the apartment. I knew that I had to first get better at this point. Now I had another thing to worry about; I was on insulin, plus high blood pressure as well. When it wasn't one thing, it was another.

The high blood pressure was okay. I knew that I had to stay away from salt but sugar... I love my apple pie and cheesecake. I had to fight my flesh really badly when it came to this. My body was crying out for help, and I had to be strong most of the time, while days I felt like giving up. This was all new to me; I was not thinking about lupus too much, not even the stroke. The only thing I thought about from the stroke was my eye, as I could not see.

The sugar thing was kicking my rear end really well. I had to be checking my sugar level with each meal or sometimes just on how I felt. This was too much. I didn't need to feel sorry for myself at all. My body was getting bigger each day; I could feel my skin stretching.

I knew that I needed to fix the apartment upstairs, but I didn't have anyone to help me at all. My mother told me that I was on my own, and she was right; I did as much I could, but getting over all this was too much for me.

One day, I called my cousin Tina, and she told me all that was being said about me. She let me know that they were all upset with me because I told my nephew to go back to his mother. Even the other sister I spoke with was mad at me. She told her it was my fault that her son was in jail.

I was hurt to know all my life, I was there for all of them, even my own sisters who didn't have a place to stay, and I opened my house to help out those who didn't have it. I tried to help, and this was the payback. Even my own mother hated me because I loved the Lord too much. My daughter even turned on me because she didn't want to hear about Jesus.

I guess this was the reason no one called me or even visited me in the hospital. It was good to know. I knew that I had to get better really fast and stop feeling sorry for myself. Now I know that this was just a plan of the enemy. I had to stand up now and live for Jesus; they all hated me because I would not compromise with their lifestyle.

I know that there is a God, and I have to live for him; I know that there is a place called hell and a place called heaven. I have to choose which place I want to spend the rest of eternity in.

When people asked me how I was feeling, I would tell them what my family thought of me, that I was crazy. My cousin would call me and ask me how I was feeling; I would just tell me down and out. I told her, "I don't know if I'm going to die today or tomorrow, but I would love to keep my daughter's sweet sixteen birthday party." She laughed and told me that sounded good; this took my mind off things.

Tina told me not to worry at all; she would see to it that Abi had her party. She would send things that she ordered online and send them to the house; I asked her how much it cost. She told me what my dad did for her was only a payback, and since he loved me so much, it was the least that she could have done. My mother was on the phone most of the time, talking to her kids. I didn't let it get the best of me. I was more focused on how to get better. This sugar thing was kicking my rear end; it made me feel so different. I didn't know how to handle this at all. My body would shake a lot. I didn't know if the sugar was low.

One day, I almost passed out due to the fact it was low. I shook as if I was a pressure cooker. I didn't like the feeling at all; now, I would take food with me anywhere I went. I didn't want to pass out at all. I knew I had to move on, but if I had to follow how I felt each day, I probably would have been in a nursing home by now. I had to start getting myself lined up with the Word of God and do whatever the Holy Spirit told me to do. I stayed away from negative vibes, which meant staying away from people that felt sorry for me.

I notice that sometimes, I love the attention of being sick, but sometimes, I really feel that way. I had to fight that feeling to get to where I wanted to go. I knew I had to get the apartment ready because the mortgage had to be paid. I even needed help, but I didn't have the money to pay someone to help me. I knew my brother would have help, but he was the only one working at his home, so he could not get the time off to do so. The little I was getting from my job could not do too much, but it was helping.

Chapter 41

This, too, didn't last long due to what the doctor put on my report. She told me that I could never work again; I didn't believe that at all. I knew I was sick, but the God I serve would not let me suffer for long. I know that one day, I am going to get well and do my Father's work.

I knew that I could not go back and do the kind of work I used to do; it took too much out of me, but I had to find something else to do. I always heard a voice telling me to finish my book, but whenever I tried to do it. I would get distracted and go and do something else. I didn't know what it was, but I could not find time to sit down and type things I'd been through; it felt as if something was holding me back, or I would get up and find other things to do except what the Lord told me.

Now I started to face upstairs and face my own battle. I could not do too much. My mother told me that she was not going to help me at all, and Abigail agreed as well. I had to go upstairs and try to do little each day. I remember my legs getting weak, and I fall on my bottom. I still got up and took out some of the things the tenant left in the apartment.

I would get a call from my cousin; she was updating me about Abigail's party. I would tell her that I fell on my bottom and that my legs were weak. She told me to ask the church people to help, but I didn't. They all knew my situation, and no one offered. I let her know that when God told me to help, I would just do it, and then people would wonder how I knew. I didn't tell them that the Lord told me because they would think that I was nuts, but I know that he is talking to them.

They chose not to listen; I told her that I have my sisters and nephews; they knew my situation, but they refused to help. They totally forgot what I'd done for them, but God knew. This is the cross I have to bear; I knew that I had to get this place ready. I went upstairs and worked as much as possible. My body cried out most of the time, but I had to trust God for everything.

Every day, I would go upstairs and do what I could do. I could hardly see most of the time due to the sugar, plus I could hardly see out of my eye that was affected by the stroke. One day, I got so upset by the fact that I was doing this so that I could have a roof over my head. I went downstairs and told my daughter that she needed to help me, but she wanted to listen to her grandmother.

I lost it; I told her to get her whatsoever upstairs and help me. I told her that she was going to benefit from it; I put her straight. I could not do too much. My body felt like it was giving up on me. Then God answered my prayers; my brother came down the following weekend. He did as much as possible; I did not have to pay him at all. He always tells me when he wins the lotto, I'll be okay. Then he told me that God would not mind if I bought the lotto at all. He even said that my pastor would be happy if I won. I asked him why. He said, "Sis, I know you; you would even want to give them some of your winnings." Then he asked me if the church would help me at all; I told him that they pray for me, and that was it. He looked at me and shook his head; he was right with what he was saying.

When I read the Bible, it said that the old churches help each other, but today, if you don't have money, don't call them. I don't know if they think that I have money due to the fact that I have a house. I still have to pay bills as well. My mother gave me three hundred for rent and a hundred for the cable. I would have to find the mortgage, light, gas, insurance, and water bill, plus my medical insurance, as well as co-payment for each doctor's visit and co-payment for my meds, not to mention my credit card bills and things for Abi and myself as well.

My mother helped out with her food stamp, which I'm grateful for. Whatever she cooks, I try not to complain but give God thanks. This was my life, trying to fix this place to help pay the bills to keep a roof over our heads. Somedays, I felt like giving up, then my cousin would call me and tell me that my mother was talking about me with my sisters. My sister didn't keep her mouth at all. She would talk about her poor mother working her soul out while my daughter and I just sat down and rested.

I did the best I could, but I guess I had to do more. I felt really bad because I never let her do all of the work. So I made a point of cleaning up the bathroom; my heart sometimes was racing so fast. I could hardly stand up due to the fact that my legs were weak. I would tell my daughter to clean the bathroom at times, but my mother would tell her it was okay, and she would do it. Mother would complain that she was not doing a good job.

I know that she needed to learn, but you could not please my mother at all. Even when we went to the grocery store, she would take her own time, not realizing that I had to ask someone to take us. I could see the expression on their faces. For some of them, I would give money for gas just to take us; some got upset; it's not like I go to the store every day, but once a month; but people would get tired of me. I tried to stop bothering them, but sometimes, I didn't have any choice.

I would do all these things for people without a problem, but no one was Angela. I would tell one person to drop me off, then I would call another one to pick us up. I didn't want them to get tired of us because they didn't care at all. They would say that they were not going to the store and in a rush. I didn't have any vehicle to help us, and that girl took my van and didn't even one day call and ask me if I needed help.

One day at the grocery store, I got a call from one of my church sisters. She asked me if the apartment was rented. I told her that I was fixing it; she told me that she had some church sister who was looking for someplace to live. I told her that it was not ready as yet, but she wanted to come and look at it. I told her fine, but when I got home. She called me as soon as I got home.

I told her it was not ready yet, but she was determined to come and see. When they came, the red flag came up. My spirits could not take them at all, even though they were church people. I just felt funny about them, but it was not ready yet; it seemed as if this lady was a pain.

She would call me so often, asking when it would be ready. I told her that I had to wait until my brother got here to help me. Things were happening all over, and the old tenant called for her security deposit. I told her that I was waiting for my brother to finish because they did a lot of damage and didn't move out until after the 11th. She saw me one day at the bus stop. She told me a lot of bad words. She was just cursing me out. She told me that I was evil, and that was the reason why these things were happening to me.

My daughter just walked away from us, but I felt embarrassed. This woman was acting this way; she was going to make sure that I was dead. I could not understand what was going on. When we got on the bus, the lady was quiet. I just sat down. I wished the earth could just open up and take me in. While I was on the bus, I could not cry for anyone to see me like this. I didn't know if my daughter was embarrassed of me. We did what we had to do. Then we went back home.

I went into my room while she went into my mother's room. I don't know if she told her what had happened; I picked up the phone and called my cousin and asked her to call her lawyer's friend and ask him to write me a letter for me.

I didn't want to ask anyone at all; she told me that I didn't owe her anything at all. She told me that they had moved out after the 10th and had damage to the house. I don't like the embarrassment at all. I got the letter and gave them half of their deposit. I called the son, and he came and got the money. I told him the next time I saw his mother talk to me the way she did, I would call the police for harassment.

I didn't do these people anything at all, but everyone wanted to put me down. I paid them and went on to the next thing; I did what I had to do. My brother came down and helped me with the finishing touch. Then the same lady came this time; she wanted to know if the place was ready, but my brother was there. He saw her, and she told me she would move in right away because she didn't want me to rent it to someone else. When she left, my brother asked me what was wrong with this one.

I told him that my spirits didn't like her; he told me to tell my spirits that my bills wanted to be paid. Then he said that they were older people, and they were my kind, church people. He was talking; I still didn't feel them at all, then he spoke to her and told her that the place would be ready for next month, but she insisted on moving in while he was still fixing it.

He looked at me and told me it was not a lot left to do, she could move in, and then he would get the little things done. I still didn't feel it at all; then, he reminded me of all the bills I had to pay. She still insisted on moving early. I asked her if she was going to pay for the two weeks. She told me that she didn't have it at all; we had changed the carpet, the kitchen sink, and the bathroom sink, as well as fixed the bath.

My brother also varnished the floor, painted the whole place, and fixed the light fixtures. He was rushing too much to prepare the place for this lady, and I think she could have waited. He told me to get help, so I did. I asked Marie's son-in-law to help. He came and fixed the tile on the floor and finished the painting.

She got her way after all; she did move in two weeks early, but my brother told me that he saw a few roaches as well. He told me what to buy to get rid of them; if I had money, I would have called the extremity. I got what he said and bombed the place out; I called the lady, and she came and looked over the apartment.

She was smiling and happy, but my spirit was killing me; I hated to ignore the spirit. It was not even two days since she moved in; she called me to let me know that the bathroom sink was leaking. I could not call my brother to fix it; he was in New York. I had to call a church brother who charged me eighty dollars to fix it. I called my brother and told him what had happened. He asked me if this person went to church, and I told him yes. He said he only had to put some kind of tape on it, but because I was a woman, they were robbing me blind.

I knew that; when the two weeks were over, she called me to let me know that the light was not working. Now I had to call an electrician, who was another church brother. If I had called my own brother, he would ask me if I didn't know anyone else.

I didn't have any money at this time to call anyone else. He came, and he didn't charge me at all. He told me to get the things he needed. I got a ride and got what he needed; then, he fixed it for me. It seemed as if my brother didn't do a good job. Paying all the bills and the back bills was too much, and now my work insurance had stopped due to the fact that the doctors told my job that I was not coming back to work.

She actually put on the paper that I would never go back to work. I didn't even realize it until the scheduler called me crying. I told her not to cry for me but just pray because the God I serve would take care of me. The road to recovery was not easy; most of the time, I would find myself crying, and I felt like people were pointing their fingers and asking, "Where is her God that she talks so much about?"

Then some days, I was bold and told the devil to get behind me. I knew that my mother thought that I was losing my mind because I would talk a lot about God, Jesus, and the Holy Spirit. I didn't care at all. I knew what I heard. I would spend most of my time listening to the Bible on my iPod and listening to gospel music as well. My pastor's wife and some sisters would come over and pray with me, which helped a lot.

I didn't go to church at all due to the fact I could pick up any sound. It seemed as if I lost one sight and got my hearing. This was one of the things I got from my sickness. I could hear things really loud, and sometimes it gave me a headache.

My cousin called me and asked where I was keeping the party for Abi. I told her in the backyard; then she told me to look around and see if I could find anywhere to rent. I thought that it was too much, but then I remembered that I could ask the church for their hall. I called my pastor, and he told me it was free for all members. I gave him the date, and he told me to call another brother in charge of these things. I called him, and he told me all kinds of prices. I knew that the pastor told me that it was free. Then he told me he would get back to me. I went and called Abi's cousin, who cooks for events like these. He told me whenever I was ready. My cousin was waiting for me to decide where I was going to keep this thing, but I still had to wait on the brother from church.

One day, I got a call from the young lady who owns me my money for my van. She told me that she could only pay me five hundred dollars a month. I was happy to hear that. Now I could help my cousin with some of the expenses with Abi's party. Then I called my cousin and let her know. I was helping my cousin with Abi's party; my church brother told me they had an event that same day; it took him long enough to find that out, but we kept it in the back of the yard.

I would go out with Marie and get food kinds for the party. My mother told me that she was not going to help at all with the cooking. I knew Marie would have done it, but I wanted her to come and enjoy herself. Things were running smoothly; I would do what I had to do.

I sent invitations to a lot of people, but they did not show up at all; even Abi's cousin, who was to cook, didn't call at all. I had to get someone else to cook. This, too, was a big thing, my mother didn't eat from people, so she didn't want any of the food. Now she was at the party, cooking food for her family, while I was having food catering. I thought to myself that she could have cooked instead, but that was her behavior. As I watched all that was going on, I tried to maintain my cool. My sister came but still did not come outside to the party. I saw most of my co-workers. I asked Abi where her friends were. She told me she didn't know. Not one from her school showed up; most of them were people I knew, and some from her church.

I did my best and could not wait until everything was over. For the treatment I got from this party, it was not worth it at all. The day went by, and I was just helping to clean up. As I watched my sisters get what they needed and leave, I just thanked my brother and his wife for all the help they had given. Then my cousin got her thanks another way. This was over, and now my real life has begun. I went to church for the first time since I had the stroke. It was Father's Day.

I was so happy to be in the house of the Lord; I was greeted a lot, and I felt really good. I don't know what I could have done; I knew that I had to find something to do. It seemed as if whenever I thought about things, I would get a call about what I was thinking. I got a letter from social security. They wanted me to come in for an interview to see how I was functioning mentally. I kept asking God to help me with this interview. I didn't want anyone to think I was crazy like my mother had told everyone.

I prayed so hard; the day came, and I took a cab to the interview. They told me I was too early, so I had to go back home. I didn't have any money to take the cab again, so I took the bus this time. I left the house early again; I didn't know my way at all. I asked the driver, and he told me I had passed the stop three blocks back. Now I had to come off and walk it back.

My legs were so weak, but I kept on going. When I got there, I was early again. So I sat down and waited until I was called. In the meantime, while I was waiting. I saw this doctor calling the ambulance for a patient that he was interviewing. I got so nervous that I asked God to help me with this man. I didn't want him to put me down as crazy, for my mother to prove she was right.

When I went in, I was just praying and asking God to help me; he even had a dog in his office with him. I was just playing with the animals as if I was okay, but I was scared to death. He asked me questions I could not answer, but I trusted God, and he answered most of them. He gave me things to do; I did most of them.

Then he asked me some more questions; I failed some but answered the rest. When the interview was over, he asked me how I got there. I told him by bus. This poor man didn't know what I went through to reach him. I got on the wrong bus and had to catch another one. I could not see the stop, and the bus took me three blocks down the road. Then I had to walk it back. It was too much; I just kept my cool. I didn't want my mother with me at all. I went with the Lord. When I got home, I was so tired. I just went to bed; the rain was even falling, and I got wet, things I had to face.

As the months went by, I was waiting to hear from them, and the tenant was now complaining about roaches. She even called my church sister, who I knew well; now, this woman was on my case, as well as my church sister. She would call her own sister and complain that the house had a lot of roaches and I was not doing anything about it. I heard everything that she was saying because I was in her sister's van when she called her.

Her sister had her on speakerphone; I could not believe what I was hearing. This woman would call me whenever she needed help. She was always borrowing money to pay her bills, and now she made me sound like the crazy landlord. When I went home, I went upstairs and asked the lady what was happening to the apartment; she then told me that she had roaches.

I told her to call me and let me know the next time things like this happen. She didn't need to let anyone else know. This was the wrong thing I did. She called me for everything; I could not handle this at all. I was going under a lot of stress. I went out and got some gel from The Home Depot. She wanted me to call the exterminator to fix the problem. I told her that I did not have that kind of fun; if she had the five hundred dollars that she owed me, I would be sure to help. She didn't call me for that once more. The next call I got was not pretty at all.

This time, her sister had tripped on the concrete on the walkway; then, my church sister told them that it had happened to her a lot, which was one of the reasons she was careful when she came to my place. All these years, I didn't get a complaint about that; my mother dressed the lady's forehead. I asked her if she wished to go to the emergency room, and she told me that she was going to church.

The next day, I went upstairs to see if she was fine, and she told me no. I asked her again if she wanted to go to the ER, but she still refused. I just walked away and shook my head. I knew that this was what the Lord was telling me about; it didn't stop there. Her sister called me up one day and let me know that I needed to fix the walkway. It sounded like a threat to me. I had to call a friend and see how much it would have cost me to fix the situation. The price he gave me was about a thousand and change. I knew that he must be crazy with these prices.

The tree in the yard had lifted up the concert, so it had a space lifted up. Now he wanted to remove all of the walkways and make a new one. I didn't have that kind of money at all; the money that I had put away for Abi was almost made because I had to make up the mortgage as well as other expenses. I did what I knew best, I called my brother, and he came, not right away, but he came and fixed it.

I just had to thank God for him; it seemed as if he was the only one who was helping me. I then told him it was the same reason I didn't want to rent this lady the place; she wanted me to get a washer and dryer hooked up for her. I told her no way. I didn't have money to pay my bill, plus to get all that for her. She pushed and pushed until she got her way. I just shook my head; God knows.

I could not handle this woman. My brother called me and told me he was going to Puerto Rico and that his brother-in-law was getting married. He told me I didn't have to worry about a thing. I asked Abi if she wanted to go. She had money from her party. I went and got our tickets on my credit card, and we just went.

Before I left, I went to my doctor and asked them if it was safe for me to travel. They told me that it was fine. I didn't think twice. I just went and left all my worries behind. My mother didn't want to go at all; everywhere my brother and his family were, we were there.

When I came back, it was the same thing all over again; now I had gotten a letter from social security. They had denied me benefits. I could not understand why they had all of my doctor's records. I just could not understand at all; then, I went back to the office. One of the officers told me that I had to reapply once more. He even told me to get a lawyer this time; I did what I had to do. I reapplied; then, I went and got a lawyer to help me. I had to call someone I knew who had helped me in the past. I went in, and she took over my papers, which I had done most of it. Now I had to wait. I was stressed out most of the time because the bills were too high, and I was not getting any income. Only on the rental, and it seemed as if whenever this lady paid me, she wanted me to fix something.

I had it really hard, but I could not give up at all. I had to fight through this. As the day went by, things were the same. Abi was getting ready to go back to school; I had to do what I could. I didn't have much on my credit card to spend; after all, we went to Puerto Rico, which I didn't regret at all. When I heard the news that a hurricane was heading to Puerto Rico, I was devastated by the fact that I had just left the island. It was hit not once but twice. I felt so sorry for the people that were affected by the storm. I know what it felt like to have gone through that. In Jamaica, we have a lot of high mountains, but I saw some of the mountains in Puerto Rico.

The island was not that big at all, but God was with them for anyone to come through that storm. This was the life we had to deal with; we had to face some pretty ugly things. As the winter approached, I was faced with doing the thing I feared the most. I had to go to the government for help.

Marie took me to where I could apply for help; I had to wait in a line that was outside the building. This was no fun; I never thought that it would have come this far. I had to put pride in hiding myself and stand in line like everyone else. I thought with all the illness I had, I would have gotten help, but I was wrong. After staying in that line for an hour, I had to wait another hour and a half just to be called for an interviewer; it was no fun.

They treated people with no respect and thought that everyone was on drugs. I was only there because of my health problem.

Chapter 42

I should have listened to my brother and nephew. They told me to sue the hospital for all they did to me. But no, I had to follow what the Lord told me, after all. I was a child of God, and he would work it out. When they finally called me and checked over my paperwork, it was over before it began.

She told me that they could not help me at all due to the fact I had a home, plus I was getting income through that. She told me that I could have gotten a food stamp. The amount that I was qualified for was eighty-two dollars a month for my daughter and myself. I thought to myself, *How in the world would I ever survive the winter?*

I called around but always got a slap in the face; the mortgage was more than the rent, and I knew the gas bill was no joke in the winter. I needed help, so I called up and made an appointment to see RCT. They help you with your winter bills. I didn't know if I would qualify for that as well, but I had to try.

I went there, and they told me they could only give me 500 hundred for the year, so I had to find the rest. I called the gas company, and they told me that they had a program that would match whatever I could come up with, but they had to check out everything I had told them. The only thing they didn't ask me was what I had for dinner.

It was really hard to live like this; I fight most of the time. I never gave up at all, even though I felt like it. The winter was really bad. We would have to pay for people to do the snow; then, my tenant called me with another complaint. She was not getting any heat; when I went upstairs and saw the condition of the place. I could not believe it at all; I went into her niece's bedroom to feel the heater; this was too much. She had a dirty plate on the bed and forks and a spoon on the floor. The only clean room in the apartment was her sister's room.

The place was a mess. She had the nerve to tell me she had roaches. They had food all over the place, bottles from soda to water. I kept thinking that mice would be next; I should really be careful what I say. I felt as if I was walking outside the yard. I called the plumber, and he told me the pipe wanted to bleed. When he came and did that, he didn't even charge me at all; I called her and asked her if she was getting heat, and she told me yes.

Then we had a snowstorm; this time, we had freezing rain and so on. She called me at about 6:00 a.m. for me to clean the ice. She told me that she had to go to work. I told her that I could not do anything at this time. I would have to wait until the rain was over before I could do anything.

She was on a ramp page; I could not take it anymore. One day, I was on my way with Abi to an appointment; when the lady called me once more, complaining that the apartment was too hot. I got upset that I lost it and told her that the place was not a penthouse and that if she did not like it, she should find somewhere to go, and I hung up my phone.

I then called my church sister, the one who told her about the place, and told her the first thing that came to my mouth. I told her whenever she got those crazy people from, to not introduce them to me. I was sick and tired of them, but she told me she could not talk to me and hung up her phone. I was so upset. Then Abi told me to calm down. I finally did, but that church sister didn't take it lightly at all. She had my name all over Hartford, telling people that I was crazy and how I cursed her out.

She even told the ladies to move out of my place. When I got the rent from her, I called the plumber. It seemed as if he had turned off the switch by accident. This switch controlled the heat upstairs; whenever it got too hot, it would control the level, but he did not turn it on. When my brother came to visit, he noticed it. I told him that I could not take this lady. Now she had her sister giving me the rent, which I still had to put into the apartment because she would find something else for me to fix.

The next call I got was from the church sister asking me if I went into their apartment because they noticed something there that wasn't there before. I just sent her a picture of how the apartment was before they came in, and I needed it to be the same way when they left.

I could not believe this church lady; I knew her before Abi was born, and to think how she sold me out like that. She even went and told the young lady who had the van that Abi was not listening to me at all. She wanted to know if I needed her to talk to my child. I just shook my head and thought I could trust them. I was always there to help them whenever they needed me, but now it was every man for themselves. She told the lady that I was crazy and not to listen to me at all.

I got all kinds of bad verbs from people; I kept thinking I was evil and not doing what God called me to do. I was getting into fights with everyone, so I stayed by myself most of the time. I knew my sister didn't think much of me either, and everyone else had gone. I still did what I knew best; I thanked God for all the trials and tribulations I had to face because, without them, I would not know to handle certain things when they came my way.

One day on my way to church, I came out of the house and stepped down on the walkway. I heard and felt a sound in my foot. It felt as if I had pulled something. I still went to church because the pastor's wife had called me and asked if I could be a greeter that Sunday. I told her fine.

It was too late now to let her know, so I took my time and walked to church. I was in a lot of pain, but I still stood there and greeted each person that came in. Then one of the sisters told me that I was standing at the wrong door; I didn't want any fuss with these church people. I moved and went to where she told me to; then another one told me I was still standing in the wrong place. I just smiled and looked up to Jesus and told him to keep me, just keep me.

It was time for service to begin, and everyone went in. I was still in the lobby holding the door for the latecomers. When I went in, I could feel my foot hurting a lot. I asked one of the sisters for some ice, then I put it on my foot. When I went home, I was just crying. I put some ice on it and kept it elevated. This did not last; I was in pain the whole night.

I didn't want to go to the emergency room on a Sunday evenly, especially at UConn. I waited the following morning and asked sister P to take me. I was surprised when my mother told me she was coming as well. When I went, it was fractured; they told me how sorry they were, and they put it into a hard case. They told me to see an orthopedic; I didn't care at all for their doctors. So I went to the one that my daughter had gone to. He looked at it and told me that it was broken. I didn't want those hard cases, but it seemed as if they had new boots that I could take off at night. I was glad about that; now, I was once more in bed. I still moved around; I didn't want to feel sorry for myself. Everyone I spoke to told me the same thing. It was too much for me, and now that my foot was fractured, I had to take care of myself; I spent some of my time in bed, while other times, I would move around. I would sometimes work on my book, but it seemed as if I would totally forget what to write or sometimes didn't care. I knew the Lord wanted me to finish this book, but I always felt like something or someone was holding me from completing my mission.

I had to press and press, but it felt like a fight; I didn't like the feeling of being in one place too long, then I started to go out more. I knew that my body needed rest due to everything else, but I could not stay in one place too long. Now I was putting on too much weight, and I was getting tired a lot. I would actually feel my skin stretching away; I could not do any exercise at all due to my bones. I would go to the doctor for my checkup.

One of my co-workers would call me and ask if I needed help. I thanked her a lot because God always sends help when you need it, not the ones that you expect. After going back and forth to the doctor's offices, my foot was getting better. I was just thanking God for everything. I could start to go back to church once more.

I had gotten a letter from the tenant; she stated she was leaving within a month. I was happy but surprised at the same time. I knew that I had to get on top of things. I could not wait to get to church. I knew someone who was always on the road. The kind of work he did, he was always counteracting with people. I told him that the apartment was going to be ready in a month. If he heard about anyone who needed a place, to let them know. I could not wait until these people left; now, she was even more moody than before.

I just had to wait until that day came. I still went to church even though my foot was in a booth. I got all kinds of facial expressions and questions. It seemed as if I was always telling people what had happened. I sounded like a broken record; I would make it through. During all this time and the winter, my bills were back up. I had to pay the bills and sometimes didn't pay the mortgage on time. Now everything was in a mess. I had to know what I was doing at this time. I knew I had to pay back the security deposit plus fix the place up. This was too much for me. I knew that I didn't have anyone to call up to help me due to the fact that people always depended on me for help.

I had to trust God for this one. He was always there to help me in times like this. I didn't know what was happening then, but now my faith in the Lord was wavering. My brother would call me a lot and ask what I was going to do. I would start getting nervous a lot; my heart was beating fast most of the time. I was under so much stress; the only thing that came to my mind was my life insurance; I had this for over fourteen years now. I had to call them and cancel it. Then I lost a lot of money from my policy just to pay my mortgage. I had just cleaned up my bills, and now I really had to know what I was going to do now; when the month came and gone, the tenant moved out.

This was another thing; she took off the washing machine she had upstairs, and now the water was coming down in my apartment. I called her to let her know I was getting a lot of water. She told me that she was far away, and I didn't want to go into the apartment without her being there. I had to turn off the water main and call my church sister and tell her what was taking place. She then came to the house with one of the tenants. They cleaned up the water and told me it was from the machine.

I was so upset at this point; the water was still coming downstairs, so I told them to call a plumber for them to fix my house. She did that, and when he came, he told me that the pipes needed to be changed. I was really upset at this point. I just told them fine and got another plumber for myself. He charged me two hundred and forty dollars to fix it.

I had to fix it out of the deposit that I had for her, which she had owed me five hundred already. This was too much; when she finally moved out and gave me back the keys, I thought that I had a lot of work to do. They came and cleaned up really well; the only thing I needed to do was to clean up the stove, and some parts of the walls needed painting. I knew I had to get started and do what I needed to do.

This time, my mother came and helped me upstairs; I didn't do too much due to my broken foot. This didn't go long before I got someone else. My church brother had gotten a young lady with three children; his son was a young man in his twenties. I told her I needed more information, which she did not give me. Then she told me later she would bring them. She did not live in the town of Hartford but in Bridgeport.

I did not hear from her for almost two weeks; I then called my church brother and told him that I didn't hear from her. He told me to do what I needed to do, which I did. I put up the sign for the apartment to be rented. I don't know if she heard that I did it; she called me the next day and told me that she was coming to fill out the rest of the paperwork. She did come, but this time, she came with a U-Haul truck. She came with her furniture and everything. I just stopped, and then a funning feeling came over me. I didn't like this one bit. I told my mother that something didn't feel right. She came in the middle of the month like everyone else.

I asked her where the rest of the paperwork that I had asked for was, and she told me all kinds of stories about her work schedule and the kids. I told her that I don't do things like this at all; I was still hesitant to let her in, and she even came with half of what I told her. She said she was waiting for the rest of the money from a friend.

She had to use five hundred to rent the truck. I don't know if she thought I was some joker or what. My mother asked me if I was going to let her go back since she was here already. I just looked at her and went and called my sister; she understood what I was talking about. She told me to let her go back with her things and wait until the next person came.

That was just what I felt, but my mother thought I should have rented her the place. She was outside in the truck with the kids waiting for me to give her the okay. Then my mother asked once more what I was going to do; I just let her in, and the next thing I heard from her—I called myself a Christian.

The lady was happy, but I knew in my heart that something was wrong. I told her that she still owed me for the two weeks, and she told me she knew. This woman moved in with her three children and her uncle, who she said lived in Jamaica. I asked her for the rest of the information, which she still did not give me. Her child was another story; it seemed as if he was challenged. I could not get ready for this; he would be all over the place.

I had to keep calm at times, then sometime, when I could not take the noise, I would take him outside and let him play. I knew that I must be the craziest landlord ever. The things people do to me and get away with... This didn't last long; in the next three weeks, she had her friend move in with four children. I don't know if this girl had a brain or not, but she did. I watched and waited for a week, then I called her and asked her what was going on.

She told me it was her friend and she had problems with her boyfriend and needed a place to stay. I told her they had to leave because she could hardly handle her son, and now I had to face four more kids. This didn't sit too well with her; she would leave the kids at night and go with her friend, and the children would have fun all night; this was too much for me.

During that time, I had a bad feeling one night. I felt my body shaking; I got up and checked my sugar level. It was low, so I went into the kitchen to make something that I could bring back up. When I opened the cupboard door to get a can of milk, I saw a mouse. I don't know what happened. I jumped so fast and screamed out. When I landed on my feet, I knew I was in trouble. I felt like I was walking on pins and needles. I was just crying; I knew I had done something to both my feet. I didn't go to the hospital at all. I know their protocol.

I stayed home that weekend in pain. I could not explain it; I had to call my daughter whenever I was going to the bathroom. I had to go through a lot at this time; I waited until Monday morning and took a cab with my mother once more. This time, the two feet were broken; what else was next? I jumped from a mouse and broke my two feet; it seemed as if everyone had a laugh at me. To think about it, I had to laugh too due to the fact of fear I broke both my feet. Now the doctor wanted to do surgery, but my mother told him no.

He told me that my bones were brickle and they didn't look good. I knew that due to the fact of my sickness. Mother told him that my other foot had healed before and now I should just wait and see. To tell you the truth, she was right; because my bones were so brickle, it did not make any sense to put screws in both of my feet. Now I had to be in bed, which was no fun, and I had to wear these boots that looked like ski boots.

Now I was in bed, and the beginning of the month came, and the lady didn't pay the rent. She even went over the grace period. I knew the mess had started; I asked her for the rent, and she hid. I had to wait before I took action; I told her that if she knew that she could not afford the place, she should move out and find something that she could afford. She told me that she could, and her son was the one who was holding her up.

I then told her that her friend and her children would have to leave. My water bill was going up, and all the noise they were making upstairs was no fun. This lady was in another world. She didn't care at all. She had all kinds of men coming into the place, and I was so upset that one day something bad was going to happen.

She came with the rent at the end of the month and fifty dollars for the water bill. I asked when her friend was leaving, and she told me soon. The month came, and the second week, the friend moved out, then I realized that she could not afford the rent. I never got another dime from her; she hid most of the time. I knew I had to do something at this point because if I sat back and were a Christian lady, I might be on the street as well. I had to take her to court, which was no fun.

I had to go to court with my two feet broken, which was no joke at all. People would make fun of me, while others would think I was being silly wearing winter boots in the summer. I got a lot of criticism from people who didn't know my situation. I had to go on with life and do what needed to be done. I had no money for a cab, so I had to take the bus and take my time. I would get a ride from Marie and another co-worker, which I am grateful for. This went on for a while; I had to depend on people to get around most of the time because the bus system was not working with my broken feet. I just had to wait until my feet were healed enough to take action.

This lady knew the system so well; she knew everything that needed to be known about the court system. I was stressed; I knew I was dependent on this money to pay my mortgage, and now I was in a hole once more. I went to court with this lady every month for her to move out. I told her to just move with what she owed me so that I could get the place ready. She told me that she loved the place and she was not going anywhere.

I didn't know what to do; I even called my church brother and told him what she was doing. He didn't care at all. He said I should have fixed my business myself; I called my pastor and told him as well, and he told me that I should take her to court, which I did. I realized that I was on my own with this problem. Whenever I went to court in Hartford, it seemed as if they gave these people a lot of privileges while the landlords had to suffer. I don't think that it is fair what they are doing in Hartford housing court. I was a landlord that had to pay my bills just like everyone else, or else I, too, would be on the street.

They don't care how hard you work to have something, and then someone wants to bring you down with them. They gave this lady up until December to move out, which was three and a half months. Then they told me if she didn't move out, I would have to do the eviction process, which would take another month.

Whenever I went to court, I had to find money to pay the sheriff just to give her a notice. This is a lot of money-making things. I didn't know if I was coming or going. The mortgage people were calling me for their money as well as everyone else. The house was even going into foreclosing. My daughter would be going to school next year, and all the savings I had were gone, and now they wanted to take the house from me. I got a call from my brother, and he told me to buy a lotto.

He didn't have any money to help me, so he told me to buy a lotto; I was hesitant to do so, but when these people wanted their money, they would do anything. I did go and buy the lotto, but I did not win at all. Now the devil was giving me all kinds of ideas to let them come and shut off the water because I owe them 600 hundred dollars as well. I was tempted to do a lot of evil things, but I knew in my heart that God was watching me, and I still had to do the right thing. I had to wait until this woman left the house before I could do anything to the apartment.

Chapter 43

I went to God again and told him that he was the only one who could help me now. This fear thing was kicking my ass, and it made me feel like I should not pray at times. I didn't wait on him at all; I went and called all the people who owed me money. Some told me yes and never called back, while the girl who owed me for my van threatened me and told me that she was not going to steal for me. Then she had the nerve of calling the same church sister and telling her that she was praying for God to kill me for my own money.

I asked her, "What did you tell her?" She said, "Nothing." I just smiled and told her thanks. No wonder I was going through all of this. I was getting in a fight all over; these people were not praying for me; they wanted me on my face. I was bitter and angry at the same time. I knew that God would not deal with me at this point. I didn't care at all. I was so angry. I wanted everything and everyone to just give me what they owed me and leave me alone.

God didn't answer me at all. I knew because he told me to finish what he told me to do. I was still doing my own thing; my mother told me to call the church and ask the pastor for help. I told her no because if God had told him, he would bring it. Then she told me to ask Marie; I didn't want to because of pride, but I had to because these people wanted the house so badly. I had no one that could help me.

I finally called Marie, and she lent me a thousand dollars. It was not enough, but it still put me up for a month. The only thing I got from God was to call all the people that owed me and tell them to keep the money. I was really upset with the Lord, but I didn't question it because I knew that it was the Lord's voice. I knew the devil would tell me to do that. I did what I was told and texted each of them and removed them from my contact number. I was upset for a while, but I knew what God was doing with me. He wanted to get me back with him, but I was too far gone with all these people.

I knew what I needed to do, and I should have done it for a long time. I was still waiting for my social security to kick in, but that was too much time; finally, the lady moved out most of her things and gave me back my key. I didn't waste any time. I went and called my brother to see if he could come and help me, but he told me that he was busy.

I asked a guy next door how much it would have cost me to paint the apartment. The price he gave me, I had to call back my brother and tell him to leave his wife and child and take the thirty dollars bus. He was too busy because he was helping his wife's family to move that same weekend. I told him that she had a lot of brothers, and I needed mine to help me, but he told me it was his wife.

I was upset, of course, and I asked God what I should do. Then I called another church brother of mine, who got another member from the church who helped me. He painted out one room and did a little touch-up there. I had to call a co-worker, and she came and took me to Home Depot, where we rented the machine to clean the carpet. She helped me with the shampooing because I could not do too much. The young lady had left things in the apartment as well. I still had to ask the same brothers to move them into my garage.

I didn't have much, but they took what I had. This time, my mother was helping me; she knew that if I lost the house, she, too, would be out of a place to live. While I was still cleaning the place up, a couple of people came by to look at the apartment. I was thinking twice at this time. I didn't know if I should take it to the agency, but I didn't have that kind of money to do so. This young man came and said that he loved the place. I was very skeptical about renting him the place, but my mother liked him a lot. I didn't go by my feelings but by the spirit. He never gave up.

Christmas came and went; I didn't have anything to give to anyone. My finances were tight, so I had little to give. My faithful friends, who always look out for me, stopped by and gave me gift cards. I bought things the house needed, like toilet paper, soap, and so forth. Abi paid our phone bill because she had gotten a summer job.

She didn't give it up; this was helping her a lot. The money that Mother was giving me helped out with the rest of the bills. I owed Marie, and I knew that I had to get a job to pay her back really soon. I had to trust the man Christ Jesus for everything at this point. I had no one to help me but him. I went and let the young man move in. My mother told him because of her, that was the reason he got the place. She was right because I did not trust anyone at this point.

I know I had to trust God for everything, but I was still waiting on that social security disability. I had gotten a letter from them, which I had a case in January. I went with my lawyer, who told me he would only collect if I did. We went, and I told them all that I'd gone through, and they read my medical reports, from lupus to stroke, diabetes, high blood pressure, and osteoporosis. They still turned me down. They told me that my own doctors at UConn told them that I was okay to work, and to top it off, UConn Hospital sued me over medical bills.

What more can one take? I didn't think I could cope anymore. I told God to just take over because this was too much for me. The next thing that happened to me was unthinkable; my daughter was doing her own thing. She didn't want to listen to me at all when it came to God. She was dropping her grades at school; the more I spoke to her, the more she got upset. It went to the point that we had a fight, not verbally but physically. She was out of control; I prayed and did my best, but she was set in her ways, and no matter how I told her what life was all about because I didn't want her to get hurt. She told me that she would not make the same mistake I did.

I learned a lot from her about God and how often he told me not to go there. I still ignored him and sinned even more. When sin brings us into condemnation, we think that Dad will turn his back on us, but he is the God of forgiveness who says he will never leave us. I believe in God; I could never deny my Father or my Savior, Lord Jesus Christ. I knew I had to finish this book that he told me to.

I don't know if all the trials I'm going through can help anyone; I know God is always there with me.

When I think about my past and see where he took me from, I was actually going through the same thing these people went through in the Bible. King David and Joseph went through with their siblings; they treated them badly, and they still had to forgive them.

The Bible says to honor your mother and father, and your days will be longer on the earth (Exodus 20:12). This was one of the reasons why I prayed for my daughter because I saw what had happened to David's son Absalom. I hope she won't turn her back on him. I wish her all the best in life.

If only Abi knew how much I love her, but she still thinks that I didn't show her the love she wanted. I didn't know the kind of love that she was looking for; the only love I knew was what I'd learned from Abba.

One day, coming from one of my doctor's visits, I saw her at the bus stop kissing a young man. I didn't know if I was to come off the bus and create a sense of or if I was glad about her being happy. When she saw me, I really didn't know what had run through her head, but she was thinking something else. When we got home, she went into her grandmother's room. Then I called her to ask her about this guy; she was at the top of her voice. I kindly let her know that I was talking to her alone and not the entire neighborhood.

She was still yelling and telling me he was her man, and she kept disrespecting me. I lost it and hit her, then she told me more things I dare not repeat, so I hit her even more. I think she got too much, so she started to fight me back. I got hit even in the eye that was blind; we fought until my mother came into the room and told me to leave. She then went on the phone and called all she knew; I was too embarrassed to do so. I was in a lot of pain; I knew that I should not have been in this kind of confrontation, but it happened.

We didn't speak for a long time. She felt as if she was grown. I still have the mentality that children should respect their parents. Her prom came, and this was another story; we both got hurt. Everyone kept telling me to leave her alone, but how could I?

She was on the wrong side of the road, and I knew that she was going to get hurt. As a mother, I still didn't listen to what people had to say; I went and called my pastor's wife. She gave me the best advice, which I took. She didn't like it one bit, but I had to do what was best for her. Graduation came, and she graduated with a scholarship; the college she chose was far away from home. This was not good for me, but I had to let her go, not out of my heart, but she had to fly on her own now.

I didn't have any money to help her at all, so I did the best I could. Whenever she called for help, as parents do, we helped. I had to sacrifice a lot of bills to send her money. She came on Christmas break; then went back to school once more.

Before you knew it, another crisis after another, tenants were acting up; now they had to leave once more. Things were the same, trying to make ends meet. Marie had given work with her mother for two days, and I had gotten a baby to take care of as well, so it helped out a lot. I still could not do hard work because I never knew when my bones were going to give out. The apartment had been empty for a while now, and I was facing foreclosure once more; this time, my sister Althea helped out so that I could keep the house. My brother told me to sell it and be done with it, but I needed somewhere to live, as well as my mother and daughter.

I still paid off most of the money and still owed them two thousand dollars, but I knew God would see me through this. In the month of March, I got a call from my daughter. It was spring break, and she needed money, so I had to put a bill on hold and send it to her.

The apartment was rented at this time; then, everything took a turn for the worst. The whole world was facing COVID-19. This is another story. This was too much for me, but I had to trust God with this one. My daughter came home, and now we all have to face the unexpected thing in life. God is in control.

I know that life can be cruel at times, with all the tests I got from people in general, not to mention crises, some of which I will never understand. While others, we just have to ride it like the surfer riding the waves. I question it a lot. Boy, if you think about it, most people in the Bible went through something. I have to forgive them the way Jesus forgives me; this is what it boils down to, forgiveness and love. This world would never get any better until we all come to realize that there is the devil whose motivation is to kill and destroy what God had created.

He hated God so much that he wanted to destroy whom God loved the most, that is, us. You would think we care for each other, but we are just pure evil, and our hearts have the world in it. If we truly love Abba, we will do everything in our hearts to change. This COVID-19 is a test as well as everything else, like black lives matter, sex trafficking; you name it. As Christians, we all need to wake up and start doing what the Lord has commanded us to do. He said we have to love our neighbor as ourselves.

This is the reason why we need Jesus Christ. Only he can help our sinful nature. We are born in sin due to the fact that Adam brought it upon us, but Jesus Christ came to redeem us from it all, even though he didn't have to. He loved us so much that he came and paid the ultimate price for all of our sins. I know that he is coming back soon, and he's coming back for all those who are ready to go with him.

Then after that, it will be a judgment on earth for those who didn't accept Jesus Christ as our Savior. I thank the day that I had those couple (2) abortions, and killing my innocent babies was something I had to pay for, but glory be to God, who sent Jesus to pay for my sins. Now I know that I can finally be free. I can truly say I forgive everyone who hurt me, and I apologize to anyone I have offended in any way.

If the world could only stop and read the Bible, where our Father had given us instructions before leaving this world, because no one knows how their lives are going to end. We have to live each day as if it is our last. So, please, I'm asking each and every one to forgive each other so that our heavenly Father can forgive us. And remember to accept Jesus Christ as your Savior and believe it as well because God is coming back really soon. We all need love and forgiveness one and for all.

As for myself, I don't know when my end will come. I'm just going through everyday life with struggle, and I trust God, and I know he will help me through it all. I only have to believe in Jesus. The good Lord always leaves us with something to remember.

Milton Keynes UK
Ingram Content Group UK Ltd.
UKHW030647201123
432908UK00017B/1985

9 798890 412188